SPSS/PC+
Made Simple

Paul R. Kinnear & Colin D. Gray

*Department of Psychology,
University of Aberdeen*

 LAWRENCE ERLBAUM ASSOCIATES, PUBLISHERS
Hove (UK)   Hillsdale (USA)

Copyright © 1992 by **Lawrence Erlbaum Associates**

Reprinted 1993, 1994, 1995

Lawrence Erlbaum Associates, Publishers
27 Palmeira Mansions
Church Road
Hove
East Sussex, BN3 2FA
UK

British Library Cataloguing in Publication Data

A catalogue record for this book is available from the British Library

ISBN 0-86377-297-8

Printed and bound in the UK by Redwood Books, Trowbridge, Wiltshire from camera-ready copy supplied by the authors.

CONTENTS

Contents

Contents

Contents

Contents

Contents

PREFACE TO THE FIRST EDITION

In recent years, the analysis of psychological data has been greatly assisted by the development of statistical computing packages. Those who have used the Statistical Package for the Social Sciences (SPSS; the current version is SPSS-X) on a mainframe will agree that it is one of the most powerful and comprehensive packages currently available. That package, however, as even its greatest admirers will admit, would be a daunting prospect indeed for the newcomer with little or no previous experience of computing. Recently, however, a PC version of SPSS, known as SPSS/PC+, has been developed, which is much more accessible and friendly than its mainframe parent.

SPSS/PC+ is by no means simply a watered-down version of SPSS-X. The plus (+) in its name is well deserved, for it has a very special feature, absent from the mainframe package: SPSS/PC+ has a **Menu and help** mode of operation. By selecting from the Menu, the user can 'paste' correctly-written commands on to an area of the screen known as the **scratch pad**. Once there, they can be executed at the touch of a key. This confers an enormous advantage, because the user can begin to analyse data immediately, without first acquiring a knowledge of SPSS syntax.

This is a practical book, intended as an **introduction** to the use of SPSS/PC+. It is by no means a comprehensive treatment; indeed, with the needs of the beginner foremost in mind, we have been highly selective in the material we have included. The book should, however, serve as a useful preparation for more advanced texts.

While this book is neither a text on statistics nor a primer on experimental design, it does contain some general advice on the use of elementary statistical techniques. The advent of the computing package has brought sophisticated statistical methods within reach of a wider range of users than ever before. Amidst this plenitude, however, lurk pitfalls into which the unwary user can only too easily stumble. It is one thing to command the computer to perform a procedure; it is quite another to select a test correctly from the often bewildering variety of available options. A successful run is no guarantee that the method chosen is either appropriate for the data or that it provides the best answer to the question addressed by the research. Wherever possible, therefore, we try to alert the reader to features of the output that would suggest that the statistics might be misleading. We also offer some guiding principles for the selection of statistical tests and make some suggestions for further reading.

There has been a widespread tendency for researchers to follow rather rigid procedures in data analysis, in which too much emphasis is placed upon formal statistical testing and the obtaining of 'significance', and too little upon thorough exploration of the data. SPSS/PC+ has powerful graphs and displays which can yield insights that routine performance of formal tests would miss. (Note, however, that in this book we consider only those graphs and displays that are provided by the basic SPSS/PC+ package.)

The book is divided into two parts. The first part (Chapters 1 to 5) introduces the reader to the SPSS/PC+ system and offers some general advice on statistical analysis. These chapters should be read sequentially, because the material they contain is hierarchically organised.

The second part of the book comprises a set of 'stand-alone' chapters, which describe the use of SPSS/PC+ to solve various kinds of problems (how to compare two means, how to analyse nominal data, and so on). Readers who have worked their way through Chapters 1 to 5 should be able to move directly to any of the chapters in the second part and perform the routines described there. To help the reader, we have repeated, in each of the chapters in the second part, some of the material that was introduced in the first part.

Computing packages are subject to continuous revision. While we can assure the reader that all the commands and procedures described in this book have been thoroughly tested by the authors on version 4.0.1 and really do work at the time of writing, it is quite possible that during the final preparation of the manuscript for publication, yet another revision of SPSS/PC+ may already have appeared. Any changes, however, would almost certainly be slight.

The authors wish to thank their colleagues and students at Aberdeen for the many helpful comments they received while writing this book. In particular, they would like to thank John Lemon of the Computing Centre at Aberdeen University for reading part of the manuscript and making several helpful suggestions. They would also like to thank Peter Bates for preparing the illustration.

Paul R. Kinnear

Colin D. Gray

July, 1992.

In this revised edition, a substantial set of exercises has been added. Each exercise is more than a set of cookbook instructions: wherever possible, the reader is encouraged to manipulate the given data set, in order to heighten appreciation of what is being measured by the statistics concerned.

Some techniques, such as non-parametric tests, which receive only a brief mention in the body of the text, are more thoroughly explored in the exercises. Also, in the exercises on ANOVA, there is guidance on the making of multiple comparisons. Where shortage of space prohibits fuller treatment of an important topic, the reader is referred to an appropriate statistical textbook for further guidance.

Paul R. Kinnear

Colin D. Gray

July 1994.

CHAPTER 1

THE PERSONAL COMPUTER

1.1 INTRODUCTION

Computers now play an essential role in the analysis of data in many disciplines, including psychology. Computers are designed to obey sets of instructions known as **programs**. Fortunately, however, it is not necessary to be able to write a program to make use of a computer, because there are available pre-written sets of programs known as **packages**. The earliest packages were designed for use with large **main-frame** computers. Nowadays, however, many are available on small machines known as **personal computers (PCs)**. One of the most widely used and versatile of the statistical packages is the **Statistical Package for the Social Sciences (SPSS)**, a version of which is available on PC. The purpose of this book is to show you how to use **SPSS/PC+**, without assuming any previous experience with SPSS on a main frame computer.

There are different kinds of PC: some are **stand-alone** machines, intended for independent use; others are part of a **computer network**, in which the users' PCs are linked to a central machine known as the **file server**. In either case, the procedure for operating SPSS/PC+ is basically the same, except for a few minor details, such as the manner in which one begins a session (a procedure known as **logging in**), how one ends a session (**logging out**), and how one instructs the computer to **print out** the work that the package has done. In this chapter, we shall describe some of the main physical features of the PC, including its **keyboard** and **disk drive**. Then we shall consider some basic procedures, such as the preparation of a new disk (**formatting**), logging on and logging off.

1.2 THE COMPUTER KEYBOARD

1.2.1 Arrangement of the computer keyboard keys

(The reader will find it helpful to have a PC keyboard available while reading this section.)

The number and letter keys on a PC keyboard (see page 3) are arranged exactly as they are on an ordinary typewriter: from left to right, the letters of the top row appear in the order Q,W,E,R,T, ... and there is a row of number keys above the top row of letters. On a typewriter, there is a SPACE BAR running along the bottom of the keyboard, a single press of which moves the printing head a space to the right. On the computer keyboard, there is also a space bar, a press of which moves a blinking image on the screen of the VDU one space to the right, without printing any character on the screen.

Some keys have two items printed on them, one above the other. All keyboards (typewriter or computer) have a **SHIFT** key which, when pressed and held down, gives the upper item when the item key is then pressed. For example if, while holding down the shift key, you then press the key with the two items 8 and *, you will obtain *. If a letter key, such as E, is pressed while the shift key is held down, the letter will be typed in upper case (eg E); if the shift key is not held down, the letter will be typed in lower case (e).

Be sure to make a clear distinction between the **zero key** (in the row of number keys) and the **letter O key**, in the top row of letters. They may look similar on the keyboard, but a computer does not find the letter O an acceptable substitute for the number zero.

On a computer keyboard, there are several additional keys with specifically computing functions. For example, for convenience, there is an extra set of number keys, known as the **number pad**, situated in a rectangular area to the right of the main keyboard.

1.2.2 A glossary of keys for future reference

The following is a list of keys intended for your future reference as you work through the book. At this point, they will be described briefly, and you should try to identify them on a PC keyboard at the earliest opportunity. Note that in this book we shall use square brackets around a word such as **Alternate** or **Delete** (e.g. **[Alt]**, **[Del]**) to indicate that a single key is to be pressed: the letters of the word are not to be typed out individually.

ALTERNATE (Alt)

This, the bottom left key on the keyboard, is used like the shift key: it works only in

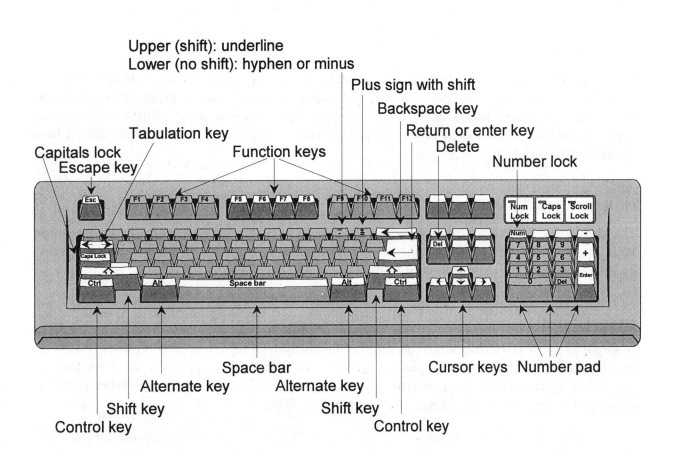

Upper (shift): underline
Lower (no shift): hyphen or minus

Plus sign with shift
Backspace key
Return or enter key
Delete
Capitals lock   Number lock
Escape key   Tabulation key   Function keys

Space bar
Alternate key   Alternate key
Shift key   Shift key   Cursor keys   Number pad
Control key   Control key

combination with other keys, being held down while the latter are pressed. For example, one might hold down the Alternate key while pressing E, an operation for which we shall use the notation **[Alt]/E** .

BACKSPACE

The long horizontal key with the left-pointing arrow is the **Backspace** key. When you are typing from a computer keyboard, your current position is indicated by a small blinking image which continually appears and disappears. This is called the **cursor**. If you press **[Backspace]**, the cursor will move one space to the left and delete any character that happens to be in that space.

CAPS LOCK

The **Caps Lock** key is a **toggle** switch: a single press produces a change, which is reversed when the switch is pressed again. If you are typing in lower case, a press of **[Caps Lock]** causes all subsequent letters to be typed in upper case. Another press returns you to lower case. Note that **[Caps Lock]** affects letter keys only: only with the letter keys, does it have the same effect as **[Shift]**.

CURSOR KEYS (← ↑ → ↓)

The four keys with thin arrows pointing up, down, left and right are known as the **Cursor keys**, because they move the cursor in the directions indicated. In SPSS/PC+, they are also used to locate lists of options known as **menus.**

DELETE (Del)

A single press of **[Del]** erases the character at the position of the cursor and replaces it with the next character on the right. The position of the cursor on the screen, however, is unchanged. The effect of continuing to press **[Del]** has the effect of "sucking in" text from the right and deleting it, while the cursor remains in its original position.

ESCAPE (Esc)

The **Escape** key is often used to change (or "escape") from one activity to another. When you are using SPSS/PC+, you will often be reminded (by receiving a **prompt** on the screen) to press **[Esc]** in order to return to some previous stage, such as a menu.

FUNCTION KEYS (F1-F12)

Along the top of the keyboard is a row of **function keys**, labelled **F1** to **F12** (only keys F1 to F10 are used by SPSS/PC+). Their use will be described in later chapters.

RETURN (or ENTER or ⏎)

On an electric typewriter keyboard, there is a **Return** key, the pressing of which enables the typist to begin a new line by moving the printing head to the left **margin** of the writing area of the paper. On the PC keyboard to the right of the letter keys, is a large key, marked with ⏎. On a computer, its main function is to **enter** (ie to transmit to the computer) a line which has just been typed by the user. It is therefore sometimes known as the **Enter** key. But when the user is typing material on the screen, the same key also returns the cursor to the start of the next line and is therefore also called the **Return** key. In this book, we shall use the symbol ⏎ to refer to this dual-purpose key.

SHIFT KEYS (⇑)

The two keys that are identically marked with fat, upward-pointing arrows are the **Shift** keys. Either key can be used. Their function was described at the beginning of this section.

1.3 HOW A COMPUTER WORKS: DISK DRIVES AND FILES

1.3.1 Computers in general

A computer is a device for processing information. This processing has three aspects:

    (1)   **input** of information to the system;

    (2)   **central processing** of information by the system;

    (3)   **output** of information from the system.

There are several ways of entering information into the system. One way is by typing it in from a keyboard. But there are other ways. Information can be stored in labelled containers known as **files**. (In the present case, these "containers" are actually patterns of electro-magnetic disturbance on **disks**, but it is useful to think of files as storage boxes.) Instead of typing information into the system from the keyboard, it can be entered from a file. Files can contain different kinds of information. They can be used for the storage of **data**, which can then be used as input. They can also store **commands**, ie lists of instructions for the central processor of the computer to carry out. The contents of files and the results of executing commands can be viewed on the computer screen, known as a **visual display unit (VDU)**. The results can also be stored in a file.

The term **hardware** refers to the physical units of a computer; the programs which operate the computer are known as **software**.

1.3.2 Disks and disk drives

By the operation of a piece of hardware known as a **disk drive**, information is stored in and read from files on **disk**. There are two main types of disk:

(1)   **floppy disks**, which are portable (ie they can be inserted in and removed from the computer hardware);

(2)   **hard disks**, which are an integral part of the hardware and cannot be removed.

A disk drive operates in two modes:

(1)   in **write mode**, it transfers information to files on a disk;

(2)   in **read mode**, it extracts information from files on a disk.

There are different kinds of floppy disk drive, designed to handle disks of varying size and storage capacity. Some disks (the 5¼" type) are contained in a bendable cardboard sleeve. Others (the 3½" type) are smaller, with rigid plastic containers. Disks also vary in their storage capacity. A **high-density** disk stores more information than does a **double-density** disk. Although a high-density disk drive can also read from and write to a double-density disk, the converse does not hold: a double-density disk drive can neither read from nor write to a high-density disk.

A 3½" floppy disk has a **write-protect** notch. When you can see through the notch, the write-protect mechanism is in operation: fresh information cannot be stored on the disk. To write information to the disk (or to edit files thereon), a plastic tab must be drawn across the notch, so that you can no longer see through it. Occasionally the tab can slip into the open (write-protect) position and cause the computer to signal a fault when it tries to open a file on the floppy disk. This situation is easily corrected by removing the disk from the drive, sliding the tab shut, and replacing the disk.

The construction of files (particularly those containing large sets of data, or long lists of commands) may require hours of work. Occasionally floppy disks become damaged, or **corrupted**, and the information they contained is lost to the user. This, we assure you, is a highly unpleasant experience and probably very bad for the blood pressure. The moral is clear: **always duplicate important files on back-up disks: it is well worth the trouble**.

Before a new floppy disk can be used to record material, it must be **formatted**, that is, prepared for use with a specific system. This procedure will be described later.

1.4 SOME BASIC PROCEDURES

1.4.1 Logging in

Before you can use a computer, you must first **log in** (sometimes the term is **log on**). Computers vary in their logging in procedures, and you may need to seek local advice about the computer you intend to use. Some computers start automatically when turned on; but others require you to insert a special logging-in disk before turning on the machine.

When inserting a 5¼″ floppy disk, keep the label facing upwards and insert the side with the plastic indent into the slit. Insert a 3½″ disk by keeping the label facing upwards and inserting the metal part into the slit.

Turn on the power supply switch. After several seconds the screen should show some display, either a prompt such as C:\>, or (in the case of networked computers) a menu of options. This menu may contain, in addition to SPSS/PC+, an item for formatting a disk (see the next section). In this book, we shall assume that the system has been set up, or **configured**, for use with a floppy disk supplied by the user. When choosing the SPSS/PC+ option, you will be prompted at some stage to remove the logging-in disk (if used) and insert your own formatted disk. If you do not respond to such a prompt, you will unable to continue. This is because when SPSS/PC+ is loaded up, it automatically tries to open up working files on the disk that the system expects.

If the prompt C:\> appears, you may need to type in a special code, such as **spsspc**, to start up the SPSS/PC+ program. Seek local advice for the exact details.

Further details about logging in to SPSS/PC+ will be given in Chapter 2.

1.4.2 Formatting a floppy disk

Before a new floppy disk can be used, the computer must be allowed to check the magnetisable material of the disk for blemishes. The computer also installs a special program, which regulates the writing and reading of files to and from the disk. This is known as **formatting** the disk. Once a floppy disk has been formatted, it can be used thereafter without further formatting. **Always format a second disk as a back-up copy**. This will allow you to duplicate important or lengthy files on separate disks.

You may need to seek local advice about the formatting procedure. There are two common ways of formatting a floppy disk:

a)   If your PC starts up with MSDOS (**Micro**Soft **D**isk **O**perating **S**ystem), the prompt C:\> will appear on the screen (the hard disk drive is usually labelled C), with a blinking underline cursor to the right of >. To format your floppy disk in the floppy disk drive (normally labelled A), type in **format A:** and press ⏎ . (If there is more than one floppy disk drive, you may wish to use drive B, in which case the command is **format B:**). You will be prompted to insert the disk and to press ⏎ yet again. The formatting process will then begin, its progress being monitored on the screen.

When formatting is complete, you will be prompted to supply a name for the disk (to which you could respond by typing SPSS and pressing ⏎). You can decline the opportunity to name your disk by simply pressing ⏎ directly. At some point, you may be asked whether you want to format another disk. Answer appropriately and press ⏎ once again.

If the disk drive is of the **high-density** type and you wish to format a **double-density** disk, you may have to use a format instruction with additional parameters (eg **format a:/t:80/n:9** which specifies 80 tracks and 9 sectors in disk drive A).

b)   If you are working on a network, there may be a formatting option on the menu. If so, select it and press ⏎ . Formatting will then proceed as before.

We strongly recommend that you always write your name and application (eg SPSS/PC+) on the labels of your disks. If you have omitted to do this before formatting, take the formatted disk out of the drive and write the information on it before you continue your session.

1.4.3 Logging out

When you have finished a session, you must **log out** of the computer. This usually means simply removing the floppy disk, and turning off the computer (though many network managers prefer computers to be left on between users). In the case of an SPSS/PC+ session, however, a more complicated procedure is required to effect an orderly termination. Details will be given in Chapter 2.

1.5 SUMMARY

1)   Computer keyboards differ from typewriters by having extra keys with special computing functions.

2)   The information that a computer uses (including its own operating system) is stored in labelled **files** as patterns of electro-magnetic disturbance on storage devices called **disks**. **Hard disks** are permanently installed in the computer and are physically inaccessible to the user, while **floppy disks** are portable and work by being inserted in, or removed from, a **disk drive**. Some disk drives are quite specific about which disks they can handle, however, and users must ensure a correct match. A disk drive is identified by a letter followed by a colon. The user's floppy disk drive is usually identified by the letter A, but if there is more than one floppy disk drive, B may be the appropriate letter.

3)   Before a new floppy disk can be used, it must first be **formatted**, that is, prepared for use by the system. Be sure to format more than one disk, so that duplicates of important files can be stored on a **back-up** disk. The usual command is **format A:** (or **format B:** if disk drive B is being used).

4)   The procedure for beginning a session at the computer is known as **logging in** (or **logging on**), and for finishing as **logging out** (or **logging off**).

CHAPTER 2

INTRODUCTION TO SPSS/PC+

In this chapter, after a preliminary look at the **Menu and Help** sytem, the reader will be invited to set up and run a short session on SPSS/PC+, during which the all-important **DATA LIST** command will be briefly introduced. (DATA list and the other **data commands** will be considered in detail in Chapter 3.) In addition, a number of simple but important basic procedures, such as editing, file handling and printing out hard copy, will also be described.

The text will be much easier to understand if, while studying it, the reader is also logged in to SPSS/PC+ and can perform the various exercises suggested. There is nothing like "hands on" experience for effective learning in computing.

2.1 LOGGING IN AND ACCESSING SPSS/PC+

It is essential that the user have available a **formatted disk**. (The procedure for formatting is described in Chapter 1.) Also, since the precise procedure for accessing SPSS/PC+ will vary from installation to installation, local information must be sought. If the user has available a stand-alone PC with SPSS/PC+ stored on its hard disk, a DOS (Disk Operating System) prompt will appear when the machine is turned on. To access SPSS/PC+, the user must type **spsspc** (or something similar) and press ↵ . If the user's machine is part of a network, a menu may appear, with SPSS/PC+ as one of the options. In either case, the user will be required to insert the formatted disk before gaining access to SPSS/PC+. This is because when one logs in to SPSS/PC+, files are opened on the user's disk: the process of logging in cannot be completed until this has been achieved.

2.2 THE MENUS

2.2.1 Modes of operation of SPSS/PC+

There are basically two ways of using SPSS/PC+:

(1)   by typing in commands directly from the keyboard;
(2)   by choosing from a **menu** of options. (An abundance of information, or **Help**, is available to assist the user to make the right choice.)

The first method requires a knowledge of SPSS syntax, and would only be suitable for those who have already had considerable experience with SPSS on a mainframe computer. In this book, therefore, we shall concentrate upon the second, or **Menu and Help,** mode. By using Menu and Help, you can by-pass the obstacle of SPSS syntax and start to analyse psychological data right away. Eventually, however, a knowledge of syntax will have been acquired automatically, and it will then be found more convenient to type in the instructions directly.

2.2.2 The screen windows

When SPSS/PC+ is first accessed, the screen briefly shows the Title Page in colour, after which the image resolves into two rectangular areas (the upper green, the lower blue), known as **windows**. The upper window contains the **main menu**. The lower window is known as the **scratch pad**, because the user can type commands and data directly on it from the keyboard. It will be seen later, however, that one of the advantages of operating in **Menu and Help** mode is that much of the typing that would otherwise be required is avoided by choosing items from the menu with the highlight and pressing ⌡ . The chosen items will then be **pasted** on the scratch pad.

Direct pasting of commands from the menus has the great advantage that the commands will appear written in correct syntax. Computing packages (and SPSS/PC+ is no exception) insist that instructions be written in a prescribed syntactic form, with punctuation in the correct places. For example, commands in SPSS/PC+ must be terminated with a period (.), otherwise what was intended to be the next command would be treated as a continuation of the present one.

Notice that in the menu, some words are written in UPPER CASE. This means that they are **key words**, ie essential parts of a command. The user moves the highlight on to them by means of the cursor keys and pastes them directly on the scratch pad by pressing ↵ . Items prefaced with a slash (/) are **subcommands**. A command may have several subcommands. As with a command, a chosen subcommand can be pasted on the scratch pad by pressing ↵ . Items prefaced with ! are requests to supply essential information, but are not themselves pastable. For example, the user may be required to type in names for the variables at that point. With such commands, there is usually an instruction in the right panel telling the user how to enter the items: for example, the user may be instructed to press **[Alt]/T**, in which case a box will appear in the middle of the screen, into which the variable names can be typed. (Variable names can also be directly pasted, however, provided the DATA LIST command - see below - has been previously executed. This can be a very useful shortcut.)

2.2.3 More about the windows: moving around and making choices

The menu window is itself sectioned into several areas. On the left is the menu proper, comprising a list of items. On the right, there is information about the items to help the user make the correct choice. The user can highlight any item on the menu by moving the ↓ cursor key down to it. Notice that as each item on the menu is highlighted, fresh information appears in the window opposite, explaining the term.

At the beginning of an SPSS/PC+ session, the first menu to appear is the **MAIN MENU**, the top item in which (**orientation**) is highlighted. To the right, is a panel explaining, in general terms, how SPSS/PC+ operates. We recommend that the reader routinely study the information in the panels that accompany the menu choices: they are a mine of useful information. Most items have an arrowhead pointing to the right, which indicates that more details and information are available and can be accessed by pressing the → cursor key.

The SPSS/PC+ menu system is hierarchically organised. The items in the main menu can be thought of as the names of the chapters in a book: to move down to an item and select it is to choose a new chapter. By moving to the right, the user can read the chapter. With **orientation** highlighted, for example, the reader should move to the right by pressing the → cursor key and read about the menu windows. When reading one of the sections on the right hand side, you may find an arrow indicating that there is more material below, which cannot be seen through the window. This material can be read by holding down **[Alt]** and pressing the ↓ cursor key as often as required.

2.2.4 Writing on the scratch pad

When cursor control is located in the menu window (ie SPSS/PC+ is in **Menu and Help** mode), a square white rectangle can be seen blinking in the scratch pad window. While this rectangle is blinking, the user cannot type anything directly on the scratch pad. Cursor control can be transferred to the scratch pad by pressing **[Alt]/E** (the E is for Edit), which will cause the blinking rectangle to change to a white underline cursor. It is now possible to type material directly on the scratch pad. The cursor can be moved by the arrowed cursor keys, and also by pressing ↵ , which starts a new line. To transfer control back to the menu, press **[Alt]/M** (the M is for Menu) or **[Esc]**.

Exercise:

Press **[Alt]/E** to obtain an underline cursor on the scratch pad. Write three or four very short lines of words (jumbles of letters will do) on the scratch pad. After writing three or four words, press ↵ to start another line and proceed to write two or three more lines in the same way.

2.2.5 Clearing the scratch pad

Now, clear the scratch pad. This can easily be done by positioning the cursor after the last character and pressing **[Backspace]**, or by positioning the cursor at the first character and pressing **[Del]**. Hold down the keys as long as necessary.   When there is a large amount of material to be removed, it is easier to use the function keys, as described in section 2.3 .

2.2.6 Checking the contents of the scratch pad

During a long session with SPSS/PC+, the user may write many commands on the scratch pad. On the other hand, only a screenful of the scratch pad's contents can be viewed at any one time. By using the ↑ and ↓ cursors, however, the entire contents of the scratch pad can be inspected.

2.2.7 Occasional problems with the scratch pad

Problems can arise when the user is entering data or preparing commands on the scratch pad. Below, for reference, are four common causes of difficulty. For the moment, however, we suggest that the reader omit this section and pass on to section 2.3.

1) **The screen turns blue and shows the prompt: SPSS/PC+**

The user has inadvertently entered **direct command mode**, which bypasses **Menu and Help**, which is part of the **REVIEW text editor**. To return to **REVIEW** (and so to Menu and Help), type **Review.** (note the period), and then ↵ .

[With networked computers, the problem is sometimes more serious, and arises because the memory capacity of the computer has been exceeded. If so, the execution of commands can overwrite some of the memory allocated to the SPSS/PC+ system itself. The only solution (albeit an unsatisfactory and drastic one) is to remove one's floppy disk, turn the computer off and start again. This possibility underlines the need to save commands and data to files on disk before running programs: this practice can save hours of work.]

2) The cursor fails to move to a new line when ↵ is pressed

In the bottom right hand corner of the screen, the abbreviation **Ins** (insert) should be visible, indicating that the REVIEW text editor is in **insert mode**. If, however, the user should inadvertently press the zero key on the number pad, the editor will switch to **overwrite mode**. To restore **Ins** to the screen, press the zero key again. On pressing ↵ , the cursor should now move to a new line.

3) You wish to insert an additional command above those already written on the scratch pad, but cannot get the top line to move down to make room.

Move the cursor to the top leftmost character already written on the scratch pad. Type the first few characters of the new command and press ↵ . The original first line will now be repositioned below the new line of characters. Move the cursor back to the end of the first line and continue with the rest of the command.

4) While the user is typing, characters cease to appear on the scratch pad and an error message indicates that line length has been exceeded.

Press ↵ , or press **[Delete]** a few times, to remove any superfluous characters further along the line.

2.3 THE FUNCTION KEYS (F1 TO F12)

Lying along the top of the keyboard, is a row of twelve keys with the labels **F1** to **F12** (though SPSS/PC+ uses only F1 to F10). They are known as the **function keys**.

Function keys are primarily for editing material on the scratch pad, but they are also used for writing to and reading from files on floppy disk, and for listing the files on a disk. When **[F1]** is pressed, a mini-menu headed **info:** appears along the foot of the screen with the first item, **Review help**, marked with a dark rectangle. If ↵ is now pressed, the screen will show two large lists of items: the upper list is a **Guide to Review Function Keys**; the lower is a **Guide to Menu Commands**. The upper guide lists the various functions of keys F1 to F10. The most important keys are as follows.

F1   can list the **guide to the function keys**, or the **names of the files on the floppy disk**, or the **names of the variables**.

F3   reads a previously written file from floppy disk to the scratch pad.

F7   marks lines of material on the scratch pad.

F8   deletes, moves, or copies lines previously marked with F7.

F9   saves material on the scratch pad to a file on floppy disk.

F10   executes commands that have been written on the scratch pad, and also logs the user out at the end of an SPSS/PC+ session.

The lower guide lists the various combinations that involve the **[Alt]** key. Two examples (mentioned in the previous section) are **[Alt]/E** and **[Alt]/M**.

There is no need to memorise either list: pressing **[F1]**, and then ⏎ will restore them to the screen at any point.

When a function key is pressed, a mini-menu appears at the foot of the screen. Items on this smaller menu are selected either by highlighting them with → and pressing ⏎ , or by typing the upper case letter in the item name (this is not always the first letter). For example, when **[F1]** is pressed, the mini-menu contains, among its options, **File list** and **menu Help off**. In the case of **File list**, the letter **F** is in upper case, so this item can be selected by pressing **F**; but with **menu Help off**, it is the letter **H** that is shown in upper case, and that option is therefore selected by pressing **H**.

To leave the function key guides and restore the menu and scratch pad windows, press **[Esc]**.

2.3.1 Marking a block of lines with [F7]

A block of lines on the scratch pad can be marked with **[F7]** prior to deletion, copying, moving or execution. Place the cursor on the top line of the material to be marked and press **[F7]**, followed by ⏎ . Move the cursor down to the bottom line of the material to be marked and press **[F7]** again. Both the top and bottom lines, as well as all those intervening, will turn yellow: the scratch pad now contains a **marked area**.

2.3.2   Using [F8] to delete, move or copy a marked block

A block marked by using **[F7]** (see section 2.3.1) can be deleted, moved to another part of the scratch pad, or copied by using **[F8]**. To delete the block, press **[F8]**, followed by **D** (for delete); the material in the marked block of lines on the scratch pad will disappear. To move the marked block to another part of the scratch pad, position the cursor at the new location, press **[F8]**, followed by **M** (for move); the material will then move to the new location.   The same procedure applies for copying, except that **C** is selected; a copy of the block will then appear at the new location.

2.4 A RUN OF SPSS/PC+

2.4.1 Preparing commands

In this section, the reader is asked to prepare a simple set of SPSS/PC+ commands, enter some data and run the program. Normally these commands would be prepared with the aid of **Menu and Help**, but on this occasion, we ask the reader to type the following lines directly on the scratch pad. Press **[Alt]/E** to transfer control from Menu and Help. When the end of a line is reached, press ↵ to go to the next line.

```
DATA LIST FREE/Maths French.
BEGIN DATA.
76 89 42 54 56 66 32 12
END DATA.
LIST.
```

The **DATA LIST**, **BEGIN DATA** and **END DATA** lines are known as **data commands**. (These and the other data commands will be discussed fully in Chapter 3.) **Only by writing data commands can the user enter data into SPSS/PC+.**

The first line is the **DATA LIST** command. It states that there are two variables, called *maths* and *french*, and that the data will follow in **free-field format** (this term will be explained later). Note that the line of data is preceded and followed by the **BEGIN DATA** and **END DATA** lines, respectively. From the number and order of the variables named in the DATA LIST command, it can be seen that the line of data the user has just typed was transcribed from the following set of examination results:

Maths French

76	89
42	54
56	66
32	12

The final line is a command for listing the data on the screen. The LIST command will be discussed more fully in Chapter 4.

Notice that each command ends with a full stop, or period (.): **all SPSS/PC+ commands end with a period.**

2.4.2 Executing the commands

The commands on the scratch pad will continue to be mere lines of characters on the screen until they are submitted for **execution** by SPSS/PC+. Only then will they be treated as commands or data, and processed by the computer. The computer checks that the commands have been typed in the prescribed manner, and that the data are consistent with the specifications in **DATA LIST**. Provided that it finds no errors, SPSS/PC+ will perform whatever procedures or computations are requested after the data commands (in this example, it will obey the LIST command).

Execute the commands as follows:

i)   Move the cursor with the ↑ key up to the first command (ie DATA LIST.).

ii)   Press **[F10]**, and then ↵ .

Fuller details on the execution of commands are given in section 4.2.1.

2.4.3 Screen listing of the output

Provided there are no errors in your typing, the output will be listed, a screenful at a time. With each screenful, the word MORE will appear in the top right corner of the screen. Press the space bar to continue the listing. The screen will initially display, or **echo**, the commands (but not the data) and will then list the scores for *maths* and *french* in two columns, as in the examination results table in 2.4.1 . Eventually, the **Menu and Help** window and the scratch pad will reappear.

If there are any errors, the screen will display an error message and return the user to the

Menu and Help window and scratch pad. Check carefully that you have not omitted a period or mistyped one of the key words in the commands.

You have now executed your first set of SPSS/PC+ commands and seen your first example of output. In order to preserve the commands for future use and to obtain a hard copy of the output, however, it is necessary to learn about file handling, which is the topic of the next section.

2.5 FILES AND FILE HANDLING

2.5.1 Command files, data files and listing files

There are different kinds of files. When using a computing package, the user will often command the contents of a file to be displayed, or **listed**, on the screen of the VDU. A **listing file** contains a display (or listing) of computer output. A **data file** contains only data that are to be entered into the system. A **command file** always contains instructions (**commands**); but it may also contain data for analysis.

2.5.2 Naming files

Computers typically have several disk drives (see section 1.3.2), each of which is represented by a letter: a floppy disk drive is usually labelled A or B; a hard disk is usually labelled C; and (in a network) the central file server's hard disk is usually labelled F.

When a file is named, the name begins with a letter specifying the disk drive in which the file is to be found. For example, a file named A:TTEST.LIS would be found on a disk in floppy disk drive A.

Notice that the file name A:TTEST.LIS has three parts:

(1)   a **letter** identifying the disk drive;
(2)   a word, the **filename** (one word), naming the contents of the file (this word must contain no more than eight characters);
(3)   an optional **extension**, (which must contain no more than three letters).

Note the punctuation: it is essential. There must be a colon to the right of the letter identifying the disk drive; and there must be a period (.) to the left of the extension (if used). The letter

A in the file name A:TTEST.LIS tells SPSS/PC+ that the file is to be found (or created) on a disk in drive A. The filename TTEST reminds the user that its contents concern t-tests. The extension .LIS indicates that it is a listing of computer output. By the file name, therefore, we are reminded that the file contains the results of one or more t-tests.

Other recommended extensions include .CMD for a command file and .DAT for a data file. Note that a data file should contain only data: the data should not be sandwiched between the **BEGIN DATA** and **END DATA** commands, as in the example in 2.4.1 .

2.5.3 Saving the entire scratch pad to a named file on disk

Ensure that there are no unwanted lines of data or commands on the scratch pad by running the cursor up to the top and down to the bottom of the scratch pad window. Unwanted material can be eliminated either by using the **[Del]** and **[Backspace]** keys, or by marking and deleting a block of lines, with **[F7]** and **[F8]**, as described in sections 2.3.1 and 2.3.2 .

To save the material on the scratch pad, press **[F9]**. When the prompt **write whole file** appears at the bottom of the screen, press ⏎ . A box labelled **Name for file:** will appear with SCRATCH.PAD written in it. Delete this label with **[Del]**, type in your file name (eg A:scores.CMD) and press ⏎ . The file *scores.CMD* will then be written to the floppy disk in drive A.

Rather than save the entire contents of the scratch pad, it is sometimes more convenient to save only a section which has been marked as in 2.3.1 . When the section has been marked, press **[F9]** and move the marker at the bottom of the screen to **write marked area**, instead of **write whole file**. Press ⏎ , and continue as before, naming the file and pressing ⏎ once again.

[The reader may have noticed the **SAVE** command in the Menu. This command is reserved for saving material to special **system files**, which are discussed in a later section.]

2.5.4 Accessing a disk's directory of files

You can confirm that your floppy disk does indeed contain a file named *A:scores.CMD* in the following way. Press **[F1]**, **F** (for **File list**) and ⏎ . A box with the symbol *.* will appear. The asterisk (*) is known as the **wildcard** symbol and (depending on whether it lies to the left or the right of the period) represents either a generic filename or a generic extension. Delete the *.* , type **A:*.CMD** and press ⏎ . The upper window should then list any files with a CMD extension, including *scores.CMD*.

Should you wish to obtain a list of all the files on the disk, you would type in **A:*.*** . To obtain a shorter list containing only the **data** files on the disk, you would type **A:*.DAT**. To obtain a list of all files with the filename *TTEST*, you would type **A:TTEST.*** .

2.5.5 Restoring the contents of a file
to the scratch pad

As a double check that the disk really does contain the data, the user can read the data from the file on to the screen. Press **[F3]**, and then **I** (for insert), which will bring to the screen a box labelled **File to insert**.

(If pressing **[F3]** does not work initially, it may be necessary to press **[F1]** and ⏎ , after which **[F3]** will work.)

Type **A:scores.CMD** in the box and press ⏎ . The contents of the file will appear on the scratch pad, proving that the saving operation has been successful.

[The reader may have noticed the **GET** command in the Menu. This command is reserved for reading material from special **system files**, which are discussed in a later section.]

2.5.6 Saving output to a named file on disk:
using the SET/LISTING command

When the user logs in and accesses SPSS/PC+, the system opens up certain files on disk. One of these is called **SPSS.LIS**. When a program is run, the output is displayed on the screen. At the same time, the listed output is transferred to the file **SPSS.LIS** on disk.

There are two problems, however. Firstly, during a single SPSS/PC+ session, the user will often execute several sets of commands (or the same set several times while correcting errors), and on each occasion, a listing of the output will appear on the screen. All these listings will be accumulated in the file SPSS.LIS, which thus becomes something of a dustbin, containing much information that is no longer needed by the user. Moreover, although the system will close the file SPSS.LIS (while leaving its contents stored on disk) when the user logs out, all the file's contents will be wiped out whenever the user logs in again with the same disk.

To save selected listing to a named permanent file, write the **SET/LISTING** command on a line above **DATA LIST**, at the head of all the commands.

(Should the reader be unable to type this command on the first line of the scratch pad, see hint 3 in section 2.2.7 .)

For example, suppose we want to save the listing from the example of the Maths and French examination marks. The SET/LISTING command would appear as follows:

SET/LISTING 'A:scores.LIS'.

Several features of the syntax are worth noting. Firstly, this statement is a **command**. In SPSS/PC+, **all commands end with a full stop or period (.)** . Note that inside the single quotation marks, the entire file name appears, including the label of the disk drive and the extension (if there is one).

We recommend that the SET/LISTING command be written on the scratch pad only after a successful execution of all the commands.

The SET/LISTING command is executed by moving the cursor up to the SET/LISTING command line, pressing **[F10]**, and then ⏎ . The output listing will be saved to disk as it appears on the screen. This procedure is an essential preliminary to the process of printing out a permanent record, or **hard copy**, of selected output (see section 2.6).

2.6 PRINTING OUT HARD COPY

2.6.1 Printing during an SPSS/PC+ session

While the contents of a file on disk can be read on to the screen at any time (by using **[F3]**, then **I**), the user will often wish to obtain a print-out, or **hard copy**, of the listing for more detailed examination. The arrangements for printing from a computer vary from installation to installation, so local advice must be sought. There are, however, a number of general points which are worth making here.

To print a file, the user must leave SPSS/PC+ temporarily and return to the computer's basic operating system, which is known as **DOS** (Disk Operating System). Proceed with the following steps.

1)   Return to the MAIN MENU by pressing **[Esc]** the required number of times. Move down to **run DOS or other programs**. Press ⏎ , which will paste the word DOS on the scratch pad.

2)   Press **[Alt]/T** to obtain a box.   Type in the command

   PRINT *full file name.*

   and press ⏎ .

   (On some systems, the command is NPRINT, rather than PRINT.) As with all commands, there is a period at the end. Note that **there are no quotes around the full file name**.   For example, to print the previously saved listing file **scores.LIS**, the command is

PRINT A:scores.LIS.

3)   Execute the command by pressing **[F10]**, then ⏎ .

On completion of step 3, the printing routine will run. The prompt MORE may appear in the top right hand corner of the screen, in which case press the space bar to continue. Eventually, when printing is complete, the user will be returned to the SPSS/PC+ menu display.

2.6.2 Printing after logging out
of SPSS/PC+

The user can also print out files after logging out of SPSS/PC+. The computer's own DOS system would then be used. (It may be necessary to select DOS from a menu.) When the DOS prompt (say C:\ >) appears, type **PRINT** *full file name* and press ⏎ .

2.7 SYSTEM FILES

Note: This section should be omitted on a first reading, because we do not recommend the use of systems files to the beginner.

A **system file** is a special type of file which stores information in binary form, and whose contents, therefore, cannot be read or edited on the screen. Nevertheless, system files can be very useful, because SPSS/PC+ can process the information they contain much more quickly than the information in ordinary files. For example, the **data commands**, comprising **DATA LIST, VARIABLE LABELS, VALUE LABELS,** and **MISSING VALUE** (see Chapter 3) may be very extensive for a data set with a large number of variables. Should the user intend to analyse the same data set repeatedly, over a series of sessions with SPSS/PC+, these data commands would be more economically stored (in terms of processing time and convenience) in a system file than in an ordinary file. A system file can be read using the **GET** command on each subsequent run. While at no time do the data commands appear on the screen during such runs, they are nevertheless obeyed by SPSS/PC+, as will be seen from the output listing.

2.7.1 The SAVE and GET commands

(These commands are used only for saving **system files** to disk and for reading them.)

Suppose that the user intends to perform several correlations on a set of data and intends to build a command file with the filename CORR. (The full file name will be A:CORR.CMD) On the scratch pad, the user types out the data commands, before going on to prepare the correlation command. After executing the data commands once to ensure that they have been correctly written, the user can save them to a system file by typing the following command and executing all the commands again:

SAVE OUTFILE 'A:CORR.SYS'.

(Note that **the extension .SYS is obligatory**.)

Thereafter, the data commands can be dispensed with and replaced with the command:

GET FILE 'A:CORR.SYS'.

for subsequent analyses.

2.8 LOGGING OUT OF SPSS/PC+

There is a standard (and essential) procedure for finishing a session on SPSS/PC+. When in the MAIN MENU, move the highlight down to **FINISH** and press ↵ . The word FINISH will appear on the scratch pad. Now, simply press [F10], then ↵ . You will then be returned to DOS and receive the DOS prompt.

2.9 PLAN OF A TYPICAL SPSS/PC+ SESSION

In the diagram below, are shown the main steps in setting up and running an SPSS/PC+ session. The remainder of the book is organised around this scheme.

A session on SPSS/PC+ falls into two phases:

(1)   **data entry and exploration** at a general level;
(2)   **statistical analysis**.

Phase 1: Data entry and exploration

Step 1 (Chapter 1)   **Log in** to the computer. If necessary, format a new floppy disk.

Step 2   **Access SPSS/PC+**.

Step 3 (Chapter 3)   **Prepare the data commands**, beginning with the **DATA LIST** command, which gives information about the data and the names of the variables.

Step 4 (Chapter 3)   **Enter the data** between the **BEGIN DATA** and **END DATA** commands. (This step is omitted if the data have already been written to a special data file.)

Step 5 (Chapter 3)   (This step is optional, but highly recommended.)
Add clarificatory labels about the variables with the **VARIABLE LABELS** command, and **decode the numbers** making up the grouping variables with the **VALUE LABELS** command. Add **information about missing values** with the **MISSING VALUE** command.

Step 6 (Chapter 2)   **Execute these data commands** to ensure that there are no errors and to enable SPSS/PC+ to generate a **table of variable names**. If necessary, correct the errors and re-execute the commands.

Step 7 (Chapter 4)   Continue with **commands for listing and exploring the data**.

Step 8   **Execute these additional commands**. Inspect the results for any errors you may have made when typing the data in. This step also helps the user to appreciate the distribution and nature of the data prior to further statistical analysis.

Step 9 (Chapter 2)   **Save all the commands and the data** (if included) by writing them to a file on the floppy disk using **[F9]** and supplying a filename.

In **Phase 2 (Statistical Analysis)**, which is described in Chapter 5, the user chooses appropriate statistical tests and methods.

2.10 SUMMARY

1)   To **log in** to SPSS/PC+, the user must at some point insert a formatted disk.

2)   **Key words in the menus** can be **pasted** on the scratchpad by pressing ↵ .

3)   To **type directly on the scratch pad**, press **[Alt/E]**; to return control to **Menu and Help**, press **[Esc]**.

4)   To **move around the menus** without pasting anything on the scratch pad, use the **arrowed cursor keys**.

5)   To **clear several lines of material from the scratch pad**, mark an area with **[F7]** and delete the marked (yellow) area with **[F8]** and **D** (for delete).

6)   The **function keys (F1 to F10)** are used for editing material on the scratch pad, for writing to and reading from files on floppy disk, for executing commands, for switching windows, and for several other purposes.

7)   To **write material to a file on the floppy disk**, press **[F9]**, then ↵ , type the name of the file, and press ↵ . To **read the contents of a file on to the scratchpad from the floppy disk**, press **[F3]**, then **I** (Insert), and then type the name of the file. During both procedures, the user must give the full file name:

a **letter** indicating the disk drive (eg A:);
a **filename** indicating the content of the file;
an optional **extension** indicating whether the file is a listing file (**.LIS**), a command file (**.CMD**), or a data file (**.DAT**).

The syntax of a full file name is:

letter: filename. extension

8)   To **enter data into SPSS/PC+**, one or more **data commands** are essential. The principal data command is **DATA LIST** (more fully described in Chapter 3).

9)   If **data are to be typed on the scratch pad**, they must be preceded by the command **BEGIN DATA** and followed by the command **END DATA**.

10)   **Commands are executed** when the user presses [**F10**], then ⏎ .

11)   To obtain a **directory** of the files on a disk, press [**F1**], then **F** (for **File list**), type in A:*.*, and press ⏎ . Alternatively, the list of files can be reduced by requesting only files with one particular extension (eg A:*.CMD). The * is the wildcard symbol meaning "anything".

12)   To **save output listing to a named file**, use the **SET/LISTING** command. This is placed above all the other commands on the scratch pad. The execution of this command is an essential preliminary to printing out hard copy of the listing. The format of the command is

SET/LISTING 'A: *filename*'.

Note carefully that the filename is enclosed in single quotes and the command is terminated with a period (.).

13)   **System files** can save computer processing time. It is often advantageous to use the **SAVE** command to store the data commands in a system file. It is then necessary only to write a **GET** command on the scratch pad to enable SPSS/PC+ to read the data commands from the system file when other commands are executed. System files cannot be read on the screen or edited.

14)   **Printing** can be directed either while the user is logged in to SPSS/PC+ or from the computer's DOS system. The usual command is

PRINT *A:filename* .

Note that there are no quotes around the file name.

15) To **terminate a session on SPSS/PC+**, move the MAIN MENU highlight to **FINISH**, press **[F10]**, and then ↵ .

16) A typical SPSS/PC+ session consists of two phases:

1) **data entry and exploration**;

2) **statistical analysis**.

CHAPTER 3

PREPARATION OF DATA COMMANDS

3.1 INTRODUCTION

This chapter describes the entry of the data into the SPSS/PC+ system and the writing of commands that clarify and label the data. The procedures will be discussed under seven headings:

(1)   the preparation of the results for typing in from the keyboard;

(2)   the location of the **DATA LIST** command in the **Menu and Help** window;

(3)   the preparation of the **DATA LIST** command;

(4)   the inclusion of data in the data commands, between the **BEGIN DATA** and **END DATA** commands;

(5)   the entering of data from a separate **data file**;

(6)   the inclusion of **VARIABLE LABELS** and **VALUE LABELS** commands to clarify the names and codes of the variables in the output;

(7)   the identification of missing data by using the **MISSING VALUE** command.

Finally, there will be a section describing the optional use of **titles**, **subtitles**, and **comments**. These are not data commands but can, along with **VARIABLE LABELS** and **VALUE LABELS**, improve the intelligibility of the output.

3.2 PREPARATION OF THE RESULTS FOR TYPING IN FROM THE KEYBOARD

When an experiment has just been completed, the results will almost certainly not be in a form suitable for analysis by computer: there will simply be a large pile of completed experimental records or questionnaires. The researcher must not only extract an orderly set of data from all this but also give SPSS/PC+ clear commands about the form that the data will take. Typically, SPSS/PC+ expects a data set in which each row contains various kinds of information about one particular subject in the investigation: their age; their gender; their performance scores(s) achieved in the experiment; and so on. Such characteristics, or properties of the subject are termed **variables**. The computer must be given a list of the names and types of the variables, and the order in which in which their values will be entered. SPSS/PC+ expects a series of values, each of which relates to a separate variable; moreover, the order of the variables (eg height, weight, score) must be the same for all subjects. When the values of all the variables of a particular subject have been typed in, the data for the next subject will then be typed. SPSS/PC+ will assume that the new values refer to the same pre-specified list of variables in their order of specification in the DATA LIST command. The end result of the data entry process is a rectangular array, or **matrix**, of values, in which the rows represent subjects (or **cases**) and the columns represent variables. A data set ready for typing in might be as follows:

VARIABLE

Subject	score	IQ	gender	age	blood group
1	10	120	F	23	B
2	15		M	38	AB
3	19	110	M	30	B
.	.	.	.	.	.
100	8	101	M	25	O

Notice that the second subject's IQ is missing; perhaps his or her intelligence protocol has been mislaid. There is a potential problem here, because SPSS/PC+ expects to receive a series of values or symbols, one for each of the pre-specified variables. If a missing value or symbol is not flagged in some manner, SPSS/PC+ will read the next value or symbol as the one intended for the previous variable (in this example, M would be read as the value for the missing IQ). Consequently, all the remaining data will be ascribed to the wrong variables. As will be seen later, it is good practice to establish **missing value codes** for any variables that may have missing values. Obviously this code must be some number or symbol which is different from the usual entries (eg a negative value for IQ, an X for gender).

In summary, before data can be entered into SPSS/PC+ from the keyboard, they must be organised into a table whose columns represent variables and whose rows represent subjects. It is, therefore, a good idea to write the data out on a sheet before typing them in to the computer, especially if you decide to use **fixed-field format** (see below). The computer must be apprised of the names and order of the variables on which each (and every) subject is recorded. These are the column headings of the data matrix that is going to be entered into SPSS/PC+. As explained above, a missing value code should also be established, so that the data are entered in their correct places. It is important to think carefully about the variable names, bearing in mind that a name cannot exceed eight characters in length.

The following are some routine questions the user should ask when preparing the data set.

3.2.1   Which variables are measurements and which are grouping variables?

A **measurement** is a number indicating **how much** of some property an individual possesses. Measurements may either take the form of values on an independent scale with units, as in height or weight, or they may merely be statements of a person's rank on the variable in relation to those of other people. A **grouping (or coding) variable**, on the other hand, is a set of arbitrary code numbers, each number often denoting a category of some qualitative variable (whether a characteristic of the subject such as gender, or an experimental condition under which the subject was tested). For example, one could use the code numbers 1 and 2 to denote *male* and *female* respectively. Code numbers are also used to denote ranges of values of a quantitative variable, such as IQ, height or weight.

In a psychological **experiment**, at least one variable (say task complexity) is manipulated by the experimenter, with a view to studying its effect upon another variable, say, the subject's performance. The values of the former, known as the **independent variable**, are thus **assigned** to the subjects in the experiment; whereas those of the latter, known as the **dependent variable**, are measured during the course of the investigation. Sometimes this distinction is identified with that between grouping variables and measurements; but this is incorrect, since (with nominal data), a dependent variable may also be a grouping variable.

The distinction between measurements on the one hand and grouping variables on the other may seem somewhat artificial, when it is considered that grouping variables may be constructed from measurements by defining categories in terms of arbitrary cut-off points. The important thing to remember is that the numbers in a grouping (code) variable do not represent

how much of some characteristic an individual possesses: they are just code numbers indicating category membership, even if the categories have been constructed from true measurements.

3.2.2 Will the data be located in the data commands or in a data file?

Data commands are statements about the data, but need not necessarily contain the data, which can be stored elsewhere, in a separate **data file**. There is, then, the consideration of whether the data should be typed into a separate **data file** or incorporated in the **data commands**. The answer to this question depends on the size of the data set. For example, if the experiment is a small-scale comparison of three training methods, with ten subjects using each method and just one dependent variable (say performance on a test), it is much simpler to include the thirty scores in the data commands. If, however, fifty males and fifty females have been asked to attempt three or more tasks, so that there are more than three hundred scores, then it is better to create a separate data file, which will be easier to edit, and which can be used as input for a succession of different analyses, each with its own set of data commands.

3.2.3 Are the data to be typed in freefield format or in fixed-column format?

In **freefield format**, the data comprise a succession of items separated either by spaces or commas: there is no requirement that the values of a particular variable will occupy any particular column on the screen. SPSS/PC+, however, assumes that any space or comma marks the end of one datum and the start of the next. In **fixed-column format**, the data on a particular variable always occur in specified columns on the screen. Freefield format is simpler to use and is fine for small data sets; but it is not recommended for large data sets, because of the greater risk of erroneous entries in those circumstances.

Here are some examples of data in **free-field format**. It is immaterial whether the data for each subject are entered on separate rows or begin wherever the data from the previous subject finish. When the data are extensive, it is preferable to start a new row for each subject. However, when there are only a few variables (eg gender and score), it is more convenient to type the data along rows, starting a new row only when the previous row is full. So the same data set can be entered like this:

12 23 21 23 34 43 32 12 23 3 33 22 36 45 45 21 28 8 34 23 78 133 34 2 33 65 45 4

or like this:

12 23 21 23 34 43

32 12 23 3 33 22

36 45 45 21 28 8 . . . .

or like this:

12,23,21,23,34,43,32,12,23,3, ...

If commas are used as separators, as in the third style, **a missing value** can be registered by inserting two commas one after the other (, ,); however we prefer to use a pre-specified value for a missing datum, as described in the next section.

The choice of fixed-column format requires the user to work out carefully which columns will be used for each variable by taking into account the largest possible value of any datum (including the decimal point if necessary). For example, gender would require just one column, IQ requires three columns; but what about annual salary? If the values of a variable are decimal fractions, to how many decimal places will the values be given? In fixed-column format, all this must be specified **before** the data are entered and the user may have to make arbitrary decisions.

The table of numbers between the horizontal lines below shows a set of values laid out in **fixed-column format**. Each row represents the data for a subject. The first column is gender, columns 2-4 contain an examination marks, columns 5-7 contain psychological test scores, and columns 8-13 contain sums of money.

Columns

1	2	3	4	5	6	7	8	9	10	11	12	13
1	1	3	2		9	2		6	1	.	5	0
1		9	9	1	1	2	1	1	2	.	7	5
2		8	4		7	5	1	5	5	.	9	0
1	1	2	3	1	0	9		9	9	.	8	5

3.2.4 Are there any missing data and if so, how will they be represented?

The data sets yielded by surveys or experiments are often incomplete: a participant may   not wish to reveal his or her salary; an entry in an experimental protocol sheet may be indecipherable; an experimental condition may have inadvertently been skipped.

Although it is possible to register a missing datum by leaving a blank between commas in freefield format or omitting data in the appropriate columns in fixed-column format, we strongly recommend specifying certain values or symbols for missing data. Obviously care must be taken to choose values or symbols which could not occur as data. Common practices include using a number that lies outside the range of possible values for the variable or using a negative number (provided, of course, that there are no negative data). For example, if the possible range of values is 0-6, the missing-value code might be 9 (or better still, -9); if the maximum score is 60, the missing-value code might be 99 (or -99); and so on.

3.2.5 How are the variables to be named?

There are a number of rules governing the choice of **variable names** (which are entered as part of the DATA LIST command). A variable name must meet the following requirements:

a.   it must **never** exceed eight characters;
b.   it must **always** start with a letter;
c.   it must contain neither a **blank** nor **special symbols** such as &, !, or / (the period (.) and an underlining symbol (_) are allowed);
d.   it cannot be any of the **keywords** that SPSS/PC+ has reserved as special computing terms such as AND, NOT, EQ, BY, and ALL.

Names can be in upper or lower case. Cryptic variable names can be expanded in a special command called VARIABLE LABELS, which comes after DATA LIST (or after END DATA, if the data are included in the data commands).

3.2.6 Have any data to be recoded?

Computers are well suited to the processing of **numerical data**, whether in the form of whole numbers (integers) or decimals. When data are being gathered, however, those on categorical variables such as gender are usually recorded by using letters. Such symbols are known as **alphanumeric data**. It is quite possible, of course, to assign arbitrary **code numbers** to the categories of a variable such as gender or blood group; indeed, this is often necessary at some point in order to perform certain statistical analyses. It is usual, however, to postpone this translation until the data have been entered into SPSS/PC+, because it is much easier to understand them when they are in alphanumeric form.

3.3 FINDING THE DATA LIST COMMAND
IN THE MENU

Use the ↓ cursor key to move the highlight down the MAIN MENU to **read or write data**. Press ↵ or the → cursor key to move into the **read or write data** menu, and move down to **DATA LIST**. Notice that DATA LIST is written in upper case on the menu. This means that these words are an essential part of the command and can be pasted directly on the scratch pad by pressing ↵ . The words DATA LIST will now appear on the scratch pad. In the upper window, a new menu, with the title DATA LIST, now appears. Information about this command is given on the screen.

(Alternatively, type **DATA LIST** on the scratch pad, and press **[Esc]** to obtain the DATA LIST menu.)

3.4 PREPARATION OF THE DATA LIST COMMAND

In the DATA LIST menu, are the words **location of data**. To the right, is a panel explaining **location of data**. It states that data can either be read in from a file on disk, or typed in directly from the keyboard after the **BEGIN DATA** command.

In detail, the two procedures are as follows:

(1)   To read in data from a file, move the highlighting down to **FILE** and press ↵ . A box will appear, in which the user must type the **file name** of the data file (which might be, for example, A:TTEST.DAT) and press ↵ .

(2)   If a data file is not being used, the data will be typed after the **BEGIN DATA** command, which follows the DATA LIST command.

The next step is to specify the format of the data by selecting, from the DATA LIST menu, the **FREE/**, the **FIXED/** or the **TABLE/** option. Press ↵ to paste your choice on the scratch pad. Note that the TABLE/ option is similar to FIXED/; but when the commands are executed by SPSS/PC+, a table will appear on the screen (and in the listing file) showing the names of all the variables, their starting and finishing columns, the type of format, and the maximum width of each variable (ie the number of columns occupied by its maximum value). This option is recommended when there are many variables, because it is very helpful to be reminded of the precise location of data relating to a particular variable in a large data set.

If you have selected **FREE/**, a new menu, headed FREE/, will appear in the upper window and you will be prompted to name the variables. Read the Help on the right side and move the highlight down the menu to see some examples. Then press **[Alt]/T** and type the variable names in the box, remembering the restrictions about variable names (see section 3.2.5 above). **The order in which the variable names are entered must be that in which those variables are organised in the data.** Type the names one after the other with a space (or a comma and a space) between each name. Note that the name of a variable for which the data are alphanumeric must be followed by a bracketed expression comprising the letter **a** (or **A**), followed by a number indicating the maximum number of characters in a datum: for example, the notation *gender (a1)* means that a datum can extend to only one character (M or F); on the other hand *subject (a3)* means that the variable *subject* can extend to three characters, as in s99. This is explained in the menu, under the item **(A)**.

If you selected **FIXED/** or **TABLE/**, a new menu headed FIXED/ or TABLE/ will have appeared in the upper window and you will be prompted to name the variables and specify the column locations for each variable. The FIXED/ or TABLE/ menus include an item **string variables**. String variables are just long alphanumeric variables such as people's names; note that the letter *A* (or *a*) must be typed after the column locations of such a variable name.

When specifying the variable names, the user is given the opportunity to take shortcuts. Suppose the variables are *Time1, Time2, ..., Time20*. Instead of typing in all those labels, each differing from its neighbour only in the number at the end, the user can type *time1 TO time20*. The vital components are the use of the keyword **TO** (upper or lower case) and integers at the end of the variable name with no embedded space (ie *time20*, not *time 20*). For free-field format, the command is:

DATA LIST FREE/time1 TO time20.

For fixed-column format, the command is:

DATA LIST FIXED/time1 TO time20 1- 60.

assuming two columns for each time measurement, plus a space between data. TABLE/ can be used instead of FIXED/. Examples are given in the Help panels.

This completes the DATA LIST command. It should finish with a period (.); if it does not, enter the scratch pad with **[Alt]/E** and type in a period.

3.5 INCLUSION OF DATA IN THE DATA COMMANDS

If the data are not located in a separate data file, they must be typed in after the DATA LIST command, between the **BEGIN DATA** and **END DATA** commands. This can be achieved either by transferring control to the scratch pad (by typing **[Alt]/E**) or by staying in the menus and performing a pasting operation. To paste from the menu, press the ↵ cursor twice to get back to the **read or write data** menu and then use the ↓ cursor to highlight **BEGIN DATA**. Read the information about BEGIN DATA and press ↵ to paste BEGIN DATA on the scratch pad. A blinking cursor on the scratch pad indicates that SPSS/PC+ is expecting the user to type in the data. When doing so, it is essential to bear in mind the ordering of the variables that was specified in the DATA LIST command. If BEGIN DATA has been pasted from the menu, the words END DATA will be on the scratch pad already; but if BEGIN DATA has been typed in by the user, the words END DATA must be typed in manually. In that case, **note that the period (.) must be added.**

The following examples should clarify the procedures that have just been described.

3.5.1 Example 1

Suppose that ten people use a mnemonic technique to commit a list of words to memory. A day later, they are asked to reproduce the list, and the number of words recalled by each person is noted. Their performance is to be compared with that of a control group (also containing ten participants) who memorised the same list of words by rote. The subjects' recall scores are as follows:

Mnemonic group	12 19 13 15 16 21 18 17 10 20
Rote group	11 12 9 12 15 8 13 11 18 7

With only 20 scores, it is easier to enter the data by including them in the data commands, in free-field format. Since there are no missing data, no missing data code need be specified. Since the dependent variable is the number of words recalled, a suitable variable name would be *recall*. Since the independent variable is the group (mnemonic or control) to which a subject has been assigned, a suitable name for that variable would be *group*. This grouping variable can be defined as a coding variable by assigning the code value 1 to the mnemonic group and the value 2 to the control (rote learning) group.

The commands on the scratch pad should appear as follows:

```
DATA LIST FREE/group recall.
BEGIN DATA.
1 12 1 19 1 13 1 15 1 16 1 21 1 18 1 17 1 10 1 20
2 11 2 12 2 9 2 12 2 15 2 8 2 13 2 11 2 18 2 7
END DATA.
```

Note that in free-field format, it is immaterial how the data are distributed among lines. It is even possible to have each person's data on a separate line thus

1 12
1 19
1 13
. ...

It is also immaterial whether the commands are in upper or lower case letters; but we consider it best to reserve upper case for SPSS/PC+ command words and lower case for variable names.

3.5.2 Example 2

Twenty subjects take two ability tests. Their scores are as follows:

	Test 1	Test 2
Subject 1	15	22
Subject 2	10	12
. . . .	. .	. .
Subject 20	18	26

With so few scores, it is simpler to include the data in the data commands. In this example, both variables are sets of measurements, so there is no grouping variable, and thus no need for any coding variables. The scores obtained under test 1 and test 2 have been given the variable names *test1* and *test2*, respectively: **note that there must be no spaces among the characters in a variable name**.

The commands on the scratch pad should appear as follows:

```
DATA LIST FREE/test1 test2.
BEGIN DATA.
15 22 10 12 ..... 18 26
END DATA.
```

3.5.3 Example 3

Twenty subjects are given a battery of ten psychological tests. The subjects' test scores are recorded, together with their gender, their age and the level of education they have attained. With a data set like this, in which several measurements are made on each person, it is better to enter the data in **fixed-column** format from a separate data file. In this case, however, we shall incorporate the data into the data commands. Note that alphanumeric variables must have **(a)** or **(A)** after the variable name, but no digit is placed immediately after the **a** or **A**.

The commands should appear as follows:

```
DATA LIST FIXED/gender 1(a) age 3-4 educlevl 6 test1 TO test10 8-37.
BEGIN DATA.
M 21 4 24 32 24 31 25 67 49 83   7 63
M 20 3 30 21 25 30 28 50 40 76  21 45
F  34 4 36 45 34 29 32 40 43 70  18 48
END DATA.
```

In the first line, to the right of the / sign, the variables are listed in order. After each variable name, comes a range of numbers specifying the columns containing the values of that variable: for example, *age 3-4* tells the computer to reserve columns 3 and 4 for the values of the variable *age*. The entry for the variable *gender* reads: *gender 1(a)*, where *(a)* indicates that this is an **alphanumeric** variable. With fixed-column format, there is no need to indicate the width of an alphanumeric variable, because that is done by the column specifications.

The use of the keyword **TO** in the expression *test1* TO *test10* is a shorter alternative to writing out *test1 8-10, test2 11-13, test3 14-16, ..., test10 35-37*. (Strictly, we do not need column 37, but to use the shortcut, each of the ten variables must receive the same column allocation.)

Note that when specifying the columns in which the values of a particular variable are to appear, the user may allow extra columns for spaces between the values. If three columns have been specified for a value that cannot exceed two digits, the user has the choice of either preceding or following the numerical value with a space: for example, the value 7 in the first row of data could have been typed into column 32 instead of column 33.

3.6 ENTERING DATA FROM A DATA FILE

When the data set is large, it is usually more convenient to prepare a separate data file than to type all the data into the data commands between the BEGIN DATA and END DATA commands. A data file is prepared by typing data directly on the scratch pad without any accompanying statements or commands. Enter the scratch pad with **[Alt]/E** and type in the data, either in free format or in the format you will eventually specify in DATA LIST. Having written your data on the scratch pad, save them to a named file (section 2.5.3). A suitable file name is A:PSYCTEST.DAT (ie disk drive A, filename PSYCTEST, and the optional extension .DAT to show that it is a data file).

The following example will serve as an illustration of these points.

Two hundred students of architecture have been given a battery of tests and questionnaires. There are many variables, including examination results, tests of spatial ability, previous experience with construction kits, and whether any of the students' relatives are (or were) architects.

For a data set of this size and complexity, it is best to enter the data into a separate file in fixed format. The allocation of the values of each variable to specified columns must be carefully decided beforehand, making sure that each variable's column allocation is sufficient for the largest possible value the variable can take. The TABLE/ format option is selected, so that the column location of each variable will be included at the beginning of the listing file when the commands are executed by SPSS/PC+ thus:

DATA LIST FILE 'A:ARCHSTUD.DAT' TABLE/gender 1 (a) conkit 3 archrels 5
    maths 7-8 physics 9-10 english 12-13 french 15-16 spatabil 18-19 . . etc..

This commands SPSS/PC+ to read data from a file stored on a floppy disk which will be inserted in drive A. The name of the file is A:ARCHSTUD.DAT. The data are in fixed format, with column allocations as specified.

3.7 THE VARIABLE LABELS AND VALUE LABELS COMMANDS

The addition of certain optional commands after the basic DATA LIST command can work wonders for the comprehensibility of SPSS/PC+ output. Details of these subcommands are to be found in **labels and formatting**, in the **read or write data** menu. (Alternatively, type **VARIABLE LABELS** or **VALUE LABELS** and press **[Esc]**.) Look at the examples in the help panel before writing your own commands.

Examples:

VARIABLE LABELS Archstud 'Architectural Students' spatabil 'Spatial Ability'
    age 'Age in Years'.

VALUE LABELS gender 'M' 'Male' 'F' 'Female' / educlevl 1 'One A Level'
    2 'Two A Levels' 3 'Three A Levels' 4 'Scottish Equivalent'
    5 'Irish Equivalent' 6 'Other Qualifications'.

Note that symbols, such as M and F, must be in quotes. In the VALUE LABELS command, variables must be separated by /; but this is not so in the VARIABLE LABELS command. Note also the period (.) at the end of each command.

3.8 THE CODING OF MISSING DATA

Suppose that we have a set of data on a group of children, including their ages, their genders and their performance on several psychological tests. Unfortunately, in several cases, the gatherer of the data has failed to record a child's gender. It has been decided to record gender by means of a coding variable, in which 1 denotes a boy and 2 a girl. A suitable missing value code could be any number other than 1 or 2: for example, 9 would be a reasonable choice. This decision is communicated to SPSS/PC+ in the following command:

MISSING VALUE gender (9).

Whenever the number 9 occurs as a value of the variable *gender*, the computer will now treat it as a missing value and ignore it accordingly when calculating such statistics as the mean and standard deviation.

The choice of a code for a missing item obviously must be one which cannot occur as a datum. As mentioned earlier in this chapter, some people choose a value such as 9, or 99, or 999 which is beyond the possible range of data values, while others prefer the convention of using a negative value such as -9 (provided, of course, that negative data values cannot occur). As another example, suppose that when pressing a button in response to the appearance of a light, people typically show reaction latencies of around 800 to 1500 milliseconds. A reasonable missing value code here might be a number such as -1, since negative reaction times are impossible:

MISSING VALUE reactime (-1).

Missing value codes can be assigned to several variables in a single MISSING VALUE command such as:

MISSING VALUE gender (9) reactime (-1) score1 TO score9 (999).

This declares that when 9, -1, and 999 are encountered as values among the data for the variables *gender*, *reactime*, and for the nine variables *score1* to *score9* respectively, SPSS/PC+ will register these data as missing values.

Further details about the **MISSING VALUE** command and examples of its use are given in **labels and formatting** in the **read and write data** menu. This information can be obtained either by retaining control in the menu system and using the cursor keys, or by transferring control to the scratch pad, typing MISSING VALUE and using **[Esc]**.

3.9 TITLES, SUBTITLES AND COMMENTS

The optional addition of a title at the head of the data commands can serve to remind the user which experiment is being analysed. The **TITLE** command prints the title on every page of the listing. For example, the command

TITLE 'Colour Blindness Study'.

prints **Colour Blindness Study** on every page after the page number. If the text is not in single or double quotes, it is reproduced in upper case letters. A title can be up to 58 characters long and can include apostrophes and periods, provided it starts and finishes with double quotes, followed by the usual period **after** the concluding double quote.

The **SUBTITLE** command adds a left-justified subtitle beneath the title (if any). The same rules apply as for the TITLE command, except that it can be up to 64 characters long. For example, the command

SUBTITLE Ishihara Test Scores.

prints **ISHIHARA TEST SCORES** on each listing page, until replaced by another subtitle. Note that the subtitle will be printed in upper case, because no single or double quotes were included in the command.

It is often useful to write **comments** among commands to remind oneself of the purpose of the exercise without causing them to be printed in the listing. This is done by using an asterisk (*) as the first character. A comment can extend over several lines and include several sentences, provided no line finishes with a period before the final period marking the end of the comment. For example, the comment

*This section examines males only. The data includes all those
tested from 1985-1992.

would be echoed in the listing among the commands, but would not appear on each page of results.

Incidentally, the asterisk is invaluable for "commenting" out commands temporarily when several commands are about to be submitted for execution with **[F10]**. To do this, move the cursor to the first character of the command and type in an asterisk (*); this will have the effect of turning the command (including all its subcommands) into a non-executable comment.

Details of **titles**, **subtitles**, and **comments** can be found in the menu, under **titles and comments**. This is part of **session control and info** within the MAIN MENU. Alternatively, type **TITLE** on the scratch pad and press **[Esc]**.

3.10 SUMMARY

1)   Before preparing a **DATA LIST** command, it is important to spend some time deciding upon the following points about the data:

a) Are there any **grouping variable**s and if so which are they?

b) Are the data going to be typed into a separate **data file** or incorporated in the data commands between **BEGIN DATA** and **END DATA** commands? This decision depends on how many data there are, because large sets of data are more conveniently handled in separate data files.

c) Are the data going to be typed in **free-field** or in **fixed-column** format? Again, the right decision depends upon the amount of data, especially the number of variables. Fixed-column format is preferred when there are many variables.

d) Are there any **missing data**? If so, how will they be coded?

e) What **variable names** will be used, bearing in mind the restrictions on such names (particularly that their length cannot exceed eight characters)?

2)   The **DATA LIST** command is found in the **read or write data** menu. Alternatively, type DATA LIST and press **[Esc]**. Examples and details of the various options are given in the help panels. Data may be accessed from a separate **data file** or inserted between **BEGIN DATA** and **END DATA** commands within the data commands.

The command for free-field format is

DATA LIST FREE/ *variable names.*

The command for fixed-column format is

DATA LIST FIXED/ *variable name and columns.*
or
DATA LIST TABLE/ *variable names and columns.*

(The **TABLE/** option lists the columns for the variables in the output.)

When data are stored in a separate **data file**, the command needs an extra component to identify the name of the file, thus:

DATA LIST FILE 'A:*filename*' **FREE/** *variable names.*
or
DATA LIST FILE 'A:*filename*' **FIXED/** *variable names and columns.*
or
DATA LIST FILE 'A:*filename*' **TABLE/** *variable names and columns.*

For example, if the data are in a free-field file *A:testdata.dat*, the command is:

DATA LIST FILE 'A:testdata.dat' **FREE/** *variable names.*

3)   A **data file** is prepared by typing the data (without any commands) directly on the scratch pad and then saving to a named file with **[F9]** and typing in a file name (eg A:testdata.dat).

4)   Extra information about variable names and the codes used for grouping variables can be added with the **VARIABLE LABELS** and the **VALUE LABELS** commands. Information about these will be found in **labels and formatting** in the **read or write data** menu:

VARIABLE LABELS *variable name 'label'   variable name 'label'* etc .
VALUE LABELS *variable name value 'label'   value 'label'* etc
                 /variable name value 'label'   value 'label' etc .

If a value is not a number (eg a letter such as M), it must be in single quotes.

5)   Information to enable the computer to recognise missing values is added with the **MISSING VALUE** command, which is also to be found in **labels and formatting**:

MISSING VALUE *variable(s)* (*value*) *variable(s)* (*value*) etc .

6)   A **title** and **subtitles** can be added by using the **TITLE** and **SUBTITLE**

commands. These result in listing being annotated with the information contained in these commands and can assist in identifying the experiment or survey being analysed. Should the user want extra comments to appear in the command file, but not in the output listing, one or more **comment statements** can be used. A comment statement is one prefaced by an asterisk (*). Comments interspersed among commands serve as a useful reminder of the purpose of each block of commands.

CHAPTER 4

LISTING AND EXPLORING DATA

4.1 INTRODUCTION

The SPSS/PC+ package has been designed to carry out a wide range of statistical tests with amazing ease and rapidity. Before the user can proceed with any data analysis, however, certain preparatory steps must first be taken.

First of all, it is essential to check whether the data have been correctly entered into the computer: a chain is no stronger than its weakest link. It is of paramount importance that the user check thoroughly to ensure that all subsequent inferences rest upon a firm foundation of correct information. Having checked that the data have been correctly entered, one might be tempted to proceed immmediately to command SPSS/PC+ to perform various formal statistical tests. The user is strongly warned against this, however.

The process of data analysis should be thought of as taking place in two phases:

(1)   **Exploration and description of the data**.
(2)   **Confirmation of data characteristics**.

It is to the second phase of analysis that formal statistical testing belongs: the performance of a t-test or an analysis of variance should be seen as the end-point of a careful consideration of the features of your own data set, rather than an automatic first step.

There are two main reasons for taking such a cautious approach. Firstly, the user who proceeds

45

immediately to carry out various tests may miss the most illuminating features of the data. Secondly, the performance of a statistical test always presupposes that certain assumptions about the data are correct. Should these assumptions be false, the results of statistical tests may be quite misleading.

The researcher who explores a data set thoroughly may find therein characteristics of great psychological significance. There is always the possibility, however, that these patterns are chance occurrences and that, were the research to be repeated with fresh subjects, they might disappear. The purpose of a statistical test is to **confirm** the characteristics of a data set, in the sense that the researcher wants to be able to say, with a high degree of certainty, that a characteristic of the data has not arisen through chance and to be confident that were more data to be gathered, it would reappear.

The psychologist works with several kinds of data:

(a) **Measurements on an independent scale with units**. (These are called **scalar** or **interval** data.)

(b) **Ranks** (or ordered categories).

(c) **Nominal data**, which are merely statements of qualitative category membership.

Suppose we have a set of measurements, say the heights in inches of a group of women. There are usually three things we want to know about such a data set:

(1) the general **level**, or **average value**, of the scores;

(2) the **dispersion** of the values, ie the degree to which the individual values tend to **vary** around or **deviate** from the average, as opposed to clustering closely around it;

(3) the **distribution shape**, ie the relative frequencies with which scores are to be found within various regions of the total range of the variable.

In this book, we must assume that you already have some knowledge of the statistics that measure the level and dispersion of a set of scores. The most well-known measures of level are the **mean**, the **median** and the **mode**; and dispersion is measured by the **standard deviation** and **quantile range** statistics. We also assume that you understand some terms relating to the distribution of the data set, such as **skewness**, **bimodality** and so on. Should you be a little rusty on these matters, we strongly recommend that you read the relevant chapters of a good text on the topic, such as Gravetter & Wallnau (1992), chapters 1 to 4, Howell (1992), chapters 1 and 2, Anderson (1989), chapters 1 to 3. Hartwig & Dearing (1979) provide a readable account of a set of more recent statistical measures known collectively as **exploratory data analysis (EDA)**.

Before considering the various statistical measures available on SPSS/PC+, it might be useful to remind the reader of the procedure for executing commands (the procedure was briefly described in section 2.7.2) and to describe how to correct, amend or supplement existing commands on the scratch pad.

4.2 COMMANDS: EXECUTION, CORRECTION, AMENDMENT, AND SUPPLEMENTATION

4.2.1 Executing commands

In previous chapters, it was seen that while control is in **Menu and Help**, certain commands can be pasted on the scratch pad. These commands, however, are not executed at that point. To have them executed, the user must use the function key **[F10]** as follows. Press **[Alt]/E** to transfer control to the scratch pad. Next, use the cursor keys to move the cursor up to the top line of the commands (anywhere on the top line will do), press **[F10]** and then ↵. SPSS/PC+ will execute all the commands from the cursor downwards. The commands will appear successively on the screen as they are executed, followed by a screenful of output, with the word MORE written in the top right corner. This display will remain until the **space bar** is pressed, which will bring more output to the screen.

It is also possible to execute a block of marked commands using the **[F7]** key to mark the starting and ending commands of the block (see section 2.3.1), pressing **[F10]**, selecting **run marked Area**, and pressing ↵.

4.2.2 Making corrections to commands

Sometimes, instead of the expected screenful of output, an **error messsage** appears (there may be multiple error messages). Such errors, however, cannot be corrected until the listing is complete and the commands on the scratch pad reappear on the screen. It may be necessary to press the space bar several more times in response to a succession of MORE prompts. Once the commands do reappear, it may be found that the multiple errors resulted from omitting a period (.) at the end of one of the commands (eg DATA LIST). Corrections can be made to the commands on the scratch pad by pressing **[Alt]/E** and moving the cursor to the appropriate place(s). If help is needed from **Menu and Help**, press **[Alt]/M** or **[Esc]** to restore the menus to the upper half of the screen.

If you wish to see the listing again in order to check on the details of the error message(s), it can be shown on the upper half of the screen in place of **Menu and Help** by pressing **[Alt]/S** (the S stands for Switch). The cursor will be there, too, to enable you to scroll up and down the listing using the ↑ and ↓ cursor keys. The listing can be left in place while corrections are made to the commands by pressing **[Alt]/E** to transfer the cursor back to the scratch pad. At any time, the **Menu and Help** display can be restored in place of the listing by pressing **[Alt]/S** again.

After the errors have been corrected, it may be necessary to execute all the commands again by moving the cursor to the topmost command, pressing **[F10]** and ↵ . If, however, the error was very minor (eg a misspelt variable name), it may suffice to leave the cursor on the corrected line before pressing **[F10]** and ↵ .

4.2.3 Amending or supplementing commands

Once commands have been executed without error, the user frequently alters existing commands, or adds additional commands or subcommands. This is easily done by working directly on the scratch pad, or by returning to the **Menu and Help** mode and pasting the required material on the scratch pad. As in the case of corrections mentioned above, it is not necessary to run the cursor up to the top line prior to execution, because SPSS/PC+ retains details about executed commands in a temporary **active file**. It is only necessary to move the cursor to the first of any new or altered lines on the scratch pad before pressing **[F10]** and ↵ .

4.3 THE LIST COMMAND

A quick check on whether the data have been transcribed accurately can be made by using the LIST command. Use the ↓ cursor key to move down the options in the MAIN MENU to **analyze data**. Next, with the → cursor key, move into the **analyze data** menu and down to **reports and tables**. Move to the right into the **reports and tables** menu, in which LIST is the top item. Press ↵ to paste LIST on the scratch pad and read the information about the options for LIST. An alternative (quick) way of getting to the LIST menu is to type LIST on the scratch pad and then press **[Esc]** for the menu. The LIST menu will appear in the upper window.

Example: Suppose the following commands have been written on the scratch pad:

```
DATA LIST FREE/group score.
BEGIN DATA.
1 12 1 19 1 13 1 15 1 16 1 21 1 18 1 17 1 10 1 20
2 11 2 12 2 9 2 12 2 15 2 8 2 13 2 11 2 18 2 7
END DATA.
LIST.
```

Run the cursor up to the top line and press **[F10]**, followed by ↵ . This will cause the values of all variables to be listed. A table is generated with two columns of numbers, one labelled GROUP, the other SCORE.

The user may want only the values of a specified variable, say *score*, to be displayed. In that case, the LIST command would be:

```
LIST/VARIABLES score.
```

This would result in the listing of a single column of values, headed SCORE.

4.4 COMMANDS FOR DESCRIPTIVE STATISTICS

Before the user embarks upon the preparation of descriptive statistics commands, it is strongly recommended that the data commands associated with the naming of variables and the input of the data be executed first.   This ensures that there are no errors in these commands or in the input of the data.   But the major advantage is that once a DATA LIST command has been executed, SPSS/PC+ generates a table of the **variable names** from which selections can subsequently be made for pasting into the descriptive statistics commands.   Besides saving extra typing, this ensures that the variable names are correctly spelt.

The **descriptive statistics** menu contains the most useful commands for exploring data, namely FREQUENCIES, DESCRIPTIVES, CROSSTABS, MEANS and EXAMINE. This menu is found under **analyze data** in the MAIN MENU. Using the → cursor key, move right into the **analyze data** menu and then right again into **descriptive statistics**. The choice of command depends upon the type of data being analysed.

The **FREQUENCIES** command gives frequency distributions for all types of data (nominal, ranks, and scalar). There are options for additional statistics, and for displays such as barcharts and histograms (see also the **EXAMINE** command below for other ways of displaying barcharts and histograms).

The **DESCRIPTIVES** command provides a quick way of generating several well-known statistics such as the mean, standard deviation, variance, maximum and minimum values, range and sum. If means and standard deviations are needed for subpopulations, use the **MEANS** command described below, instead of DESCRIPTIVES.

The **CROSSTABS** command generates contingency tables, which list cell frequencies for data classified by at least two variables. The tables also show row and column frequencies and percentages. Various statistics computed from contingency tables, such as chi-square, the phi coefficient, the contingency coefficient, lambda, Kendall's tau-b and tau-c, Pearson's correlation coefficient r, and gamma are available in the /**STATISTICS** subcommand.

The **MEANS** command computes the means and standard deviations of subpopulations (as defined by values of a grouping or coding variable). The command also has an optional subcommand for a one-way analysis of variance. **Note that this command, despite its name, cannot be used to calculate the means of variables that have not been categorised by a grouping variable; for such variables, use the DESCRIPTIVES command (described above) instead.**

The most comprehensive command for exploring data is **EXAMINE**, which has many useful options within its extensive system of subcommands. The subcommand /**PLOT** can be used to obtain a number of graphs and displays, such as histograms, stem-and-leaf displays, boxplots, and normal probability plots. Other subcommands include /**FREQUENCIES**, which generates frequency distributions of scalar data (the separate **FREQUENCIES** command described above must be used for nominal and ordinal data), /**PERCENTILES** for finding the values of specified percentiles, and /**STATISTICS** for printing a wide range of statistics. These subcommands can be selected and pasted successively from **Menu and Help**. The whole list of selected subcommands of EXAMINE may spread over several lines of the scratch pad and there should be no period (.) until after the final subcommand.

4.4.1 Example illustrating the various descriptive statistics commands

The following example demonstrates the use of all the descriptive statistics commands, though in practice one would be unlikely to include them all, because there is some overlap in the information they provide. The data, comprising the heights, weights and blood groups of twenty men and twenty women, are not fully reproduced below.

```
DATA LIST FREE / gender(a1) weight height blood(a2).
BEGIN DATA.
M 75 178 O
M 100 196 A

....
F 60 163 O
F 51 142 O

....
END DATA.
VARIABLE LABELS weight 'Weight in Kilograms'   height 'Height in Centimetres'.
VALUE LABELS gender 'M' 'Male' 'F' 'Female'/
        blood 'O ' 'Group O' 'A ' 'Group A' 'B ' 'Group B' 'AB' 'Group AB'.
```

```
FREQUENCIES/VARIABLES gender blood.
DESCRIPTIVES/VARIABLES weight height.
MEANS/TABLES weight height BY gender.
CROSSTABS/TABLES gender BY blood.
EXAMINE/VARIABLES weight height BY gender
        /PERCENTILES (25 50 75)
        /PLOT STEMLEAF BOXPLOT HISTOGRAM
        /STATISTICS  DESCRIPTIVES.
```

Note the following points:

DATA LIST command: The (a1) after *gender* and (a2) after *blood* signify alphanumeric variables, because *gender* has been recorded as M and F, and *blood* as O, A, B, AB.

VARIABLE LABELS command: This optional command provides fuller names for the two measurement variables, which are printed in the listing.

VALUE LABELS command: This optional command supplies expanded names for the levels of the two alphanumeric variables. Note that all the level symbols are in quotes (eg 'M' 'A ') and that in the case of the variable *blood*, each quote must enclose two symbols or a symbol and a space, because the variable was declared as (a2) in the **DATA LIST** command.

FREQUENCIES command: This command can process the two qualitative variables.

DESCRIPTIVES command: This command provides the mean, standard deviation, and minimum and maximum values for the two scalar variables.

MEANS command: This command includes **BY** in order to specify the subpopulations for which means are required. In this example, the subpopulations are defined by the variable *gender*.

CROSSTABS command: This command crosstabulates *gender* and *blood*.

EXAMINE command: This command explores the two variables *weight* and *height*, both in the data set as a whole and within each gender separately. The subcommand **/PERCENTILES** here includes the request for the 25th, 50th and 75th percentiles, but others can be requested. The subcommand **/PLOT** requests a variety of diagrams for illustrating the distributions of *weight* and *height*. Finally, the subcommand **/STATISTICS DESCRIPTIVES** prints a whole range of descriptive statistics for *weight* and *height*.

Selected excerpts from the listing are shown on the next few pages to illustrate the use of these commands.

Part of the FREQUENCIES listing

BLOOD

Value Label	Value	Frequency	Percent	Valid Percent	Cum Percent
Group A	A	6	18.8	18.8	18.8
Group AB	AB	3	9.4	9.4	28.1
Group B	B	6	18.8	18.8	46.9
Group O	O	17	53.1	53.1	100.0
		-------		-------	
	TOTAL	32	100.0	100.0	

Valid Cases 32   Missing Cases 0

The DESCRIPTIVES listing

Number of Valid Observations (Listwise) =   32.00

Variable	Mean	Std Dev	Minimum	Maximum	N	Label
WEIGHT	70.22	15.93	48.00	120.00	32	Weight in Kilograms
HEIGHT1	70.28	13.68	142.00	196.00	32	Height in Centimetres

The MEANS listing

Summaries of   HEIGHT   Height in Centimetres
By levels of   GENDER

Variable	Value	Label	Mean	Std Dev	Cases
For Entire Population			170.2813	13.6789	32
GENDER	F	Female	163.9375	12.0635	16
GENDER	M	Male	176.6250	12.4626	16

Total Cases = 32

Summaries of   WEIGHT   Weight in Kilograms
By levels of   GENDER

Variable	Value	Label	Mean	Std Dev	Cases
For Entire Population			70.2188	15.9287	32
GENDER	F	Female	60.1250	9.2511	16
GENDER	M	Male	80.3125	14.8805	32

Total Cases = 32

The CROSSTABS listing

GENDER by   BLOOD

	Count	BLOOD Group A A	Group AB AB	Group B B	Group O O	Row Total
GENDER						
Female	F	3	1	3	9	16 50.0
Male	M	3	2	3	8	16 50.0
	Column Total	6 18.8	3 9.4	6 18.8	17 53.1	32 100.0

Note that the upper value for each row and column total is the sum of the cell values, and the lower value is the percentage.

The EXAMINE command: part of the subcommand /PERCENTILES (25 50 75)

Percentiles

	25.0000	50.0000	75.0000
Percentiles	25.0000	50.0000	75.0000
HAVERAGE	162.2500	170.5000	181.5000
Tukey's Hinges	162.5000	170.5000	181.0000

The EXAMINE command: part of the subcommand /STATISTICS DESCRIPTIVES

WEIGHT   Weight in Kilograms

Valid cases: 32.0   Missing cases: .0   Percent missing: .0

Mean	70.2188	Std Err	2.8158	Min	48.0000
Skewness	1.0861	Median	69.5000	Variance	253.7248
Max	120.0000	S E Skew	.4145	5% Trim	69.0625
Std Dev	15.9287	Range	72.0000	Kurtosis	1.8471
IQR	18.5000	S E Kurt	.8094		

The EXAMINE command: part of the subcommand
/PLOT HISTOGRAM and PLOT STEMLEAF

HEIGHT   Height in Centimetres

Frequency	Bin Center		Frequency	Stem	&	Leaf
3.00	145.0000	***	3.00	14	.	256
2.00	155.0000	**	2.00	15	.	01
8.00	165.0000	********	8.00	16	.	00234559
9.00	175.0000	*********	9.00	17	.	000125568
7.00	185.0000	*******	7.00	18	.	0022235
3.00	195.0000	***	3.00	19	.	006

Bin width : 10.00
Each star: 1 case(s)

Stem width: 10.00
Each leaf: 1 case(s)

The EXAMINE command: part of the subcommand /PLOT BOXPLOT

The subcommand /PLOT BOXPLOT provides a separate boxplot diagram for each variable, and also diagrams with boxplots side-by-side for each variable subdivided by the grouping variable.   Thus in this example there are boxplot diagrams for *weight* and for *height* (neither reproduced here), for *weight* subdivided by *gender* (reproduced on the next page), and for *height* subdivided by *gender* (not reproduced here).

Boxplots provide a valuable visual comparison of the distributions of variables subdivided by the grouping variable, in this example of *height* by *gender*. The asterisk represents the median value. The box embraces the middle 50% of the cases (ie from the 25th percentile to the 75th percentile) whilst the extensions (known as whiskers) connect the largest and smallest values that are not categorised as outliers or extreme values.   An outlier (O) is defined as a value more than 1.5 box-lengths away from the box, and an extreme value (E) as more than 3 box-lengths away from the box.

The location of the asterisk within the box is indicative of whether the distribution is symmetric: it is clear that the distribution of heights for females is much more symmetric than that for males.   This is confirmed in the histograms and stem-and-leaf plots (not reproduced here) for height by each gender. Notice the outlier identified as Case 3 under the boxplot for males. The height of case 3 is 145 cm, a much lower than average height for males. Boxplots are especially useful for identifying outliers and extreme values in data sets.

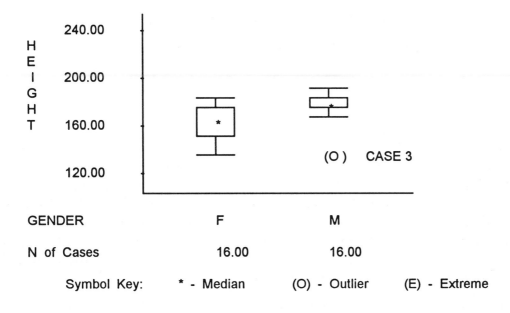

4.5 MANIPULATION OF THE DATA SET

4.5.1 The need to reduce or transform the data set

After a data set has been entered into SPSS/PC+, it may be necessary to modify it in certain ways. For example, an exploratory data analysis may have revealed that atypical scores, or outliers, have exerted undue influence, or **leverage**, upon the values of statistics such as the mean and standard deviation (for a discussion of outliers, see Hartwig & Dearing, 1979). One approach to this problem is to remove the outliers and repeat the analysis with the remaining scores, on the grounds that it is better to have statistics that describe 95% of the data well than 100% of it badly.

The use of the Pearson correlation presupposes a **linear** relationship between two variables. If that requirement is not met, the value of r can be highly misleading. Sometimes the relationship between two variables can be made linear by working not with the original values of a variable, but with a **transformation,** such as the square root, or the logarithm. Other statistical tests require that the distribution of the data have certain characteristics. Again, the use of a transformation may achieve this.

These and other manipulations are most easily achieved by saving the commands to a file on disk, so that they can be recalled to the scratch pad and modified as necessary.

4.5.2   Selection of data: the SELECT IF and PROCESS IF commands

It is often useful to be able to conduct analyses upon subsets of the data, or to exclude certain cases with outlying values. This can be achieved by inserting, immediately after the data commands, either the global **SELECT IF** command, or one or more local **PROCESS IF** commands.   Details of both commands can be found in the **modify data or files** item in the **MAIN MENU**.   Having highlighted **modify data or files**, move rightwards into that menu and then down to **select or weight data**.   Alternatively, type **SELECT IF** or **PROCESS IF** on the scratch pad and press **[Esc]**. The appropriate menu will then appear.   This contains details and gives examples of the **SELECT IF** and **PROCESS IF** commands.   Further details and examples are given when the item **( )** is expanded with the → cursor key. The commands can either be typed on the scratch pad or pasted from the menu.

Suppose that the data include a coded grouping variable *gender,* where the numbers 1 and 2 represent the categories *male* and *female*, respectively.   Perhaps the researcher wishes to select only the data from the male subjects.   The following command, inserted immediately after the data commands, will achieve this.

SELECT IF (gender EQ 1).

It can be seen from this example that the command contains a logical expression within brackets. This expression can contain **relational operators**, such as **EQ, LT,** and **GT** (see the list below), the **logical operators AND, OR,** and **NOT,**   the **mathematical operators** +, -, *, and /, and **functions**, such as **ABS** and **SQRT**. A SELECT IF command, therefore, can contain complex expressions, as in the following example:

SELECT IF (gender EQ 1 AND ABS (zscore) GT 1.96).

Should the user wish to exclude a case (perhaps because it has outliers on some variables), the command must include an alphanumeric term in quotes. (Here we assume that in the data set, subjects, or cases, have been identified as S1, S2, . . . , these values making up the variable *case.*) To exclude all the data from Subject (case) 17, the command would be:

SELECT IF (case NE 'S17 ').

Notice that when an alphanumeric variable arises in an expression, the string specifying its value (S17 in this example) must be enclosed in quotes. Moreover, **there must be sufficient characters and (if necessary) spaces to match the specification in the DATA LIST command**.   In this case, that specification was *case(a4).*   There must therefore be a space between the 7 and the right hand bracket.

The following command would select only the males from among the first 50 cases:

SELECT IF (case LE 51 AND gender EQ 1).

The following is a list of the most useful relational and logical operators.

EQ	**equal to**	
NE	**not equal to**	
LT	**less than**	**RELATIONAL**
GT	**greater than**	
LE	**less than or equal to**	
GE	**greater than or equal to**	

- -

AND	**and**	
OR	**or**	**LOGICAL**
NOT	**not**	

- -

The user may wish to make a whole series of selections during the execution of a set of commands. For example, the data for the males might be required for one run through the statistical commands and the data from the females for another. In that case, the local **PROCESS IF** command should be used instead of the global **SELECT IF** command. Several **PROCESS IF** commands can appear in the same command file, in which case each new one will override its predecessor. Note that only relational operators can be included in a **PROCESS IF** commmand; if a more complex expression is needed, a single **SELECT IF** command must be used.

The following commands will process males in the first batch of commands and females in the second batch :

PROCESS IF (gender EQ 1).
various commands

PROCESS IF   (gender EQ 2).
various commands

4.5.3 The COMPUTE command

The **COMPUTE** command can be used either to transform one or more stored variables into a new variable (say a square root or a logarithm), or to change the values of an existing variable. This versatile command can be found in **modify data value,** which is in **modify data or files** in the **MAIN MENU.** This menu can also be obtained by typing **COMPUTE** on the scratch pad and pressing **[Esc]**.

For example, suppose that from the stored variable *score*, the user wishes to create another variable *sqrtval*, which is the square root of the original variable. The command is:

COMPUTE sqrtval = SQRT(score).

Note the brackets around *score*, the argument of the function.

Within the **COMPUTE** menu, is the item **instructions**, which gives details of the other available mathematical operators and functions.

The **COMPUTE** command can be used to overwrite the values of a variable (such as *score*) with, say, the square roots or logarithms (or some other transformation) of those values. For example, the command

COMPUTE score = SQRT(score).

will overwrite the original values of the variable *score* with the square roots of those values; provided, of course, that none of the scores has a negative value. **Note carefully that the first of the two COMPUTE commands that we described preserves the original values of the variable *score*, whereas the second command overwrites them with the new values.** (The original values would still be stored in the file on disk, of course; but saving the edited data set to the same file name would result in those values also being replaced by their square roots, or whatever other transformation might be chosen.)

The **COMPUTE** command can also be used to create new variables by combining the values of two or more of the variables in the original data set. For example, the command

COMPUTE meanval = (French + German + Spanish)/3.

would create a new variable, *meanval*, each value of which is the average of those of the variables *French*, *German* and *Spanish* for any particular subject.

The most commonly used transformation functions are

LG10	**logarithm to the base 10**
SQRT	**square root**
LN	**natural logarithm**
ABS	**absolute value**

4.5.4   The RECODE command

We have seen that the **COMPUTE** command operates upon one or more of the entries in the **rows** of a data set, so that there will be as many values in the transformation as there were in the original variable.   Sometimes, however, the user, rather than wanting a transformation that will convert all the values of one or more variables systematically, may want to alter the possible values **within** a variable.   Having   defined   a variable such as social class as comprising five categories, for example, the researcher may subsequently wish to combine two or more of the original categories into a single category.   Suppose that categories 3, 4 and 5 are now to be given the single value of 3.   This can be achieved by using the command **RECODE** as follows:

RECODE class (3, 4, 5 = 3).

For a more complex example, suppose that the original five categories are to be reduced to 2 new categories, by combining old categories 1 and 2 into the new category 1 and old categories 3, 4 and 5 into the new category 2.   The RECODE command will be:

RECODE class (2 = 1)(3, 4, 5 = 2).

Notice that there is a bracketed expression for each new category.

The RECODE command can also be used to recode ordinal or scalar data into coded categories.   For example, a set of examination marks (all falling within the range from 0 to 100) can be recoded into two categories: 1 (pass) and 0 (fail) by using the following command:

RECODE exam (LOWEST THRU 50=0)(ELSE=1).

This command will convert all exam marks less than or equal to 50 to the code value 0, and all marks greater than 50 to the code value 1.   The variable *exam* held in temporary storage now contains only a set of zeros and ones; the original marks, of course, will still be stored in a data or command file on disk.   The keyword **HIGHEST** is also available.

4.5.5   The IF command

It is often useful to be able to make *conditional* transformations of variables.   For example, the user may wish to change the value of a variable only if cases are males of under 25 years of age.   Details about the use of the **IF** command can be found under **modify data value**, which is part of **modify data or file** in the MAIN MENU.   Alternatively, IF can be accessed by typing IF on the scratch pad and pressing **[Esc]**. The available operators under IF are listed in the **instructions** item of the IF menu.

For example, suppose the user wishes to divide the cases in a data set into four groups, on the basis of gender (categories 1 and 2) and age (25 and under, over 25). The four categories can be created by four IF commands as follows:

IF (gender EQ 1 and age LE 25) group = 1.
IF (gender EQ 1 and age GT 25) group = 2.
IF (gender EQ 2 and age LE 25) group = 3.
IF (gender EQ 2 and age GT 25) group = 4.

This procedure is very useful, for it enables statistical calculations to be performed on selected parts of the data set, using the variable *group* just created by the four IF commands as the grouping variable thus

EXAMINE VARIABLES *variable names* BY group.

4.6 SUMMARY

1) Commands on the scratch pad are executed by moving the cursor (with control in the scratch pad - press **[Alt]/E** if necessary) to the first command to be executed, and pressing **[F10]**, followed by ⌐ . The screen will clear and then show the various commands, followed by the output (listing), or possibly error messages, a screenful at a time. Press the **space bar** when **MORE** appears in the top right corner to obtain the next screenful.

To execute only some of the commands on the scratch pad, they must first be marked by pressing **[F7]** when the cursor is located at the starting command, and again when the cursor is located at the finishing command. This block of yellow-coloured commands is then executed by pressing **[F10]**, selecting **run marked Area**, and pressing ⌐ .

2) The **LIST** command is useful for checking the accuracy of transcription of data into the computer. Insert the **LIST** command after **END DATA** (or after the **VARIABLE LABELS** and/or **VALUE LABELS** commands, if those are used) and execute all the commands from **DATA LIST** downwards.

3)   The descriptive statistics commands are **FREQUENCIES, DESCRIPTIVES, CROSSTABS, MEANS** and **EXAMINE**.

        FREQUENCIES lists frequency distributions for qualitative variables and rankings on a quantitative variable.

        DESCRIPTIVES lists a range of univariate statistics for scalar data.

        CROSSTABS produces cross-tabulations for pairs of variables with options for computing statistics such as chi-square.

        MEANS lists the means and standard deviations for subgroups (as defined by values of a grouping variable) of measurements on an interval scale. This command cannot be used for variables that have not been so subdivided: to obtain the statistics of whole variables, use **DESCRIPTIVES** with the subcommand **/STATISTICS 1** instead.

        EXAMINE has a large range of subcommands for exploring data, including plots of frequency distributions, percentiles, and other descriptive statistics.

4)   A selection of data or of cases for analysis can be made by using the **SELECT IF** or the **PROCESS IF** command. The **SELECT IF** command can carry more complex expressions within the brackets; on the other hamd, only one **SELECT IF** command can appear in any one command file. If there are to be several conditional selections, several local **PROCESS IF** commands must be used. It should be noted that in a **PROCESS IF** command, the user is restricted to the relational operators **EQ, GT, LT, . . .** and so on. The syntax of the **SELECT IF** and **PROCESS IF** commands is as follows:

        SELECT IF *(logical expression).*

        PROCESS IF *(logical expression).*

5)   The commands **COMPUTE** and **RECODE** can be used to modify variables by transforming them, combining them or changing the possible values that a variable can take. The first two kinds of manipulations can be achieved by using the **COMPUTE** command. The syntax is as follows:

        COMPUTE *target variable = expression.*

        The third kind of manipulation is achieved by using the **RECODE** command thus

        RECODE *variable (value list = value).*

        Conditional transformations based on logical rules (such as assigning cases of age 30 or older to one category and the remainder to another) can be achieved by using the **IF** command. For example:

IF (*logical expression*) *target variable = value.*

CHAPTER 5

CHOOSING A STATISTICAL TEST

5.1 INTRODUCTION

In this chapter, we consider the second phase of data analysis mentioned at the beginning of Chapter 4: the making of formal statistical tests to confirm that the patterns we have observed in the data are not merely chance occurrences.

The choice of an appropriate statistical test depends upon three considerations:

(1)   the **question** you are asking;
(2)   how the data were gathered, ie the plan, or **design** of the research;
(3)   the **type of data** you have.

5.1.1 The question you are asking

Are you making comparisons between (or among) the averages of two or more samples? For example, you select 50 people and assign them, at random, to two groups of 25: group A and group B. Early in the morning, group A subjects are asked to read a passage and answer 30 questions on it, each person receiving a score from 0 to 30. Group B subjects are given the same passage and test, but late in the evening. You want to know whether group A shows superior recall. Your research question is about **comparing averages.**

Now consider another research question. Do tall fathers tend to have tall sons? You select 200 fathers who have sons, and measure the height of each father and that of his eldest (or only) son. You want a statistic that expresses the degree to which the variable of father's height is **associated** with the variable of son's height.

Here, then, are two different research questions, each of which requires a different statistical test. Examples of statistics for **comparing averages** are the t-test and the analysis of variance (**ANOVA** for short). For the first example (the recall experiment), a t-test might be appropriate or, perhaps a **Mann-Whitney** test: it depends upon the distribution of the data (which would be examined during the exploratory phase). If you are making comparisons among the averages of three or more groups, the **ANOVA** would be a possibility.

In the second example, where you are **measuring association**, a **Pearson correlation** would be considered.

You may, on the other hand, not be content with simply measuring the association between two variables: you may wish to make use of the existence of an association to **make predictions** about the values of one variable from a knowledge of those of another. For example, if there is an assocation between fathers' heights and those of their eldest sons, can we arrive at a rule that permits us, given the height of any particular father, to **estimate** or **predict** that of his son? This is a question in **regression**.

Perhaps you wish to predict the values of one (target) variable from those of two or more other variables. For instance, in the United States, it is common practice to try to predict university students' performance during their first year from two or more tests of ability they have taken when applying for admission to the university. The construction of a rule for predicting one variable from two or more others is a problem in **multiple regression**.

5.1.2 How the data were gathered (the research design)

In the first (recall) example, the subjects were assigned independently to either condition A or to condition B: the group to which a subject was assigned did not affect the group to which any other subject was assigned. The experiment, that is to say, would yield two **independent samples** of data. With independent samples, there is no basis for saying that the data are **paired** in any way. In the second (height) example, we also have two sets of data: fathers' heights and sons' heights. But there is an important difference: the height data are **paired**: each pair of height measurements comes from related people. Another way of obtaining paired data is to take **repeated measures**: that is, measure each subject's performance on more than one task.

The question of whether samples are independent or related is crucial for the choice of a correct statistical test. For example, if you want to compare the averages of two independent samples of scores, you might consider an **independent t-test**; but if the data are paired (either because the same subjects were tested under both conditions, or because they were related), a **paired t-test** is a possibility.

5.1.3 The type of data you have

The choice of a statistical test depends on the nature of your data. If your data are **nominal**, you might consider a **chi-square test** of some kind. If they consist of ranks, there is available a whole set of **rank tests**. To illustrate, suppose, in the second (height) example, that instead of using a tape measure to record the heights of the fathers and sons, you had merely arranged the fathers and sons separately in order of their heights, assigning the rank of 1 to the tallest, 2 to the next tallest, ..., and 200 to the shortest. Our data would then be in the form of pairs of **ranks**. With such data, the Pearson correlation would be the wrong choice: instead, one of the rank statistics, such as **Spearman's rank correlation**, or **Kendall's tau**, should be used.

5.2 A GENERAL SCHEME FOR DATA ANALYSIS
WITH SPSS/PC+

In Chapter 2, section 2.9, a scheme was presented, in which a typical SPSS/PC+ session was divided into two phases:

(1)   **data entry and exploration** at a general level;
(2)   **statistical analysis**.

On the next two pages, the scheme is repeated, but with the addition of the names of the SPSS/PC+ commands that are of most relevance to the analysis of psychological data.

5.2.1 Phase 1 - Data entry and Exploration

Prepare data file if data too extensive to be incorporated in the data commands
⇓
Prepare data commands
DATA LIST, VARIABLE LABELS, VALUE LABELS, MISSING VALUE
⇓
Execute these commands to check for accuracy and to store variable names
temporarily in an SPSS/PC+ active file
⇓
Explore data with commands from
CROSSTABS, DESCRIPTIVES, EXAMINE, FREQUENCIES, LIST, MEANS, PLOT
⇓
Execute these commands and inspect listing on screen, check for outliers, study the
distributions and so on.
⇓
If necessary, correct any errors and re-execute commands.
⇓
Save commands to floppy disk

Inspection of the listing at the end of Phase 1 will show whether the data have been correctly transcribed, whether any variables need modifying or transforming, and whether any cases are so extreme that they need to be considered as outliers and eliminated from the data set in future analyses.

5.2.2 Phase 2 - Statistical Analysis

Phase 2 may begin with modification of the data and continues with the appropriate statistical test or analysis.

If necessary, select data, compute or modify variables,

and omit missing values with commands such as

SELECT IF, PROCESS IF, COMPUTE, RECODE, IF, MISSING VALUE

⇓

Select appropriate statistical analysis from the commands below

⇓

Degree of relation-ship among variables	Significance of differences in level between/among samples	Prediction of group membership	Finding latent variables
CORRELATION REGRESSION (scalar, normal) HILOGLINEAR CROSSTABS NPAR TESTS (non-parametric tests)	TTEST ONEWAY* ANOVA* MANOVA* (scalar, normal) NPAR TESTS (non-parametric tests)	DSCRIMINANT (discriminant analysis)	FACTOR (factor analysis)

⇓

Execute commands and inspect listing on screen

⇓

If necessary, amend commands and re-execute them

⇓

Print listing file (optional)

* The uses of ONEWAY, ANOVA and MANOVA are explained more fully in section 5.4

This completes Phase 2. Inspection of the output may lead to the identification of more outliers and the need to repeat the analysis with a reduced data set. Further refinements may be added: additional statistics can be commanded; tables of residuals can be requested; and plots of the results obtained.

5.3 BASIC TERMS IN EXPERIMENTAL DESIGN

The most common statistical procedures that psychologists use are for testing differences between (or among) the means of different samples. The next chapter examines the case of two means and the subsequent four chapters extend the discussion to comparisons among three or more means. At this point, we shall introduce some basic terms in experimental design.

5.3.1 Variables: the dependent and independent variable

A **variable** is a property or characteristic of a person, an object, or a situation. Height and weight are possessed in degree, and so are examples of **quantitative variables**. Gender, on the other hand, is not possessed in degree: it is a set of two mutually exclusive categories {male, female}. Gender is a **qualitative variable**.

In research, the object is often to show that some variables, known as **independent variables**, influence (or have a causal effect upon) others, which are known as **dependent variables**. In a true experiment, the independent variable is manipulated by the experimenter, either by assigning different samples of subjects to different levels, or by testing the same subjects under the various conditions making up the variable. **Experimental research**, which is characterised by the presence of one or more manipulated variables, is contrasted with **correlational research**, where all variables are recorded as they occur in the subjects during the investigation.

5.3.2 Factor

Some experiments are of complex design, having two or more independent variables. In the context of analysis of variance (the set of statistical techniques for analysing data from such experiments), the independent variables are known as **factors** and the experiments as **factorial experiments.** A factor, then, is a set of related conditions or categories. Strictly, we should distinguish between true treatment factors, which are manipulated by the experimenter and **subject variables**, such as sex. For example, we might test for a sex difference in performance by sampling 100 men and 100 women. This is **quasi-experimentation**, rather than true experimentation, and it is only too easy to give a false interpretation to any difference that may emerge. Nevertheless, the statistical analysis is the same whether a variable is truly manipulated or a subject variable.

5.3.3 Levels

The various conditions or categories that make up a factor are known as the **levels** of that factor, even though, in the case of the gender categories, one is no "higher" or "better" than another.

5.3.4 Completely randomised experiment

If an experiment has just one treatment factor, and each subject is tested once, at one level of the factor, the experiment is said to be of **completely randomised design**.

5.3.5 Factorial experiment

When an experiment has two or more factors, it is said to be a **factorial experiment.**

5.3.6 Repeated measures

A factor is said to have **repeated measures** if subjects are tested under all the conditions comprising the factor.

5.3.7 Between subjects and within subjects factors

A factor with no repeated measures is a **between subjects** factor; one with repeated measures is a **within subjects** factor.

5.3.8 Completely randomised factorial experiment (between subjects experiment)

An experiment with two or more factors, none of which has repeated measures, is known as a **completely randomised factorial** experiment. Such experiments are also known as **between subjects** experiments.

5.3.9 Repeated measures experiment (within subjects experiment)

Experiments in which there are repeated measures on all factors are known as **repeated measures** or **within subjects** experiments.

5.3.10 Experiments of mixed design

An experiment is said to be of **mixed design** if some (but not all) of its factors are within subjects (ie have repeated measures).

5.3.11 ANOVA and MANOVA

When only one **dependent variable** is measured, one of the set of statistical procedures known as **analysis of variance** (usually abbreviated to **ANOVA**) may be appropriate (there are nonparametric alternatives). When more than one dependent variable is measured, the appropriate procedure is **multivariate analysis of variance** (usually abbreviated to **MANOVA**). Unfortunately SPSS/PC+ is confusing, because it uses its MANOVA program for repeated measures ANOVA, as well as multivariate analyses - see next section.

5.4 GUIDE TO THE COMMANDS FOR COMPARING MEANS

The Table below shows the relevant SPSS/PC+ command and chapter location for testing the significance of differences between or among samples:

Factor	One				More than one		
Number of levels	Two		More than two		Two or more		
Design	Independent	Repeated	Independent	Repeated	Independent	Repeated	Mixed
SPSS/PC+ command	T-TEST/ GROUPS	T-TEST/ PAIRS	ONEWAY	MANOVA (see note)	ANOVA	MANOVA (see note)	MANOVA (see note)
Chapter	6	6	7	9	8	9	10

Note: SPSS/PC+ utilises its MANOVA program to perform repeated measures ANOVA. This book does not describe true multivariate analysis of variance.

5.5 SUMMARY

1)   A typical SPSS/PC+ session consists of two phases. The first comprises the preparation and entry of data, the preparation of the data commands, and the execution of commands such as **EXAMINE**, **LIST**, **CROSSTABS**, **FREQUENCIES**, **MEANS**, **DESCRIPTIVES**, and **PLOT** for the checking and preliminary exploration of the data.

2)   The second phase involves formal statistical testing, with commands such as **CORRELATION, REGRESSION, T-TEST, ONEWAY, ANOVA, MANOVA, HILOGLINEAR, DSCRIMINANT, CROSSTABS, NPAR TESTS** (with its many tests as subcommands), and **FACTOR**.

3)   The following terms are defined:

Independent and dependent variables, factor, level, completely randomised design, factorial design, completely randomised factorial design (between subjects), repeated measures design (within subjects), mixed design (between subjects and within subjects factors), ANOVA, MANOVA.

4)   A schematic guide to the commands for comparing means is presented.

CHAPTER 6

COMPARING THE AVERAGES OF TWO SAMPLES

6.1 INTRODUCTION

Suppose that a psychological experiment has been carried out, in which the performance of two groups of people has been measured under two conditions, an experimental condition and a control. For example, the task could be the memorisation of the content of a written passage, and the purpose of the experiment might have been to compare the recall performance of a group of subjects who have been given special training in a mnemonic technique with that of an untrained control group. This experiment would produce two sets of scores: one from the experimental group, the other from the control. We want to compare people's typical level of performance under the two conditions. If this experiment were to be repeated, the averages for the two groups would almost certainly take different values. In statistical terms, this is because the scores actually obtained from each group are merely a **sample** from an infinite pool, or **population**, of possible values. We may find that the mean performance of the experimental (trained) group is higher than that of the control (untrained) group. But could this have arisen through chance: can we be reasonably confident that if the experiment were to be repeated, we should get the same result?

Possibly the best known statistical test for comparing the average levels of two samples of scalar data is the **t-test**, which is designed to test the difference between two **means** for **significance**. Our hypothesis is that the mnemonic technique enhances recall. This is the **experimental hypothesis**. In traditional significance testing, however, it is not the experimental hypothesis that is directly tested but its **negation**, which is known as the **null hypothesis** (H_0). If H_0 fails the test, we shall conclude that our experimental hypothesis, which in statistical terms is known as the **alternative hypothesis**, is correct.

The performance of a statistical test requires a knowledge of the **sampling distribution** of the test statistic. The **p-value** of a statistic such as t or F (or some other test statistic) is the probability, assuming that H_0 is true, of obtaining a value **at least as extreme as the one actually obtained**. Should the p-value be small, this is taken as evidence against H_0, because a value that extreme is unlikely (though possible). Traditionally, H_0 is rejected if the p-value is no more than 0.05; but in many areas, an even lower p-value, say 0.01, is now the conventional criterion for rejection. When the p-value of a statistic is at least as small as the conventional value, the value of the statistic is said to be **significant**.

Should the p-value be larger than the conventional small value, H_0 is **accepted**. This does not mean that it is actually true: it means only that the evidence is insufficient to justify rejection.

To sum up:

1)   If the p-value is greater than 0.05, H_0 is accepted and the result is **not significant**.

2)   If the p-value is less than 0.05 but greater than 0.01, H_0 is rejected and the result is **significant beyond the 5 per cent level**.

3)   If the p-value is smaller than 0.01, H_0 is rejected and the result is **significant beyond the 1 per cent level**.

In this book, we assume that you are familiar with the **t-test**, at least to some extent. If you are not, we strongly recommend that you read the relevant sections of a good statistical text. For example, Gravetter & Wallnau (1992; chapters 9-11) give a lucid account. With independent samples, the **t** statistic is calculated by dividing the difference between the sample means by an estimate of the standard deviation of the distribution of differences, which is known as the **standard error of the difference**. Should the sample variances have similar values, it is common practice to work with a pooled estimate of the supposedly constant population variance; but if they do not, the pooled estimate is not used and a **separate variance** test is made. The null hypothesis is rejected if the obtained value of t lies in either tail of the sampling distribution. The precise value of t needed for significance depends upon the **degrees of freedom** of the distribution, which in turn depends upon the sizes of the samples in the experiment; but an absolute value of t greater than or equal to 2 is usually significant, unless the samples are very small indeed. Very small samples should be avoided in any case because the test would have insufficient power to reject H_0. (The **power** of a statistical test is the probability that H_0 will be rejected given that it is false.)

The diagram on the next page shows the SPSS/PC+ commands for the various two-sample situations:-

Data derived from populations assumed to have normal distributions and equal variances		No assumptions about the population distributions	
Independent samples	Paired data	Independent samples	Paired data
T-TEST/GROUPS	T-TEST/PAIRS	NPAR TESTS /M-W	NPAR TESTS /SIGN /WILCOXON

6.2 THE T-TEST

6.2.1 Assumptions underlying the use of the t-test

The model underlying a t-test assumes that the data have been derived from normal distributions with equal variance. Computer simulations have shown that even with moderate violations of these assumptions, one may still safely proceed with a t-test, provided the samples are not too small, do not contain outliers (atypical scores), and are of equal (or nearly equal) size. Should a preliminary exploration of the data (as recommended in Chapter 4) indicate that the assumptions of a t-test model are untenable, an alternative test should be chosen from the portfolio of **non-parametric** tests, which in SPSS/PC+ are given in the NPAR TESTS menu. Non-parametric tests do not imply assumptions about population distributions and variance.

6.2.2 Paired and independent t-tests

Imagine an experiment in which a subject looks at a central spot on a computer screen and is told to press a key on recognition of a word which may appear on either side of the spot. As a check on whether the word has been truly recognised, the subject is also asked to type the word just identified. The experimental hypothesis is that words presented in the right visual field will be more quickly recognised than those in the left visual field, because the former are processed by the opposite (left) cerebral hemisphere, which is thought to be more proficient with verbal information. For each subject, the median response time to forty words in each of the right and left visual fields is recorded as in Table 1:

Table 1. Paired data: Median word recognition times in milliseconds for words in the left and right visual fields.

Subject	Left Field	Right Field
s1	323	304
s2	512	493
s3	502	491
.	.	.
.	.	.
s10	590	564

This experiment is said to be of **repeated measures**, or **within-subjects**, design, because the performance of the same subjects has been measured under both conditions (word in right field, word in left field).

Now suppose that **different** subjects had been tested with words in the right and left visual fields. The data table might appear as in Table 2:

Table 2. Independent samples: Median word recognition times in milliseconds for words in the left and right visual fields.

Subject	Left Field	Subject	Right Field
s1	500	s11	392
s2	513	s12	445
s3	300	s13	271
.	.	.	.
s10	480	s20	467

This variant of the experiment is said to have **no repeated measures**, or to be of **between subjects** design: each subject is tested under only one condition. Notice that there is no basis on which the subjects in the two conditions can meaningfully be paired; indeed, with no repeated measures, the samples can be of different sizes. It is recommended, however, that samples should always be the same size wherever possible.

The **paired t-test** is used for the paired data in Table 1. This differs from the **independent t-test** which is used for the independent samples data in Table 2. Full details and examples are given in the **T-TEST menu**, which is accessed either through **Analyze data** and **Comparing group means**, or by typing T-TEST on the scratch pad and pressing **[Esc]**. Note that the data are entered differently in the two cases, as explained below. The reader should review the information about the DATA LIST command given in Chapter 3 and use Menu and Help to write DATA LIST and the other data commands.

6.3 THE PAIRED T-TEST

6.3.1 The commands for a paired t-test

Prepare the commands on the scratch pad in the following steps:

Step 1

Write the DATA LIST command (Chapter 3). The appropriate section of the Menu can be found by either (a) typing DATA LIST on the scratch pad (after pressing **[Alt]/E** if still in the Menu and Help mode) and pressing **[Esc]** or (b) moving down the **MAIN MENU** to **read or write data**, rightwards into the **read or write data menu**, down to **DATA LIST**, and pressing ↵ to paste DATA LIST on the scratch pad.

Since the data set is small, the data can be written in free-field format and included in the data commands, rather than in a separate data file.

If the recognition times from the left and right visual fields are named *leftfld* and *rightfld*, the command is:

DATA LIST FREE/leftfld rightfld.

The data are then typed on the scratch pad after the BEGIN DATA command, as described in Chapter 3:

BEGIN DATA.
323 304
512 493
502 491
385 365
453 426
343 320
543 523
440 442
682 580

590 564
END DATA.

Step 2 (optional)

Use the **VARIABLE LABELS** command to improve the intelligibility of the listing:

VARIABLE LABELS leftfld 'Left Visual Field' rightfld 'Right Visual Field'.

Step 3

Execute these data commands by running the cursor up to the DATA LIST command (press **[Alt]/E** if necessary to transfer control to the scratch pad), and pressing **[F10]** followed by ↵. This allows you to check that these commands have been correctly written and also enables SPSS/PC+ to generate a table of the variable names. This table is very useful during the preparation of subsequent commands, because whenever variable names are required in them, the table appears in the top half of the screen. Each required variable can then be selected with the highlight and pasted on the scratch pad by pressing ↵.

Step 4

Find **T-TEST** in the Menu via **analyze data** and **comparing group means**, and press ↵ to paste T-TEST on the scratch pad. (Alternatively, type T-TEST on the scratch pad and press **[Esc]**.)

Read the examples on the screen, and use the ↓ cursor key to move down to **paired t-test**. Read the information. Move down to **/PAIRS** and press ↵ to paste /PAIRS on the scratch pad. Read the new examples and move down to **variables**.

Press ↵ and notice that a list of variables appears in the top half of the screen. Move the highlighting with the cursor key along to *leftfld* and press ↵, then move the highlighting to *rightfld* and press ↵ again. Remove the list of variables by pressing the period (.); this also completes the command.

(Alternatively you may prefer to type the variable names by pressing **[Alt]/T** to obtain a box in the middle of the screen with a flashing cursor in it. Type in the names of the variables one after the other **with a space but no comma between them**, finishing with a period (.). Press ↵ again. The variable names and period will now appear on the scratch pad.)

The command is:

T-TEST /PAIRS leftfld rightfld.

Step 5 (optional)

It is recommended that a scatterplot of the data points be constructed in order to check for outliers. If there are any, they should be removed by using the **SELECT IF** command prior to a second execution of the commands. A scatterplot is obtained by using the **PLOT/PLOT** command. Type PLOT on the scratch pad (after using **[Alt]/E** and pressing ↵ to move the cursor to the next line) and then press **[Esc]** to see the PLOT menu. Move to the bottom item, **/PLOT**, and press ⅃ to paste it on the scratch pad.

Look at the examples, move down to **vertical axis** and press ⅃ . The table of variable names will appear. Select *leftfld* with the cursor and press ⅃ . Press **[Esc]** to return to the menu, move down to **WITH**, and press ⅃ . Move down to **horizontal axis** and press ⅃ . The table of variable names will then reappear. Select *rightfld* from the variable name table, and press ⅃ . Finally, press the period (.) to remove the variable table and complete the command.

(Alternatively you may prefer to type the variable names directly on the scratch pad by pressing **[Alt]/E** and typing the vertical axis variable name followed by WITH and then the horizontal axis variable name. Finally, a period (.) completes the command.)

The command is:

PLOT/PLOT leftfld WITH rightfld.

Step 6

Save the commands to the floppy disk by using **[F9]** (see Chapter 2, section 2.5.3) choosing a filename with a .CMD extension to remind you that it is a command file. Then execute the T-TEST and PLOT commands by moving the cursor up to the T-TEST command and pressing **[F10]**, followed by ⅃ .

6.3.2 The listing for a paired t-test

The listing begins with some descriptive statistics for the two variables, followed by statistics of the distribution of differences between the paired scores, the correlation coefficient for the two variables, and the t-test with its associated degrees of freedom and p-value.

Paired samples t-test: LEFTFLD Left Visual Field
                        RIGHTFLD Right Visual Field

Variable	Number of Cases	Mean	Standard Deviation	Standard Error
LEFTFLD	10	477.3000	112.091	35.446
RIGHTFLD	10	450.8000	97.085	30.701

(Difference) Mean	Standard Deviation	Standard Error	Corr.	2-Tail Prob.	t Value	Degrees of Freedom	2-Tail Prob.
26.5000	27.814	8.796	.975	.000	3.01	9	.015

The null hypothesis can be rejected, since the tail probability (.015, or 1.5%) is less than .05 (i.e. 5%). The difference between the means is significant.

Finally, the listing displays the scatterplot of the data requested by the PLOT/PLOT command:

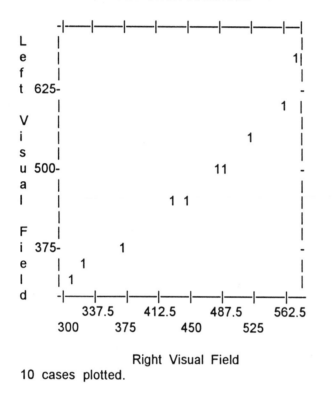

6.3.2.1 SAVING THE LISTING TO A FILE

To save a copy of the listing to a named file on the floppy disk (essential if a printed copy is needed), add a **SET/LISTING** command at the head of the commands, and submit all the commands for execution again.

6.3.2.2 PRINTING OUT THE LISTING AND COMMAND FILES

Details are given in Chapter 2 (section 2.6).

6.4 THE INDEPENDENT T-TEST

6.4.1 The commands for an independent t-test

Prepare the commands on the scratch pad in the following steps:

Step 1

Write the DATA LIST command (Chapter 3). The appropriate section of the Menu can be found by either (a) typing DATA LIST on the scratch pad (after pressing **[Alt]/E** if still in the Menu and Help mode) and pressing **[Esc]** or (b) moving down the **MAIN MENU** to **read or write data**, rightwards into **read or write data**, down to **DATA LIST**, and pressing ↵ to paste DATA LIST on the scratch pad.

Since the data set is small, the data can be written in free-field format and included in the data commands, rather than stored in a separate data file.

In this analysis, each score is identified by a code number indicating the condition under which the score was obtained. The code numbers are carried in a grouping variable. If the grouping (independent) variable is *field* and the dependent variable is *rectime*, the command is:

DATA LIST FREE / field rectime.

The data are then typed on the scratch pad after the BEGIN DATA command, as described in Chapter 3. The first number in each pair is the field-identifying code (1 or 2), and the second is the recognition time:

BEGIN DATA.
1 500 2 392 1 513 2 445 1 300 2 271 1 561 2 523 1 483 2 421
1 502 2 489 1 539 2 501 1 467 2 388 1 420 2 411 1 480 2 467
END DATA.

Step 2 (optional)

Add some labels to improve the intelligibility of the listing file, by using the **VARIABLE LABELS** and **VALUE LABELS** commands:

VARIABLE LABELS field 'Visual Field' rectime 'Word Recognition Time'.
VALUE LABELS field 1 'Left Field' 2 'Right Field'.

Step 3

Execute the data commands by running the cursor up to the DATA LIST command (press **[Alt]/E** if necessary to transfer control to the scratch pad), pressing **[F10]**, and ↵ . This allows you to check that these commands have been correctly written and also enables SPSS/PC+ to generate a table of the variable names. This table is very convenient during the preparation of subsequent commands, because whenever variable names are required in the commands, the table appears in the top half of the screen. Each required variable can then be selected by moving the highlighting along the list of names to the appropriate name, and pasting it on the scratch pad by pressing ↵ .

Step 4

Find **T-TEST** in the Menu via **analyze data** and **comparing group means**, and press ↵ to paste T-TEST on the scratch pad. (Alternatively, type T-TEST on the scratch pad and press **[Esc]**.)

Read the examples on the screen, use the ↓ cursor key to move down to **independent t-test**, and read the information. Now move down to **/GROUPS** and press ↵ to paste /GROUPS on the scratch pad. Read the new examples, and move down to **group variable**. Press ↵ and note that the table of variable names appears in the upper screen. Select *field* and press ↵ to paste *field* on the scratch pad. Press **[Esc]** to remove the table of variable names and then move down the menu to ( ). Press ↵ again to paste ( ). You will be then be prompted to fill in the values of the group variable: type 1, 2 and those numbers will appear in the box in the middle of the screen. Press ↵ to paste these values on the scratch pad.

Use the ← cursor key to get back to /GROUPS in the previous menu. Move down to **/VARIABLES**, and press ↵ to paste /VARIABLES on the scratch pad. Choose the variable *rectime* from the table of variables, press ↵ to paste it on the scratch pad, and then press the period (.) to remove the table of variables and complete the command.

(Alternatively, after pasting /GROUPS you may prefer to type the variable names by pressing **[Alt]/T** and noting that a box appears in the middle of the screen with a flashing cursor in it. Type in the name of the group variable, followed by its values in brackets, and press ↵ again. Return to the T-TEST menu with the ← cursor key and move down to **/VARIABLES**. Press ↵ to paste /VARIABLES, press **[Alt]/E** and type the variable name, followed by a period (.) to complete the command.)

The command is:

T-TEST /GROUPS field(1,2) /VARIABLES rectime.

The variable *field* is the independent variable identifying whether the word was in the left or right visual field, and the variable *rectime* is the dependent variable, recognition time.

Step 5

Save the commands to the floppy disk by using **[F9]** (see Chapter 2, section 2.5.3), choosing a filename with a .CMD extension, to remind you that it is a command file. Execute the T-TEST command by pressing **[F10]**, and ↵ .

6.4.2 The listing for an independent t-test

The listing includes an F test comparing the variances of the two groups and two t-tests, one based on a pooled variance estimate, the other on separate variance estimates. If the **2-Tail Prob.** (probability) value for the F test is less than 0.05, then the homogeneity of variance assumption has been violated and the t-test based on separate variance estimates should be used. If the F test is not significant (i.e. the p-value is greater than .05), the pooled t-test is permissible.

In this example, the F test is not significant, so the t value calculated with the pooled variance estimate is appropriate. With a **2-Tail Prob** value of .178 (i.e. 17.8%), the t value has a tail probability of 0.178, and so the difference between means is not significant.

Independent samples of FIELD Visual Field

Group 1: FIELD EQ 1.00   Group 2: FIELD EQ 2.00

t-test for: RECTIME Word Recognition Time

	Number of Cases	Mean	Standard Deviation	Standard Error
Group 1	10	476.5000	73.083	23.111
Group 2	10	430.8000	72.793	23.019

		Pooled Variance Estimate			Separate Variance Estimate		
F Value	2-Tail Prob.	t Value	Degrees of Freedom	2-Tail Prob.	t Value	Degrees of Freedom	2-Tail Prob.
1.01	.991	1.40	18	.178	1.40	18.00	.178

6.4.2.1 SAVING THE LISTING TO A FILE

To save a copy of the listing to a named file on the floppy disk (essential if a printed copy is needed), add a **SET/LISTING** command at the head of the commands, and submit all the commands for re-execution..

6.4.2.2 PRINTING OUT THE LISTING AND COMMAND FILES

Details are given in Chapter 2, section 2.6.

6.5 TESTING DIFFERENCES BETWEEN MEDIANS WITH NON-PARAMETRIC TESTS

When there are serious violations of the distribution assumptions of the t-test, non-parametric tests can be used instead. They should not be used as a matter of course, however, because should the data meet the requirements of the t-test, the comparable non-parametric test would lack the **power** to reject the null hypothesis, should that be false. It is best, therefore, to consider the parametric test first, resorting to the non-parametric alternative only if the data seriously violate the requirements.

SPSS/PC+ has a wide selection of tests in the **NPAR TESTS** menu, which is found either through the **other** option in the **analyze data** menu, or by typing **NPAR TESTS** on the scratch pad and pressing **[Esc]**. The rationale of each test is explained in the section headed **2 related samples** and (much lower down in the menu) in the section headed **2 independent samples**. The **Sign** and **Wilcoxon** tests are non-parametric counterparts of the paired t-test, and the **Mann-Whitney** test is an alternative to the independent samples t-test. Full details and examples are given in the **Menu and help** window.

6.6 SUMMARY

1)   The **t-test** can be used to test for a significant difference between the means of two samples, provided the data are normally-distributed, and the samples have similar variances.

2)   For independent samples, use the **independent t-test**, by writing a command of the form:

T-TEST/GROUPS *group variable name* **(m, n)**
        /VARIABLES *dependent variable name.*

where m and n are the values of the group variable (e.g. 1, 2).

3)   For paired samples, use the **paired t-test** by writing a command of the form:

T-TEST/PAIRS *variable names.*

A **scatterplot** is recommended. This can be obtained with the additional command:

PLOT/PLOT *vertical axis variable name* **WITH** *horizontal axis variable name*.

4) If the assumptions for the t-test are violated, a **non-parametric** test can be used. Non-parametric tests do not assume normality and homogeneity of variances; though they may require that the two distributions have the same shape. These tests are available as subcommands in the **NPAR TESTS** menu.

CHAPTER 7

THE ONE-FACTOR EXPERIMENT WITH NO REPEATED MEASURES

7.1 INTRODUCTION

Suppose that an experiment has been carried out to compare the performance of two groups of subjects: an **experimental** group and a **control** group. Provided the data have certain characteristics (ie the samples have approximately normal distributions and comparable variances), an independent t-test can be used to test the null hypthesis (H_0) of equality of the two population means. If the test shows significance, we reject H_0: we conclude that there is a difference between the two population means, which is equivalent to the conclusion that the experimental manipulation does have an effect.

The same null hypothesis, however, can also be tested by using one of the set of techniques known as **analysis of variance** (**ANOVA** for short). Despite its name, the ANOVA, like the t-test, is concerned with the testing of hypotheses about **means**. In fact, if the ANOVA and the (pooled variance) t-test are applied to the data from a simple, two-group experiment, the tests will give the same result: if the t-test shows the difference between the means to be significant, then so will the ANOVA and vice versa.

The ANOVA, however, is more versatile than the t-test. Suppose that in an investigation of the effects of mnemonic strategies upon recall, three groups of subjects were tested:

(a) a group who had been trained in mnemonic method A;
(b) a group who had been trained in mnemonic method B;
(c) a control group, who were merely asked to memorise the material as well as possible.

This type of experiment, in which each subject performs under only one of the conditions making up a single independent variable, is said to have **one treatment factor** with **no repeated measures**. It is also known as the **completely randomised experiment**. From such an experiment, we should obtain three samples of scores, one for each of the three groups. The ANOVA can test the null hypothesis that all three population means are equal, ie neither mnemonic technique improves recall (in comparison with the control group). Note that, unlike ANOVA, the t-test cannot be used to evaluate a hypothesis about three or more population means: it can substitute for ANOVA only if there are two groups in the experiment.

Why couldn't a series of t-tests be used to make comparisons among the three group means? Couldn't we simply use three t-tests to compare the control group with the mnemonic A and mnemonic B groups, and mnemonic A with mnemonic B? The problem with that approach is that when multiple comparisons are made among a set of treatment means, the probability of at least one test showing significance **even when the null hypothesis is true** is higher than the conventional significance level (ie critical p-value) of 0.05 or 0.01; in fact, if there is a large array of treatment group means, the probability of at least one test showing significance is close to 1 (certainty)! This point is explained in greater detail in Gravetter & Wallnau (1992), page 372. It is sometimes asserted that an unplanned multiple comparisons procedure can only be carried out if the ANOVA F test has shown significance. That is not necessarily true: it depends on which comparisons one wishes to make (see Myers, 1979; p. 303).

A lucid account of the rationale of the ANOVA is given in Gravetter & Wallnau (1992), Chapter 13. Basically, the ANOVA works like this. A group mean is taken to be an estimate of people's typical level of performance under that particular condition. But individual performance can vary widely and at times deviates markedly from the group mean. Think of this **within group** variability as background noise, or **error**. It may be, however, that mnemonic groups A and B achieved much higher average levels of performance than did the control group: in other words, there is high variability **between (ie among) groups**. The **ANOVA F statistic** is calculated by dividing an estimate of the **variability between groups** by the **within groups** variability:

$$\textbf{F = (variance between)} \div \textbf{(variance within)}$$

If there are large differences among the treatment means, the numerator of F (and therefore F itself) will be inflated and the null hypothesis is likely to be rejected; but if there is no effect, the numerator and denominator of F should have similar values, giving F close to unity. A high value of F, therefore, is evidence against the null hypothesis of equality of all population means.

There remains a problem, however. If H_0 is that all the means are equal, the alternative hypothesis is that they are not. If the ANOVA F test gives significance, we know there is a difference **somewhere** among the means, but that does not justify us in saying that any **particular comparison** is significant. The ANOVA F test, in fact, is an **omnibus test**, and further analysis is necessary to localise whatever differences there may be among the individual treatment means.

The question of exactly how one should proceed to further analysis after making the omnibus F test in ANOVA is not a simple one, and an adequate treatment of it earns an extensive chapter in many statistical texts: eg Kirk (1982, Chapter 3); and Howell (1992, Chapter 12). It is important to distinguish between those comparisons that were **planned** before the data were actually gathered, and those that are made as part of the inevitable process of unplanned

data-snooping that takes place after the results have been obtained. Planned comparisons are often known as **a priori** comparisons. Unplanned comparisons should be termed **a posteriori** comparisons, but unfortunately the misnomer **post hoc** is more often used.

SPSS/PC+ offers the user both planned comparisons and an assortment of unplanned data-snooping tests, such as **Tukey's Honestly Significant Difference (HSD) test**, **Scheffé's test** and so on. If these are unfamiliar to you, we urge you to read the relevant chapters in the books we have cited.

7.2 ONE-FACTOR ANOVA (NO REPEATED MEASURES)

7.2.1 The commands for the one-factor ANOVA

Suppose the results of the mnemonics memory experiment are as follows:

No Mnemonic	3	5	3	2	4	6	9	3	8	10
Mnemonic A	10	8	15	9	11	16	17	15	7	10
Mnemonic B	20	15	14	15	17	10	8	11	18	19

Prepare the commands on the scratch pad in the following steps.

Step 1

Write the **DATA LIST** command (Chapter 3). The appropriate section of the Menu can be found by either (a) typing DATA LIST on the scratch pad (after **[Alt]/E** if still in Menu and Help mode) and pressing **[Esc]**, or (b) moving down the MAIN MENU to **read or write data**, rightwards into the **read or write data menu**, down to **DATA LIST**, and pressing ↵ to paste DATA LIST on the scratch pad.

Since the data set is small, the data can be written in free-field format and included in the data commands, rather than in a separate data file. It will be necessary, however, to include a coding variable to indicate the treatment group under which each value was obtained: for example, we can assign the code numbers 1, 2 and 3 to the control, Mnemonic A and

Mnemonic B groups, respectively.

If the coding variable is *learntyp* and the number of words recalled is *recall*, the command is:

DATA LIST FREE/learntyp recall.

The data are then typed on the scratch pad after the BEGIN DATA command eg

```
BEGIN DATA.
1 3 1 5 1 3 1 2 1 4 1 6 1 9 1 3 1 8 1 10
2  10 2 8 2 15 2 9 2 11 2 16 2 17 2 15 2 7 2 10
3  20 3 15 3 14 3 15 3 17 3 10 3 8 3 11 3 18 3 19
END DATA.
```

Step 2 (optional)

Add some labels to improve the intelligibility of the listing file by using the **VARIABLE LABELS** and **VALUE LABELS** commands:

VARIABLE LABELS learntyp 'Learning Condition' recall 'Number of words recalled'.
VALUE LABELS learntyp 1 'Rote' 2 'Mnemonic A' 3 'Mnemonic B'.

Step 3

Execute these data commands by moving the cursor up to the DATA LIST command, pressing **[F10]**, and then ↵ . This allows you to check that these commands have been correctly written and also causes SPSS/PC+ to generate a table of variable names for pasting into subsequent commands.

Step 4

Find **ONEWAY** in the menu via **analyze data** and **comparing group means**, and press ↵ to paste ONEWAY on the scratch pad. (Alternatively type **ONEWAY** on the scratch pad and press **[Esc]** to access the ONEWAY menu.)

Move down the menu to **/VARIABLES** and press ↵ to paste /VARIABLES on the scratch pad. Read the examples, move down to **dependent(s)** and press ↵ to reveal the variable table. Move the highlight to the dependent variable *recall*, press ↵ and then **[Esc]** to remove the variable table. Move down the menu to **BY**, paste it on the scratch pad with ↵ , move the highlight along the variable table to *learntyp*, press ↵ and **[Esc]**. Move down the menu to **( )**, press ↵ , type in the minimum and maximum values of the grouping variable (ie 1, 3), and press ↵ .

(Alternatively after pasting /VARIABLES, press **[Alt]/E** and type the remaining details of the command directly on the scratch pad.)

The command is:

ONEWAY/VARIABLES recall BY learntyp (1,3).

If no subcommands are to be appended, ensure that there is a period (.) at the end of the command.

Step 5 (optional subcommands)

Unplanned multiple pairwise comparisons among the means can be obtained by adding an optional subcommand. Move back from the /VARIABLES menu to the ONEWAY menu with the ← key, and then down to **/RANGES**. Press ↵ to paste /RANGES on the scratch pad. A variety of possible tests will then appear in the /RANGES menu, including **Tukey's Honestly Significant Difference (HSD)** test. Select **TUKEY** and press ↵ . The command is thus:

ONEWAY/VARIABLES recall BY learntyp (1,3) /RANGES TUKEY.

Another optional subcommand is **/STATISTICS** which can provide descriptive statistics and a test for homogeneity of variance across treatments; but we shall not use it in this example.

Ensure that there is a period (.) at the end of the command.

Step 6

Save the commands on the scratch pad to a named file on the floppy disk by using **[F9]** (see Chapter 2, section 2.5.3) and then execute the ONEWAY command by pressing **[F10]**, followed by ↵ .

7.2.2 The listing for the one-factor ANOVA

The listing on the screen will include the **ONEWAY** analysis and (if the **/RANGES** subcommand is included) the results of the multiple comparisons tests.

```
- - - - - - - - - - O N E W A Y - - - - - - - - - -
```

Variable   RECALL   Number of Words Recalled
By Variable LEARNTYP Learning Condition

Analysis of Variance

Source	D.F.	Sum of Squares	Mean Squares	F Ratio	F Prob.
Between Groups	2	463.4000	231.7000	18.7415	.0000
Within Groups	27	333.8000	12.3630		
Total	29	797.2000			

Note the **F Prob** value for the F ratio in the Analysis of Variance table. If it is less than 0.05, F is statistically significant. The smaller the value of F Prob, also known as the **p-value** or **tail probability**, the stronger the evidence against the null hypothesis. In this example, H_0 can be rejected, since F Prob is very small indeed (shown as .0000 in the listing, which means that it is less than 0.00005).

The listing continues with details of the Tukey test:

- - - - - - - - - - O N E W A Y - - - - - - - - - -

	Variable	RECALL	Number of Words Recalled
By	Variable	LEARNTYP	Learning Condition

Multiple Range Test

Tukey-HSD Procedure
Ranges for the .050 level -

      3.50 3.50

The ranges above are table ranges.
The value actually compared with Mean(J)-Mean(I) is..

     2.4863 * Range * Sqrt(1/N(I) + 1/N(J))

The table below uses these ranges to show which pairs of groups differ at the 5% level. (This is the **per family** error rate: the probability that at least one comparison in the set will show significance.) The means are ordered and displayed from smallest to largest in the rows, and the asterisks indicate which pairs of groups differ significantly at the 5% level in the lower half of the matrix. Thus we can see that groups 2 and 3 each differ from group 1, but groups 2 and 3 do not differ from each other:

(*) Denotes pairs of groups significantly different at the .050 level

		G	G	G
		r	r	r
		p	p	p
Mean	Group	1	2	3
5.3000	Grp 1			
11.8000	Grp 2	*		
14.7000	Grp 3	*		

Finally the listing forms subsets of the groups as described in the text:

Homogeneous Subsets	(Subsets of groups, whose highest and lowest means do not differ by more than the shortest significant range for a subset of that size)

SUBSET 1

Group   Grp 1
Mean   5.3000
- - - - - - - - - -

SUBSET 2

Group   Grp 2   Grp 3
Mean   11.8000   14.7000
- - - - - - - - - - - - - - - - -

7.2.2.1 SAVING THE LISTING TO A FILE

To save a copy of the listing to a file on the floppy disk (which is essential if a printed version is needed), add a **SET/LISTING** command at the head of the commands, and submit all the commands for re-execution (Chapter 2).

7.2.2.2 PRINTING THE LISTING AND COMMAND FILES

Details are given in chapter 2 (section 2.6) about how to print files from the floppy disk.

7.2.3 Inputting counts, means, and standard deviations instead of data

If the sizes, means, and standard deviations of the samples are already known, these can be used instead of the raw data. The **DATA LIST** command is modified to include **MATRIX** after **FREE** or **FIXED** (see that the Menu is in **Extended Menu** mode: press **[Alt]/X** to install the extended menus). The sample sizes, means, and standard deviations are entered between the usual BEGIN DATA and END DATA commands, ensuring that all the sizes are on one line, all the means on the next, and all the standard deviations on the third. Finally, within the **ONEWAY** command, the subcommand **/OPTION 7** must be added, to direct SPSS/PC+ to read the statistics correctly.

7.3 NON-PARAMETRIC TESTS FOR ONE-FACTOR EXPERIMENTS

Should the data be unsuitable for ANOVA (as when there is marked heterogeneity of variance, or the data are highly skewed), one should consider using **non-parametric** tests, which require neither homogeneity of variance nor that the data be normally distributed. In the **NPAR TESTS** menu, are the **k-sample median test** and the **Kruskal-Wallis one-way ANOVA.** For our current example, the command for the Kruskal-Wallis would be:

NPAR TESTS K-W recall BY learntyp(1,3).

7.4 SUMMARY

1) **ONEWAY** is used for analysing data from an experiment of one-factor design with no repeated measures. The test assumes that the data are normally distributed and that there is **homogeneity of variance**. Should these assumptions be violated (the homogeneity assumption is especially important), other methods are available, such as the **Kruskal-Wallis** test, which is found under the **NPAR TESTS** command.

2) The command for **ONEWAY** is of the form

   ONEWAY/VARIABLES *dependent variable name* **BY** *category variable name* (x, y).

   where x and y represent the lowest and highest code numbers, respectively, of the category variable.

3) Subcommands for multiple comparisons (**/RANGES** *name of test*) and for additional statistics (**/STATISTICS** *numbered options*) are available. Thus the command for **ONEWAY** with a **Tukey multiple comparisons test** is:

   ONEWAY/VARIABLES *dependent variable name* **BY** *category variable name* (x, y) **/RANGES TUKEY**.

4) Sample sizes, means, and standard deviations can be used in place of raw data as input. Modify the **DATA LIST** command to include **MATRIX** after **FREE** or **FIXED**, and enter all the sample sizes on one line, all the means on the next, and all the standard deviations on the third, between the BEGIN DATA and END DATA commands. Add the subcommand **/OPTION 7** to the ONEWAY command.

CHAPTER 8

FACTORIAL EXPERIMENTS WITH NO REPEATED MEASURES

8.1 INTRODUCTION

Chapter 7 was concerned with the type of experiment (known as **completely randomised experiment**), in which there is a single independent variable, or factor. For example, in order to to see whether training in the use of a mnemonic method improves recall, we could compare the recall of three groups of subjects:

(1)   a **control** group, untrained in the use of any mnemonic;

(2)   another group trained in the use of **Mnemonic A**;

(3)   a third group trained in **Mnemonic B**.

Since the three conditions all relate to the type of mnemonic training the subjects receive, they can all be regarded as values or **levels** of a single treatment factor, which might be called *mnemonic method*:

MNEMONIC METHOD

	Control	Mnem A	Mnem B
SUBJECTS	group 1	group 2	group 3

Suppose, however, that the experimenter, having divided the subjects into the three groups, splits each group into two subgroups. Both subgroups perform under the same mnemonic condition; but one subgroup is tested first thing in the morning and the other last thing at night. If there are equal numbers of subjects in all subgroups, half the subjects in the entire experiment perform while fresh and the other half while tired. This version of the experiment now has **two factors**:

(1)   **mnemonic method**, whose levels are **control**, **mnemonic A** and **mnemonic B**;
(2)   **alertness**, whose levels are **fresh** and **tired**.

Notice that in this design, each level of either factor is to be found in combination with every level of the other factor: the two factors are said to **cross**. The design can be represented as a table in which each row or column represents a particular level of one of the treatment factors, and a **cell** of the table represents one particular treatment **combination**.

In the table below, the cell on the bottom right represents the combination "tired, mnemonic B". The participants in group 6 were tested under that treatment combination.

		MNEMONIC METHOD		
		Control	**Mnem. A**	**Mnem. B**
ALERTNESS	**Fresh**	group 1	group 2	group 3
	Tired	group 4	group 5	group 6

Experiments with two or more crossed treatment factors are called **factorial** experiments. The experiment just described is a **two-factor** factorial experiment. Note also that each subject is tested under only one treatment combination: for example, a subject, having been trained in mnemonic A and tested first thing in the morning, is not tested again in the evening. In other words, **neither factor in the experiment has repeated measures**. Factorial experiments with no repeated measures on any of their treatment factors are also termed **completely randomised factorial** and **between subjects** experiments.

The table on the next page gives the **cell means**, that is, the mean performance under each of the six treatment combinations. Also given are the row and column means, which are termed the **marginal means**:

MNEMONIC METHOD

		Control	Mnem. A	Mnem. B	row
	fresh	15	15	15	15
ALERT-NESS	**tired**	5	14	14	11
	column	10	14.5	14.5	

In a two-factor experiment, there are two kinds of possible treatment effects:

(1)   **main effects**;
(2)   an **interaction**.

If the performance level is not the same at all levels of either treatment factor (ignoring the other factor in the classification), that factor is said to have a **main effect**. For example, should the scores of those subjects tested first thing in the morning be higher than those tested at night, there would be a main effect of the *alertness* factor. Looking at the marginal row means, it is clear that this is indeed the case: the fresh subjects performed better. Turning now to the marginal column means, it is clear that performance under either mnemonic training condition was superior than under the control condition: there is a main effect of the *mnemonic method* factor.

So far, it has been seen that by looking at the marginal means alone, main effects can be discerned. Turning now to the cell means, however, it is clear that the data show another striking feature. If we look at the fresh subjects only, the performance means show a flat profile: the use of a mnemonic technique fails to produce any improvement with fresh subjects. It is quite different with the tired subjects: without the mnemonic training, their performance was markedly lower than that of the fresh subjects; whereas, when trained, they performed nearly as well as did the fresh subjects. The performance means of the tired subjects thus show a very uneven profile, which does not parallel that of the fresh subjects. The factor *mnemonic method* has different effects at different levels of the alertness factor: it works strongly with tired subjects; but it does not work at all with fresh subjects. When one treatment factor does not have the same effect at all levels of another, the two factors are said to **interact**. The analysis of variance of data from a factorial experiment offers tests for the presence not only of main effects of the factors considered separately but also of interactions between (or among) the factors.

The interaction we have just described can be pictured graphically, as plots of the cell means against mnemonic method for each of fresh and tired groups. There is thus a **fresh subjects** "curve", which is horizontal, and a **tired subjects** "curve" below it, with a different shape. The presence of an interaction is always indicated by profile heterogeneity across the levels of one of the factors.

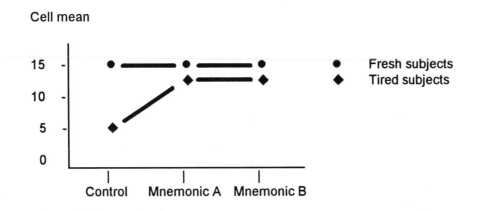

Algebraically, main effects and interactions are defined as independent: it is quite possible to obtain main effects without any interaction between the factors; and it is also possible to have an interaction without any main effects. Usually, however, the presence of an interaction requires the re-interpretation of a main effect. For example, a main effect may arise because one factor has a marked effect at one level of another factor but no effect at other levels, in which case there may be both a significant interaction and a significant main effect. This is what happened in the present example: there is a main effect *mnemonic method*; but, that factor really only has an effect with tired subjects, a fact which is brought out by consideration of the interaction between the two factors.

The manner in which the ANOVA tests for the presence of main effects and an interaction is lucidly described in Gravetter & Wallnau (1992, Chapter 15). If you are unfamiliar with such ANOVA terms as **sum of squares**, **mean square** and **degrees of freedom**, we urge you to read their chapter.

8.2 TWO-FACTOR FACTORIAL EXPERIMENT WITH NO REPEATED MEASURES

In recent years, developments in computer graphics have given an enormous fillip to the study of **human-machine interaction**. In **driving simulation**, for example, the participant sits in a car whose controls are linked to computer-generated images of an imaginary road to create a realistic driving experience. It is thus possible to test a person's performance in heavy traffic, icy conditions, or in emergencies requiring evasive action. A researcher plans to investigate the effects upon driving performance of two new anti-hay fever drugs, A and B. It is suspected that at least one of the drugs may have different effects upon fresh and tired subjects.

The researcher, therefore, decides to carry out a two-factor experiment, in which the factors are:

(1)   **drug**, with levels **placebo**, **A**, and **B**;
(2)   **alertness**, with levels **fresh** and **tired**.

There is already some reason to believe that both drugs may increase the level of arousal in tired subjects, in which case their driving should improve after ingestion of either drug. With fresh subjects, however, the effects of the drugs may be rather different: it is suspected that, with Drug A at least, their performance may deteriorate. In other words, the factors of *drug* and subject *alertness* may interact, so that at least one of the drugs may be dangerous to drivers.

In the experiment, all subjects take a flavoured drink which contains either (in the **A** or **B** conditions) a small dosage of one of the drugs or (in the control, **placebo** condition) no drug. Half the subjects are tested after reading for twenty minutes (the **fresh** condition); the other half are tested after cycling vigorously for the same time (the **tired** condition). A different sample of ten subjects is tested under each of the six treatment combinations (fresh, control); (fresh, A); (fresh, B); (tired, control); (tired, A); (tired, B).

Suppose that the experiment just described produced the following results:

		DRUG		
		Placebo	**A**	**B**
	Fresh	24 25 13 22 16 23 18 19 24 26	18 8 9 14 16 15 6 9 8 17	27 14 19 29 27 23 19 17 20 25
ALERT-NESS	**Tired**	13 12 14 16 17 13 4 3 2 6	21 24 22 23 20 13 11 17 13 16	21 11 14 22 19 9 14 11 21 18

8.2.1 The commands for a factorial ANOVA

SPSS/PC+ uses a program called **ANOVA** for analysing data from factorial experiments that have no repeated measures. The commands are prepared on the scratch pad using the following steps:

Step 1

Write the **DATA LIST** command (Chapter 3): The appropriate section of the Menu can be found either by (a) typing **DATA LIST** on the scratch pad (after pressing **[Alt]/E** if still in the Menu and Help mode) and pressing **[Esc]**, or (b) moving down the **MAIN MENU** to **read or write data**, rightwards into the **read or write data** menu, down to **DATA LIST**, and pressing ⏎ to paste DATA LIST on the scratch pad.

Since the data set is small, the scores can be entered in free-field format and included in the data commands, rather than stored in a separate data file. However it will be necessary to use **two coding (grouping) variables** to indicate the treatment combination under which each score was achieved.

If the coding variables are *alert* and *drug*, (a variable name must not exceed eight characters in length), and performance in the driving simulator is named *drivperf*, the command is:

DATA LIST FREE /alert drug drivperf.

The data are then typed in triplets on the scratch pad after the BEGIN DATA command. The first two numbers in each triplet record the conditions under which the third number (that person's performance score) was obtained. If we code the fresh and tired conditions as 1 and 2, respectively, and the control, A and B conditions as 1, 2 and 3, respectively, the scores in the top left cell of the table of results would be entered as 1 1 24 1 1 25 . . . ., those in the bottom right cell would be entered as 2 3 21 2 3 11 . . . ., and so on.

```
BEGIN DATA.
1 1 24  1 1 25 ...   ...   ...   1 1 26
1 2 18  1 2  8 ...   ...   ...   1 2 17
. . . . . . . .
2 3 21  2 3 11 ...   ...   ...   2 3 18
END DATA.
```

Step 2 (optional, but highly recommended)

Add some labels to improve the intelligibility of the listing file by using the **VARIABLE LABELS** and **VALUE LABELS** commands:

VARIABLE LABELS alert 'Alertness' drug 'Drug Treatment'
            drivperf 'Driving Performance'.
VALUE LABELS alert 1 'Fresh' 2 'Tired' / drug 1 'Placebo' 2 'Drug A' 3 'Drug B'.

Step 3

Execute these data commands by moving the cursor up to the DATA LIST command, pressing **[F10]** and ⏎. This allows you to check that these commands have been correctly written and will enable SPSS/PC+ to generate a table of variable names for pasting into later commands.

Step 4

Find **ANOVA** in the menu via **analyze data** and **comparing group means**, and press ↵ to paste ANOVA on the scratch pad. (Alternatively, type **ANOVA** on the scratchpad and press **[Esc]**.)

Move down to **/VARIABLES** and press ↵ to paste /VARIABLES on the scratch pad. Examine the examples given in the **/VARIABLES** menu, move down to **dependent(s)**, press ↵ and select the dependent variable name *drivperf* from the variable table. Press ↵ and then **[Esc]**. Move down to **BY**, press ↵, select the factor name *alert* from the variable table, and press ↵. Remove the variable table with **[Esc]**. Move down the ANOVA menu to **( )**, press ↵ and type in the lowest and highest values (ie 1, 2). Press ↵ again. Return to **BY**, press ↵, and repeat the procedure for the second factor, remembering that it has three values, not two. (Note that if the factors had the same number of values, it would only be necessary to insert one set of bracketed values after the second factor name.)

(Alternatively, after pasting /VARIABLES, you may prefer to enter the remaining part of the command on the scratch pad by pressing **[Alt]/E** and typing the required details.)

The command is thus:

ANOVA/VARIABLES drivperf BY alert (1, 2) drug (1, 3).

Ensure that the command ends with a period (.), unless a subcommand is being added.

Step 5 (optional subcommand)

An optional **/STATISTICS** subcommand can be added which displays the means and counts for each cell. Return to the **ANOVA** menu with the ← key, move down to **/STATISTICS** and press ↵ to paste **/STATISTICS** on the scratch pad. A variety of possible statistics (represented by numbers) will then be listed in the **/STATISTICS** menu. Select 3 by pressing ↵.

ANOVA/VARIABLES drivperf BY alert (1,2) drug (1,3) /STATISTICS 3.

Ensure that there is a period (.) at the end of the command.

Step 6

Save the commands to a named file on the floppy disk by using **[F9]** (see Chapter 2, section 2.5.3) and execute the ANOVA command by pressing **[F10]** and ↵.

8.2.2 The listing for a factorial ANOVA

The listing on the screen will include both the marginal and cell means, followed by the ANOVA summary table.

* * * C E L L M E A N S * * *

		DRIVPERF	Driving Performance
BY		ALERT	Alertness
		DRUG	Drug Treatment

TOTAL POPULATION

16.50
(60)

ALERT	1	2
	18.33	14.67
	(30)	(30)

DRUG	1	2	3
	15.50	15.00	19.00
	(20)	(20)	(20)

	DRUG	1	2	3
ALERT				
	1	21.00	12.00	22.00
		(10)	(10)	(10)
	2	10.00	18.00	16.00
		(10)	(10)	(10)

When these means are plotted, the graph clearly shows evidence of an interaction: the fresh and tired profiles are clearly far from parallel.

Cell mean

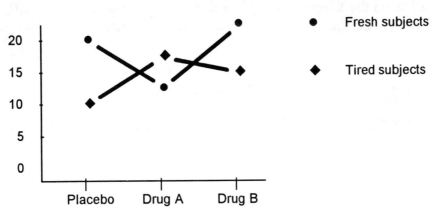

101

The ANOVA table tabulates the F ratios and their associated significance levels for the main effects and the two-way interaction. Note the **Signif of F** values for each F ratio. Both the *alert* main effect and the interaction are significant beyond the 1 per cent level, and the *drug* main effect beyond the 5 per cent level. Thus we can conclude that the drugs have different effects upon fresh and tired subjects.

* * * A N A L Y S I S   O F   V A R I A N C E * * *

	DRIVPERF	Driving Performance
BY	ALERT	Alertness
	DRUG	Drug Treatment

Source of Variation	Sum of Squares	DF	Mean Square	F	Signif of F
Main Effects	391.667	3	130.556	5.640	.002
ALERT	201.667	1	201.667	8.712	.005
DRUG	190.000	2	95.000	4.104	.022
2-way Interactions	763.333	2	381.667	16.488	.000
ALERT DRUG	763.333	2	381.667	16.488	.000
Explained	1155.000	5	231.000	9.979	.000
Residual	1250.000	54	23.148		
Total	2405.000	59	40.763		

60 Cases were processed.
0 Cases (.0 PCT) were missing.

8.2.2.1 SAVING THE LISTING TO A FILE

To save the listing to a file on the floppy disk (essential if a printed version is needed), add a **SET/LISTING** command at the head of the commands and re-execute the whole set (see Chapter 2).

8.2.2.2 PRINTING THE LISTING AND COMMAND FILES

Details are given in Chapter 2 (section 2.6) about how to print files from the floppy disk.

8.3 EXPERIMENTS WITH THREE OR MORE TREATMENT FACTORS

SPSS/PC+ can readily be used to analyse data from more complex factorial experiments, with three or more treatment factors. We should warn the reader, however, that multifactor experiments with four or more treatment factors should be avoided, because interpretation of complex interactions involving four or more factors is extremely difficult.

The ANOVA of data from an experiment with three or more factors, however, is simple on SPSS/PC+: it is only necessary to remember that a code variable is needed for each factor.

8.4 NON-PARAMETRIC TESTS FOR FACTORIAL EXPERIMENTS

As with the one-factor ANOVA, the use of the factorial ANOVA presupposes that the assumptions of a statistical model hold for the data: for example, homogeneity of cell variance is assumed, and normality of distribution. If there is marked violation of these assumptions, it may be better to use a non-parametric analysis. Meddis (1984) describes the procedure. Unfortunately, it is not available on SPSS/PC+.

8.5 SUMMARY

1)   This chapter has considered the analysis of variance of data from a two-factor factorial experiment, with no repeated measures. The use of the technique assumes normality of distribution and homogeneity of cell variance.

2)   **ANOVA** tests for the presence of a **main effect** of each factor considered separately and for an **interaction** between the factors. A factor is said to have a

main effect if performance is not the same at all levels. Two factors are said to **interact** if the effect of either is heterogeneous across the levels of the other factor.

3) The command for **ANOVA** with just one independent grouping variable is

ANOVA/VARIABLES *dependent variable name* **BY**
grouping variable name (x, y).

where x and y represent the lowest and highest code numbers of the grouping variable.

Extra grouping variable names can be added, one after the other. For example, with two grouping variable, the command is:

ANOVA/VARIABLES *dependent variable name* **BY**
first grouping variable name (p, q)
second grouping variable name (r, s).

where p and q, and r and s, respectively, represent the lowest and highest code numbers of the grouping variables.

If the grouping variables have the same code numbers, just one set of bracketed numbers is needed after the final variable name:

ANOVA/VARIABLES *dependent variable name* **BY**
first grouping variable name   second grouping variable name (x, y).

4) Subcommands for **ANOVA** include **/STATISTICS 3**, which displays the marginal and cell means.

CHAPTER 9

EXPERIMENTS WITH REPEATED MEASURES ON ALL FACTORS

9.1 INTRODUCTION

An experiment is said to have **repeated measures** on a treatment factor if each subject's performance is measured at every level of the factor. When a factor has repeated measures, its conditions can be said to vary **within subjects**, as opposed to **between subjects**. In Chapter 7, a one-factor experiment was described, in which the recall of a text by three groups of subjects was compared, each group being tested at a different level of the treatment factor. That experiment was said to have **no repeated measures** on its single treatment factor. It could also be described as a one-factor, **between subjects experiment**. In other circumstances, however, it would be better to have just one sample of subjects, and to test each subject under all the conditions making up the treatment factor. In that case, the experiment could be described as a **one-factor experiment with repeated measures**, or as a one-factor **within subjects experiment**.

As an example, suppose that in a study of performance, the independent variable is task complexity, with three levels: simple, medium and high. The experimental design can be represented as shown on the following page:

COMPLEXITY

simple	medium	complex

same group of subjects

The same design, however, can be represented somewhat differently:

COMPLEXITY

	simple	medium	complex
subject 1	—	—	—
subject 2	—	—	—
....	......	......	......
....	......	......	......
subject 30	—	—	—

In each row, the dashes represent the scores that one particular subject achieves under the three conditions. It is also clear that, although there is just one treatment factor (complexity), the design could be thought of as having two factors:

(1)   the **treatment factor**;
(2)   **subjects**, with 30 levels (if there are 30 subjects in the experiment).

Moreover, the two factors, treatment and subjects, **cross**: each level of either factor is to be found in combination with every level of the other. The one-factor repeated measures design, in fact, resembles a two-factor design (Chapter 8) with just one observation in each cell. For this reason, the one-factor repeated measures experiment is sometimes termed a **subjects by treatments** experiment.

In this chapter, we shall consider only the analysis of experiments that have repeated measures on **all** their treatment factors. In principle, of course, as with between subjects experiments, there can be any number of treatment factors.

9.2 ADVANTAGES AND DISADVANTAGES OF REPEATED MEASURES EXPERIMENTS

One potential difficulty with between subjects experiments is that if there are large individual differences in performance, searching for a meaningful pattern in the data is like trying to hear a radio programme against a background of interference. For example, in the mnemonics methods experiment described in Chapter 8, some of the scores obtained by subjects in the control condition may well be higher than those of subjects who were trained to use a mnemonic. This is because there are some people who, when asked to read through a long list, can, **without any training at all**, reproduce most of the items accurately; whereas others, unless trained, would remember very few items. Individual differences, therefore, can introduce considerable **noise** into the data from between subjects experiments.

Essentially, the within subjects experiment uses each subject as his or her own control; and the crossed nature of the design makes it possible to separate the variance that has resulted from the manipulation of the treatment factor from that arising from individual differences.

Another drawback with the between subjects experiment is that it is wasteful of subjects: if the experimental procedure is a short one, a subject may spend more time travelling to and from the place of testing than actually performing the experiment. The great appeal of the within subjects experiment is that much more extensive use can be made of the subject who has taken the trouble to attend.

In summary, therefore, the within subjects experiment has two advantages over the between subjects experiment:

(1)   it cuts down data noise;
(2)   it is a more efficient use of time and resources.

Nevertheless, the within subjects experiment also has disadvantages, which in some circumstances can outweigh considerations of convenience and maximisation of the signal-to-noise ratio. In designing an experiment, it is essential to try to ensure that the independent variable does not co-vary with an unwanted, or **extraneous** variable, so that the effects of the two are entangled, or **confounded**.

Suppose the mnemonics experiment had been of repeated measures design, and that each subject had first performed under the control condition, then under mnemonic A and finally under mnemonic B. Perhaps the improvement under mnemonic A was simply a **practice effect**: the more lists one learns, the better one becomes at learning lists. A practice effect is one kind of **carry-over effect**. Carry-over effects do not always have a positive effect upon performance: recall of the items in a list is vulnerable to interference from items in previous lists. Carry-over effects may depend upon the sequence of conditions: for example, while performance under mnemonic A may be unaffected by previous performance under the control condition, the converse may not true: it may be difficult for subjects who have been trained in the use of a mnemonic to cease to use it on demand. This is an example of an **order effect**. Carry-over and order effects can act as extraneous, confounding variables, making it impossible to interpret the results of a within subjects experiment.

One approach to the problem of carry-over effects and order effects is the procedure known as **counterbalancing**, whereby the order of presentation of the conditions making up a repeated measures factor is varied from subject to subject, in the hope that carry-over and order effects will balance out across conditions. Counterbalancing is not always sensible, however, as in the mnemonics experiment, where (as we have seen) it would make little sense to have the control condition coming last. These matters must be carefully considered before deciding to perform an experiment with repeated measures on its treatment factors.

An additional problem with repeated measures is that if there is **heterogeneity of covariance** (see section 9.3.2 below), there is a heightened risk of statistical error.

9.3 ANALYSING THE RESULTS OF WITHIN SUBJECTS EXPERIMENTS

In an exercise in experimental aesthetics, subjects were asked to produce pictures using just one of three different materials for any one picture: crayons, paints or felt-tip pens. The dependent variable was the rating a picture received from a panel of judges. The independent variable was the type of implement used to produce the picture. Since subjects would vary in artistic ability, it was decided to ask each to produce three pictures, one with each type of implement. In an attempt to neutralise order effects, the order of implements was counterbalanced across subjects. This is a one-factor experiment with repeated measures. (Alternatively, it could be described as a **one-factor within subjects** or **subjects by treatments** experiment.) To perform an analysis of such an experiment, the user has to turn to the multivariate MANOVA program. Therefore, before continuing with this example, it is necessary to explain the difference between **univariate** and **multivariate** statistics.

9.3.1 Univariate and multivariate statistics

In all the experiments that have been considered so far, there has been just one dependent variable. Statistical methods that have been devised for the processing of such data are known as **univariate** methods. The ANOVAs to which we have been referring are univariate methods. An experiment, however, may involve more than one dependent variable. In an experiment on reading, for instance, the independent variable might be the spacing of the lines in a written text. One dependent variable might be the time a person takes to read a passage. But it would also be of interest to test the **quality** of recall: perhaps reading speed is gained at the expense of accuracy. In this experiment, therefore, there would be **two dependent variables**: speed and accuracy. It would be possible to carry out a univariate ANOVA on the reaction times and recall scores separately. The problem with that approach, however, is that the outcomes of the two analyses would not be independent: if one shows significance, it might be possible to predict the outcome of the other test without actually carrying out the second analysis at all. If so, the second ANOVA is to some extent redundant.

There are available statistical techniques which permit the simultaneous analysis of data from experiments with two or more dependent variables. These are known as **multivariate methods**. For the reading experiment, one could use a multivariate extension of ANOVA known as **multivariate analysis of variance**, which is referred to acronymically as **MANOVA.** In testing whether the spacing of lines affects reading, MANOVA will take into account not only speed but also accuracy, thus utilising all the data while at the same time avoiding the redundancy problem.

9.3.2 Using the SPSS/PC+ MANOVA program to analyse data from within subjects experiments

To perform a univariate repeated measures ANOVA on SPSS/PC+, the user must, paradoxically, turn to the multivariate MANOVA program. This program interprets the data obtained at the various levels of a factor with repeated measures as **dependent** variables. Provided these are all linked with the name of the within subjects factor concerned, MANOVA will include a univariate repeated measures ANOVA in its output. Unfortunately, however, the output contains other items, many of which will be unfamiliar to one unaccustomed to working with computing packages. In the space available to us here, we can only offer the briefest outline of the rationale of MANOVA. We strongly recommend readers who wish to deepen their understanding of the topic to study the readable text by Tabachnick & Fidell (1989).

Basically, MANOVA finds a linear function of the dependent variables such that it maximises differences among the treatment groups. It then performs something similar to an ANOVA on a derived data set comprising subjects' scores on the new variable. Instead of performing an F test, however, a multivariate statistic is used such as Wilks' Lambda, Hotelling's trace criterion, or Pillai's criterion.

Provided the correct command is given, however, the MANOVA output will also include the usual **univariate ANOVA summary table** appropriate for a within subjects experiment. It is important to be aware that the model underlying the use of the repeated measures univariate ANOVA specifies certain additional requirements, over and above those required for between subjects experiments. The most important of these is that the correlations among the scores at the various levels of the within subjects factor are homogeneous. This is known as the assumption of **homogeneity of covariance**. Should that assumption be violated, the true Type I error rate may be greatly inflated. (A Type I error is the probability of rejecting H_0 when it is true.)

The MANOVA program tests for heterogeneity of covariance with the **Mauchly sphericity test**. Should the data fail the sphericity test, the ANOVA F test must be modified to make it more conservative. The **Greenhouse-Geisser** test reduces the degrees of freedom of the numerator and denominator of the F test by multiplying the original values by a factor **e**, the value of which is given in the SPSS/PC+ output under **Greenhouse-Geisser epsilon**. (The value of F remains the same as before: only the degrees of freedom are reduced.) For a helpful discussion, see Howell (1992: Chapter 14, pp. 446).

9.4 ANALYSIS OF DATA FROM A ONE-FACTOR REPEATED MEASURES EXPERIMENT

Let us return to the example described earlier. Suppose the data for the aesthetics experiment were as follows:

| | IMPLEMENT | | |
	Crayon	Paint	Felt-tip
s1	10	12	14
s2	18	10	16
s3	20	15	16
...	...	...	...
s10	23	20	18

9.4.1 The commands for a one-factor repeated measures ANOVA using MANOVA

The commands are prepared as follows:

Step 1

Write the **DATA LIST** command (Chapter 3). The appropriate section of the Menu can be found by either (a) typing **DATA LIST** on the scratch pad and pressing **[Esc]**, or (b) moving down the **MAIN MENU** to **read or write data**, rightwards into **read or write data**, down to **DATA LIST**, and finally pressing ⏎ to paste DATA LIST on the scratch pad.

Since the data set is small, the data be entered in free-field format and included in the commands, rather than a separate data file. No coding (grouping) variables are necessary.

If the levels of the factor *implement* are *crayon*, *paint* and *felttip*, the command is:

DATA LIST FREE/crayon paint felttip.

The data are then typed on the scratch pad after the BEGIN DATA command:

```
BEGIN DATA.
10 12 14
18 10 16
20 15 16
12 10 12
19 20 21
25 22 20
18 16 17
22 18 18
17 14 12
23 20 18
END DATA.
```

Step 2

Execute these data commands by moving the cursor to DATA LIST, pressing **[F10]** and then ⏎ . This will allow you to check that these commands have been correctly written and will enable SPSS/PC+ to generate a table of variable names which can be pasted into subsequent commands.

Step 3

Find **MANOVA** in the menu via **analyze data** and **comparing group means**, and press ⏎ to paste **MANOVA** on the scratch pad. (Alternatively, type MANOVA and press **[Esc]**.)

Read the overview, move down the **MANOVA** menu to **variables** and press ⏎ . Read the information on the **dependent(s)** item and press ⏎ to reveal the table of variable names. Select the variable name *all* and press ⏎ (or if preferred, select each of the names *crayon paint felttip* in turn, pressing ⏎ each time). Remove the variable name table with **[Esc]** and move back to the MANOVA menu with the ← cursor key. Move down to **repeated measures** and read the information. Press ⏎ , read the overview, move down to **/WSFACTORS** and press ⏎ to paste **/WSFACTORS** on the scratch pad. Read the instructions about the factor name and press ⏎ before typing in a new name for the factor. Press ⏎ , move down to **( )**, press ⏎ again and type in the number of levels (in this example it is 3), and press ⏎ .

(Alternatively, after pasting MANOVA, you may prefer to enter the rest of the command by pressing **[Alt]/E** and typing the required material.)

The command is:

MANOVA all /WSFACTORS implem (3).

Alternatively, if there are other variable names in the DATA LIST command besides those needed for the MANOVA command, the command is

MANOVA crayon paint felttip /WSFACTORS implem (3).

Step 4

Save the commands on the scratch pad to a named file on the floppy disk by using **[F9]** (see Chapter 2). Execute the MANOVA command by pressing **[F10]** followed by ⏎ .

9.4.2 The listing for a one-factor repeated measures analysis

The listing begins with a note stating that the **Last command is not a design specification - a full factorial model is generated for this problem**. This can be ignored.

The listing continues with sections headed **** ANALYSIS OF VARIANCE -- DESIGN 1 ****.

The first (not reproduced here) is subtitled **Tests of Between-Subjects Effects** and can be ignored.

The next section uses the **Mauchly Sphericity Test** to evaluate the homogeneity of covariance assumption, which is important for the univariate approach. If the test is not significant (ie **Significance**, the p-value, has a value greater than 0.05), then the p-value given in the ANOVA summary table, which appears under the title **Averaged Tests of Significance**, can be accepted; otherwise, one can make a more conservative test, such as the Greenhouse-Geisser. In the present case, the Mauchly test gives a p-value of 0.684, so the usual ANOVA F test can be used. In the situation where there is no evidence to indicate heterogeneity of covariance, the univariate ANOVA F test is more **powerful** than MANOVA: the null hypothesis, if false, is more likely to be rejected.

```
* * ANALYSIS OF VARIANCE -- DESIGN 1 * *

Tests involving `IMPLEM' Within-Subject Effect.
Mauchly sphericity test, W =            .90942
Chi-square approx. =                    .75963 with 2 D. F.
Significance =                          .684
```

AVERAGED Tests of Significance for MEAS.1 using UNIQUE sums of squares

Source of Variation	SS	DF	MS	F	Sig of F
WITHIN CELLS	72.73	18	4.04		
IMPLEM	39.27	2	19.63	4.86	.021

Note the **Signif of F** value for the *implem* within-subject factor in the **AVERAGED tests of Significance** section is 0.021 ie the obtained value of F is **significant beyond the 5 per cent level**, but not beyond the 0.01 level. Thus the type of implement used does affect the ratings that a painting receives.

9.4.2.1 SAVING THE LISTING TO A FILE

To save a copy of the listing to a file on the floppy disk (an essential step, should a printed version be required), add a **SET/LISTING** command at the head of the commands and re-execute all the commands (Chapter 2).

9.4.2.2 PRINTING THE LISTING AND COMMAND FILES

Details are given in Chapter 2 (section 2.6) about how to print files from the floppy disk.

9.5 THE ANALYSIS OF DATA FROM A TWO-FACTOR REPEATED MEASURES EXPERIMENT

An experiment is designed to investigate the detection of patterns on a screen. The patterns vary in shape and in solidity. The dependent variable (DV) is the number of errors made in responding to the pattern, and the two independent variables are *shape* (circle, square, or triangle) and *solidity* (outline or solid). The same sample of subjects is used for all the possible treatment combinations, that is, there are repeated measures on both factors in the experiment. As with the one-factor repeated measures experiment, the univariate ANOVA is performed by using SPSS/PC+'s MANOVA program. In this case, although each treatment combination will be treated as a separate dependent variable, the MANOVA output will contain a univariate ANOVA summary table with F tests of main effects and the interaction.

Suppose the results are as follows:

SHAPE:- SOLIDITY:-	Circle Solid	Outline	Square Solid	Outline	Triangle Solid	Outline
s1	4	2	2	8	7	5
s2	3	6	2	6	8	9
s3	2	10	2	5	5	3
...	.	.	.	.	.	.
s10	2	12	12	8	10	12

Extra care is needed when MANOVA is used to analyse data from experiments with two or more repeated measures factors. It is essential to ensure that SPSS/PC+ understands which data were obtained under which combination of factors. In the present example, there are six data for each subject, each datum being a score achieved under a different combination of the two factors. We can label the data variables as *circsol*, *circlin*, *squarsol*, *squarlin*, *triansol* and *trianlin*, representing all possible combinations of the shape and solidity factors. Should there be many treatment combinations in the experiment, however, it would be very tedious to name the variables individually. In such cases, it is much more convenient to use a shortcut when listing the variables in the DATA LIST instruction. This is achieved by making use of the keyword **TO** between two variable names which only differ in the final number (eg score1 **TO** score6, age1 **TO** age12, bearing in mind that the length of the variable name must be at most, 8 characters).

However one chooses to name the variables, there remains the problem of relating those names to specific subgroups of the data set. The MANOVA command contains an item named **/WSFACTORS**. Just as in the one-factor case used in the previous example, the within-subjects factor(s) must be named, **but the order of naming is critical when there is more than one factor.** The rule is that **the first named factor varies more slowly across the list of data than the next named factor, and so on if there are more than two factors.** This rule and an example are given in the right-hand window of the menu when **factor name** is selected within the **/WSFACTORS** menu.

In the present example, remembering that MANOVA treats each combination of levels of within subjects factors as a separate dependent variable, it can be seen that in the sequence *circsol*, *circlin*, *squarsol*, *squarlin*, *triansol* and *trianlin*, the shape factor varies more slowly than the solidity factor: progressing from left to right, the solidity level changes before the shape level. (Of course, this is arbitrary: if the sequence had been *circsol*, *squarsol*, *triansol*, *circlin*, *squarlin*, *trianlin*, the shape factor would have been changing faster than solidity. In that case, however, the data in the DATA LIST command would have been entered in a different order.)

9.5.1 The commands for a two-factor repeated measures ANOVA using MANOVA

The commands for analysing the data using the MANOVA program are prepared on the scratch pad in the following steps:

Step 1

Write the DATA LIST command (Chapter 3). The appropriate section of the Menu can be found by either (a) typing DATA LIST on the scratch pad and pressing **[Esc]**, or (b) moving down the MAIN MENU to **read or write data**, rightwards to expand this item into the **read or write data menu**, down to **DATA LIST**, and finally pressing ↵ to paste DATA LIST on the scratch pad.

Since the data set is small, the data can be entered in free-field format and included in the commands, rather than stored in a separate data file. No coding (grouping) variables are necessary. The shortcut using the keyword TO will be used to list the variable names.

DATA LIST FREE/score1 TO score6.

The data are then typed on the scratch pad after the BEGIN DATA command. Each row contains the values of the six variables *score1* to *score6*:

```
BEGIN DATA.
4 2 2 8 7 5
3 6 2 6 8 9
2 10 2 5 5 3
.   .   .   .
2 12 12 8 10 12
END DATA.
```

Step 2

Execute these data commands with **[F10]** and ↵ . This will enable SPSS/PC+ to generate a table of variable names which can be pasted into subsequent commands.

Step 3

Find **MANOVA** in the menu via **analyze data** and **comparing group means**, and press ↵ to paste MANOVA on the scratchpad. (Alternatively, type MANOVA and press **[Esc]**.)

Read the overview and move down the **MANOVA** menu to **variables**. Read the information about variables, and press ↵ . Read about **dependent(s)**, press ↵ and select *all* from the table of variables. Press ↵ and then **[Esc]** to remove the table of variables.

(You may prefer to select each of the dependent variable names or to type directly on the scratch pad *score1 TO score6*. In either case, selection is essential if there are other variable names in the DATA LIST command besides those for the MANOVA command.)

Move back to the MANOVA menu with the ← cursor key. Then move down to **repeated measures** and press ↵ . Read the overview and move down to /WSFACTORS. Press ↵ to paste this on the scratch pad. Read the information about the **factor name(s)**, especially the details about the order of the names. These names must be generic names, not variable names previously specified in the DATA LIST command. Here they might be *shape* and *solidity*. Press ↵ , type in the generic name *shape* and press ↵ . Move down to ( ), press ↵ and type 3, which is the number of levels for *shape*. Press ↵ , move back up to **factor name**, press ↵ , type *solidity*, and press ↵ . Move down to ( ), press ↵ , type 2, which is the number of levels for *solidity*, and finally press ↵ .

(Alternatively, after pasting /WSFACTORS, you may prefer to enter the factor names and their numbers of levels in brackets directly on the scratch pad by pressing **[Alt]/E** and typing in the material.)

The command is

MANOVA all /WSFACTORS shape(3) solidity(2).

Should the user prefer to enter the dependent variable names, the command would be

MANOVA score1 TO score6 /WSFACTORS shape(3) solidity (2).

Ensure that the command terminates with a period (.), unless subcommands are being added.

Step 4 (optional)

The subcommand /OMEANS displays the observed means, standard deviations and N of the variables. Move leftwards twice with the ← cursor key to the MANOVA menu, downwards to **any analysis**, and press ↵ . Move down to /OMEANS and press ↵ . The command is now:

MANOVA all /WSFACTORS shape(3) solidity(2) /OMEANS.

Step 5

Save the commands to a named file on the floppy disk by using **[F9]** (see Chapter 2), and then execute the MANOVA command by pressing **[F10]** followed by ↵ .

9.5.2 The listing for a two-factor repeated measures ANOVA

The listing begins with a note stating that the **Last command is not a design specification - a full factorial model is generated for this problem**. This can be ignored.

The listing on the screen will include several sections, each headed **** ANALYSIS OF VARIANCE -- DESIGN 1 ****.

1) **Means, standard deviations, and N**

The subcommand **/OMEANS** means obtains the listing of the mean, standard deviation and N for each of the six "variables" (treatment combinations).

* * ANALYSIS OF VARIANCE -- DESIGN 1 * *

Cell Means and Standard Deviations

Variable .. SCORE1

	Mean	Std. Dev.	N
For entire sample	3.600	1.838	10

Variable .. SCORE2

	Mean	Std. Dev.	N
For entire sample	7.700	3.268	10

Variable .. SCORE3

	Mean	Std. Dev.	N
For entire sample	4.900	3.446	10

Variable .. SCORE4

	Mean	Std. Dev.	N
For entire sample	6.000	1.155	10

Variable .. SCORE5

	Mean	Std. Dev.	N
For entire sample	5.800	3.190	10

Variable .. SCORE6

	Mean	Std. Dev.	N
For entire sample	9.000	3.018	10

2) The section subtitled **Tests of Between-Subjects Effects** (not reproduced here) can be ignored: here we are interested only in within-subjects effects.

3) Within-subject Effects

The first table contains the **Mauchly sphericity test**, which is used to check the homogeneity of covariance assumption for the SHAPE within-subject effect. In this case it is not significant, because the p-value (0.197) is greater than 0.05. Accordingly, the multivariate test can be ignored (the section is not reproduced below) and attention paid to the **Averaged Tests of Significance** (the univariate ANOVA) for SHAPE. With a **Significance of F** = 0.076, it can be concluded that differences attributable to the shape factor are not significant.

* * ANALYSIS OF VARIANCE -- DESIGN 1 * *

Tests involving `SHAPE' Within-Subject Effect.

```
Mauchly sphericity test, W =          .66634
Chi-square approx. =                 3.24763 with 2 D. F.
Significance =                        .197
```

AVERAGED Tests of Significance that follow multivariate tests are equivalent to univariate or split-plot or mixed-model approach to repeated measures.

AVERAGED Tests of Significance for SCORE using UNIQUE sums of squares

Source of Variation	SS	DF	MS	F	Sig of F
WITHIN CELLS	138.97	18	7.72		
SHAPE	46.03	2	23.02	2.98	.076

The next part examines the within-subject factor SOLIDITY. With only two levels in this factor, the multivariate and univariate approaches are identical, and no sphericity test is necessary. This factor is significant beyond the 1 per cent level, since the **Significance of F** is listed as 0.000 (meaning that the p-value is less than .0005).

Tests involving `SOLIDITY' Within-Subject Effect.

Tests of Significance for T4 using UNIQUE sums of squares

Source of Variation	SS	DF	MS	F	Sig of F
WITHIN CELLS	19.40	9	2.16		
SOLIDITY	117.60	1	117.60	54.56	.000

4) Interaction Effect

The next section examines the interaction of the two within-subject factors (SHAPE BY SOLIDITY). Since the **Mauchly sphericity test** is not significant (Significance = 0.663), the univariate test can be used. The ANOVA summary table, however, shows that this interaction is not significant (**Significance of F** = 0.270).

(The multivariate test of SHAPE BY SOLIDITY is not reproduced here.)

Tests involving `SHAPE BY SOLIDITY' Within-Subject Effect.

Mauchly sphericity test, W = .90250
Chi-square approx. = .82067 with 2 D. F.
Significance = .663

AVERAGED Tests of Significance for SCORE using UNIQUE sums of squares

Source of Variation	SS	DF	MS	F	Sig of F
WITHIN CELLS	151.30	18	8.41		
SHAPE BY SOLIDITY	23.70	2	11.85	1.41	.270

In conclusion, the listing shows that only *solidity* is significant: the other systematic sources, namely, *shape* and its interaction with *solidity*, are not significant.

{Hint: If only the univariate listings are required, the subcommand /PRINT SIGNIF (AVONLY) at the end of the MANOVA command will suppress the multivariate parts of the listings.}

9.5.2.1 SAVING THE LISTING TO A FILE

To save a copy of the listing to a file on the floppy disk (which is essential if a printed version is needed), add a **SET/LISTING** command at the head of the commands and submit all the commands for re-execution (Chapter 2).

9.5.2.2 PRINTING THE LISTING AND COMMAND FILES

Details are given in Chapter 2 (section 2.6) about how to print files from the floppy disk.

9.6 SUMMARY

1) When an experiment has **repeated measures on all factors**, the analysis can be obtained as part of the output of SPSS/PC+'s **MANOVA** program. **Univariate** analyses are preferred to **multivariate** analyses when the sphericity assumption (ie the homegeneity of covariance) holds. If the **Mauchly sphericity test** is significant, however, a conservative F test can be used. Alternatively, the user can rely upon the multivariate tests, though they are more difficult to interpret.

2) The command for a one-factor repeated measures ANOVA is of the form

> **MANOVA** *dependent variable names*
>   **/WSFACTORS** *generic factor name* (m).

The dependent variable names are the names of the levels of the repeated factor, the generic factor name is a name for the factor, and *m* is the number of levels of the factor (ie the number of dependent variables).

The command for a two-factor repeated measures ANOVA is of the form

> **MANOVA** *dependent variable names*
>   **/WSFACTORS** *first generic factor name* (m)
>   *second generic factor name* (n).

The dependent variable names are the combinations of the within-subjects factors, the generic factor names are the names for the factors, and m and n are the number of levels in each factor. The names of the factors must be listed in reverse order of the relative speed at which they vary.

When naming dependent variables, it is often useful to take a shortcut, whereby the word **TO** is used in a statement such as *score1* **TO** *score6*. Thus the command might be:

> **MANOVA** *score1* **TO** *score6* **/WSFACTORS** *generic factor name* (m)
>   *generic factor name* (n).

3) The subcommand **/OMEANS** lists the observed means, standard deviations and N for each variable.

4) The subcommand **/PRINT SIGNIF (AVONLY)** obtains only a listing of the univariate results.

CHAPTER 10

EXPERIMENTS OF MIXED DESIGN

10.1 BETWEEN SUBJECTS AND WITHIN SUBJECTS DESIGNS

It is very common for factorial designs to have repeated measures on **some** (but not all) of their treatment factors. Since such experiments have a mixture of between subjects and within subjects factors, they are often said to be of **mixed** design. The term **split-plot** is also used, reflecting the agronomic context in which this design was first employed.

In psychological and educational research, the researcher often selects two samples of subjects (eg male and female groups) and performs the same repeated measures experiment upon each group. To extend the imaginary reading experiment of Chapter 9, suppose that samples of male and female subjects are tested for recall of a written passage with three different line spacings, the order of presentation of the three levels of the spacing factor being counterbalanced across subjects to neutralise order effects. In this experiment, there are two factors:

(1)   gender (male, female);
(2)   spacing (narrow, medium, wide).

The levels of gender vary **between** subjects, whereas those of spacing vary **within** subjects. The experiment has thus one between subjects and one within subjects factor.

10.1.1 Subject versus experimental factors

It will be noticed that, unlike spacing, gender is not a treatment factor: subjects are not randomly assigned to the "levels" male and female. In other words, gender is varied by **sampling,** not manipulation, and to compare male with female is **a correlational**, rather than a truly experimental, research strategy. (Actually, the strategy of controlling a variable by sampling, rather than manipulation, is known as **quasi-experimentation**.) Authorities on the topic of analysis of variance use the term **subject factor** to distinguish factors such as gender, which are varied by sampling, from truly experimental factors, which are manipulated by assigning subjects to their various levels.

This distinction is a very important one: in correlational research, it is often very questionable whether one has truly controlled the variables of interest; indeed, several variables are often inextricably confounded, as when, in attempting to show that smoking causes lung cancer, the researcher is forced to compare self-selecting groups of people. From the point of view of ANOVA, however, subject factors are treated in exactly the same way as experimental factors.

10.2 THE ANOVA FOR A TWO-FACTOR MIXED EXPERIMENT WITH ONE WITHIN SUBJECTS FACTOR

Suppose that a psychologist designs an experiment to explore the hypothesis that engineering students, because of their training in two-dimensional representation of three-dimensional structures, have a more strongly developed sense of shape and symmetry than do psychology students. Three types of shapes are presented to samples of psychology and engineering students under sub-optimal conditions on a monitor screen. All three types of shape are presented to each subject: hence shape is a within-subjects factor. The category of student (psychology or engineering), on the other hand, is a between-subjects factor. The dependent variable is the number of shapes correctly identified.

The SPSS/PC+ program MANOVA is used for the analysis of data from experiments with repeated measures on their treatment factors. The procedure for identifying the repeated measures factors with the /WSFACTORS subcommand was explained in Chapter 9. In experiments with mixed designs, however, there are also between subjects factors. As usual, their levels are identified by means of a numerical code.

Suppose the results of the experiment are as follows:

TYPE OF STUDENT		Triangle	SHAPE Square	Rectangle
Psychology	s1	2	12	7
	s2	8	10	9
	.	.	.	.
	s6	7	14	8
Engineering	s7	13	3	35
	s8	21	4	30
	.	.	.	.
	s12	19	8	27

10.2.1 The commands for a mixed design ANOVA using MANOVA

The commands are prepared on the scratch pad in the following steps:

Step 1

Write the DATA LIST command (Chapter 3). The appropriate section of the Menu can be found by either (a) typing DATA LIST on the scratch pad and pressing **[Esc]**, or (b) moving down the MAIN MENU to **read or write data**, rightwards into the **read or write data** menu, down to **DATA LIST**, finally pressing ⌐ to paste DATA LIST. on the scratch pad.

Since the data set is small, the data can be entered in free-field format and included in the data commands rather than stored in a separate data file. A coding (grouping) variable is necessary to identify the levels of the between subjects factor.

If the coding variable is called *category* and the levels of the repeated measures factor (shape) are *triangle*, *square*, *rectangl*, (which will be treated as dependent variables by the MANOVA program), the command is:

DATA LIST FREE / category triangle square rectangl.

The data are then typed on the scratch pad after the BEGIN DATA command eg

BEGIN DATA.
1 2 12 7
1 8 10 9

```
. . . .
1 7 14 8
2 13 3 35
2 21 4 30

. . . .
2 19 8 27
END  DATA.
```

Step 2 (optional)

The meaning of the code numbers (1 and 2) can be stated in a **VALUE LABELS** command eg

```
VALUE LABELS category 1 'Psychology Students'
                     2 'Engineering Students'.
```

Step 3

Execute these data commands by moving the cursor to DATA LIST, pressing **[F10]** and ↵ . This will allow you to check that these commands have been correctly written and will enable SPSS/PC+ to generate a table of variable names which can be pasted into subsequent commands.

Step 4

Find MANOVA in the menu via **analyze data** and **comparing group means**, and press ↵ to paste MANOVA on the scratch pad. (Alternatively, type MANOVA on the scratch pad and press **[Esc]**.)

Move down the **MANOVA** menu to **variables**, and read the information. Press ↵ , read about **dependent(s)**, and press ↵ again to reveal the table of variable names. Select *triangle square rectangl* in turn, pressing ↵ each time to paste these names on the scratch pad. Remove the variable name table with **[Esc]**, move down the menu to **BY**, press ↵ , move down again to **factor(s)**, and press ↵ . Read the information about **factor name(s)**, press ↵ , paste *category* from the table of variable names with ↵ , and press **[Esc]** to remove the table. Move down to **( )**, press ↵ , type 1, 2 in the box, and press ↵ again.

Finally, the repeated (within subjects) factor is added. Return to the MANOVA menu with two presses of the ← cursor key, and then down to **repeated measure(s)**. Press ↵ , read the **overview**, move down to **/WSFACTORS**, press ↵ and read about entering a generic name for the factor. Press ↵ , type in the name (in this example it is *shape*), move down to **( )**, press ↵ , type in the number of levels (in this example it is 3), and press ↵ .

(Alternatively, after typing or pasting MANOVA, you may prefer to enter the rest of the command by pressing **[Alt]/E** and typing the required material.)

The command is:

```
MANOVA triangle square rectangl BY category (1, 2) /WSFACTORS shape(3).
```

Unless an additional subcommand is to be added, ensure that the command is terminated with a period (.) by pressing **[Alt]/E** and typing the period.

Step 5 (optional)

The subcommand **/OMEANS** lists the mean, standard deviation and N for each variable within each category, and combined across both categories. It is located in the **any analysis** item of the **MANOVA** menu:

MANOVA triangle square rectangl BY category (1, 2)
        /WSFACTORS shape(3)/OMEANS.

Ensure that there is a period (.) after the last subcommand.

Step 6

Save the commands to a named file on the floppy disk by using **[F9]** (see Chapter 2) and execute the MANOVA command by pressing **[F10]**, followed by ⏎ .

10.2.2 The listing for a mixed design ANOVA

The listing on the screen will include several sections, each headed **** ANALYSIS OF VARIANCE -- DESIGN 1 ****.

1) **Means, standard deviations, and N**

This table is obtained by the subcommand **/OMEANS**:

Cell Means and Standard Deviations

Variable .. TRIANGLE

FACTOR	CODE	Mean	Std. Dev.	N
CATEGORY	Psycholo	6.000	2.608	6
CATEGORY	Engineer	20.167	4.262	6
For entire sample		13.083	8.129	12

Variable .. SQUARE

FACTOR	CODE	Mean	Std. Dev.	N
CATEGORY	Psycholo	12.167	2.317	6
CATEGORY	Engineer	7.000	2.828	6
For entire sample		9.583	3.655	12

Variable .. RECTANGL

FACTOR	CODE	Mean	Std. Dev.	N
CATEGORY	Psycholo	7.000	2.098	6
CATEGORY	Engineer	30.833	3.430	6
For entire sample		18.917	12.738	12

2) Between-Subjects Effects

In this example, the univariate and multivariate analyses are identical, because there are only two groups. Note that *category* is significant beyond the 1 per cent level: the **Sig of F** (0.000) is less than 0.0005. There is thus a difference in performance between the two groups of students.

* * ANALYSIS OF VARIANCE -- DESIGN 1 * *

Tests of Between-Subjects Effects.

Tests of Significance for T1 using UNIQUE sums of squares

Source of Variation	SS	DF	MS	F	Sig of F
WITHIN CELLS	108.94	10	10.89		
CONSTANT	6916.69	1	6916.69	634.88	.000
CATEGORY	1078.03	1	1078.03	98.95	.000

3) Within-subject and interaction effects

The **Mauchly sphericity test** is not significant (**Significance** is greater than 0.05). Had it been significant, it would have been necessary to make a conservative Greenhouse-Geisser test with fewer degrees of freedom (obtained by multiplying the original numerator and denominator degrees of freedom by the value of **epsilon**, which is given in the output).

Tests involving `SHAPE' Within-Subject Effect.

Mauchly sphericity test, W =	.90277
Chi-square approx. =	.92059 with 2 D. F.
Significance =	.631

AVERAGED Tests of Significance that follow multivariate tests are equivalent to univariate or split-plot or mixed-model approach to repeated measures.

AVERAGED Tests of Significance for MEAS.1 using UNIQUE sums of squares

Source of Variation	SS	DF	MS	F	Sig of F
WITHIN CELLS	163.56	20	8.18		
SHAPE	533.56	2	266.78	32.62	.000
CATEGORY BY SHAPE	1308.22	2	654.11	79.99	.000

Note that both the *shape* and *category* BY *shape* interactions are significant beyond the 1 per cent level. The significant interaction is not surprising: inspection of the means in the first table shows clearly that the Engineering Students do worse with Square shapes than the Psychology Students, but better with either of the other shapes, and the significant main effect of *category* must be re-interpreted in this light.

10.2.2.1 SAVING THE LISTING TO A FILE

To save the listing to a file on the floppy disk (an essential step, if a hard copy is desired), add a SET/LISTING command to the top of the commands and submit all the commands for re-execution (Chapter 2).

10.2.2.2 PRINTING OUT THE LISTING AND COMMAND FILES

Details are given in Chapter 2 (section 2.6) about how to print files from the floppy disk.

10.3 THE ANOVA OF A THREE-FACTOR MIXED EXPERIMENT WITH TWO WITHIN SUBJECTS FACTORS

The MANOVA program can easily handle data from more complex mixed experiments, with several between subjects and within subjects factors. To extend the previous example, suppose that the shapes can be either solid or outline, in which case the design would have an additional factor, which could be named *solidity*. Although it would be feasible to name each of the six combinations of shape and solidity individually, it is more convenient to write a variable name finishing with a number (eg *score1*), the keyword **TO**, and the same name with an incremented number (eg *score6*). In naming the within subjects factors, the factor that changes more slowly is named first. The commands would be written on the scratch pad either directly or by using the pasting method explained in the previous example:

```
DATA LIST FREE/score1 TO score6 category.
BEGIN DATA.
. . . . . . . . . .
END DATA.
MANOVA score1 TO score6 BY category(1,2)
    /WSFACTORS shape(3) solidity(2) /OMEANS.
```

These commands will obtain tests of the following factors and interactions by default:

CATEGORY
SHAPE
CATEGORY BY SHAPE
SOLIDITY
CATEGORY BY SOLIDITY
SHAPE BY SOLIDITY
CATEGORY BY SHAPE BY SOLIDITY

10.4 FURTHER ANALYSIS: SIMPLE EFFECTS AND MULTIPLE COMPARISONS

The analysis of variance is a large topic in statistics, and there are available many more techniques than we can mention in this book, which is primarily concerned with computing, rather than statistics as such. For example, following the confirmation that an interaction is significant, it is often useful to follow up the initial ANOVA with additional tests of the effects of one factor at specific levels of another. Such analyses of **simple effects** are quite possible on SPSS/PC+, as are both planned and unplanned multiple comparisons. We urge the reader who is unfamiliar with such methods to read the relevant chapters in a lucid textbook such as Howell (1992).

10.5 SUMMARY

1) An ANOVA design that includes both between subjects and within subjects factors is called a **mixed,** or **split-plot**, design. In SPSS/PC+, the results of such an experiment are analysed with the MANOVA program.

2) The command is of the form

MANOVA *dependent variable names*
    BY *name of first grouping factor* (x, y)
       name of second grouping factor (p, q)
       . . . .

/WSFACTORS *first factor name* (m) *second factor name* (n) . . .

where the **dependent variable names** are the names of the within subjects factor levels or (when there are two or more within subjects factors) combinations of levels. It is often convenient to shorten the process of naming the dependent variables by giving the first variable a name such as *score1*, the last variable a name such as *score10* and separating the two names by **TO**.

When naming the **grouping (between subjects) factors**, follow the factor name with a bracketed statement of the lowest and highest code values.

When naming the **within subjects factors**, choose generic names other than those of their component levels. The order in which the factors are named is crucial: the factor that varies most slowly comes first; that which varies most quickly comes last. Each name must be followed by the number of levels in brackets.

3)   When the optional subcommand **/OMEANS** is placed after the **/WSFACTORS** subcommand, the output will include the means, standard deviations, and N of the data for each level of the between-subjects factor:

MANOVA *dependent variable names* **BY** *grouping factor* (x, y)
     /WSFACTORS *factor name* (m) **/OMEANS**.

CHAPTER 11

MEASURING STATISTICAL ASSOCIATION

___

11.1 INTRODUCTION

So far, this book has been concerned with statistical methods devised for the purpose of comparing averages between or among samples of data that might be expected to differ in general level: for example, right-handed people might be compared with left-handed people; the trained might be compared with the untrained; males might be compared with females. Consider, however, a set of paired data of the sort that might be produced if one were to weigh each of a sample of one hundred men before and after they had taken a fitness course. Previously, our concern would have been with the **comparison** of the men's average weight before the course with their average weight afterwards. One would expect expect these data to show another feature, however: the person who was heaviest before the course, is likely to be among the heaviest in the group afterwards; the lightest person before the course should be among the lightest afterwards; and one with an intermediate score before the course is likely to be in the middle of the group afterwards. In other words, there should be a statistical **association** or **correlation** between people's weights before and after the course.

The existence of a statistical association between two variables is most apparent in the appearance of a diagram called a **scatterplot** which, in the foregoing example, would be constructed by representing each person as a point in space, using as coordinates that person's weights before and after taking the course. The cloud of points would take the shape of an ellipse, whose longer axis slopes upwards from left to right across the page. An elliptical scatterplot indicates the existence of a **linear relationship** between two variables. If the slope of the major axis is positive, the variables are said to be **positively correlated**; if it is negative, they are **negatively correlated**. The thinner the ellipse, the stronger the degree of linear relationship; the fatter the ellipse, the weaker the relationship. A circular scatterplot indicates the absence of any relationship between the two variables.

The term **linear** means "of the nature of a straight line". In our current example, a straight line (known as a **regression line**) can be drawn through the points in the elliptical scatterplot so that it is rather close to most of the points (though there may be one or two atypical scores, or **outliers** as they are termed). We can use the regression line to make quite a good **estimate** of a particular man's weight after the course from a knowledge of his weight before the course: if we have *weight before* on the horizontal axis and *weight after* on the vertical axis, we need only move up to the point on the regression line vertically above his first weight, and then move across to the vertical scale to estimate his second weight. If we do that, we shall probably be in error, the difference between his true weight after the course and his estimated weight from the regression line being known as a **residual.** The value of the residual, however, is likely to be small in comparison with the man's true weight after the course.

A **correlation coefficient** is a statistic devised for the purpose of measuring the strength, or degree of a supposed linear association between two variables, each of which has been measured on a scale with units. The most familiar correlation coefficient is the **Pearson correlation (r)**. The Pearson correlation is so defined that it can take values only within the range from -1 to +1, inclusive. The larger the absolute value (ie ignoring the sign), the narrower the ellipse, and the closer to the regression line the points in the scatterplot will fall. A perfect correlation arises when the values of one variable are exactly predictable from those of the other and the Pearson correlation takes a value of ± 1, in which case all the points in the scatterplot lie on the regression line. In other cases, the narrower the elliptical cloud of points, the stronger the association, and the greater the absolute value of the Pearson correlation. When there is no association whatever between two variables, their scatterplot should be a roughly circular cloud, in which case the Pearson correlation will be about zero and the regression line will be horizontal, ie have a slope of zero.

11.1.1 A warning about the use of the Pearson correlation

It is quite possible, from inspection of a scatterplot, to do two things:

(1)   see whether there is indeed a linear relationship between the variables, in which case the Pearson correlation would be a meaningful statistic to use;

(2)   guess fairly accurately what the value of the Pearson correlation would be if calculated.

In other words, from inspection of their scatterplot alone, one can discern all the essential features of the true relationship (if any) between two variables. So if we reason from the scatterplot to the statistics, we shall probably not go seriously wrong.

The converse, however, is not true: **given only the value of a Pearson correlation, one can say nothing whatsoever about the relationship between two variables.** In a famous (and very readable) paper, the statistician Anscombe (1973) presents data which illustrate how misleading the value of the Pearson correlation can be. Basically, he shows that, wherever the scatterplot is neither elliptical nor circular (ie the variables are neither in a linear relationship nor independent), the value of the Pearson correlation is misleading. For example, data giving a zero Pearson correlation may show a very strong **nonlinear** association in their scatterplot. Two variables may be unrelated (and most of the data may show a circular scatterplot), but the presence of one or two outliers can exert considerable **leverage** and yield a very high Pearson correlation, suggesting a strong linear relationship.

The moral of this cautionary tale is clear: when studying the association between two variables, always construct a scatterplot, and interpret (or disregard) the Pearson correlation accordingly. In the same paper, Anscombe gives a useful rule for deciding whether there really is a robust linear relationship between two variables: should the shape of the scatterplot be unaltered by the removal of a few observations at random, there is probably a real relationship between the two variables.

To sum up, the **Pearson correlation** is a measure of a supposed **linear relationship between two variables**; and the supposition of linearity must be confirmed by inspection of the scatterplot.

11.2 ANALYSIS OF DATA WITH THE PEARSON CORRELATION

The principal of a tennis coaching school is of the opinion that tennis proficiency depends upon the possession of a degree of general hand-eye coordination. To confirm this hunch, she measures the hand-eye coordination of some pupils who are beginning the course and their proficiency in tennis at the end of the course.

Suppose the data for the tennis example are as listed on the next page:

Pupil	Initial Co-ordination	Final Tennis Proficiency
1	4	4
2	4	5
3	5	6
4	2	2
5	10	6
6	4	2
7	7	5
8	8	6
9	9	9
10	5	3

11.2.1 The commands for the Pearson Correlation

The commands for Pearson correlations are prepared on the scratch pad as follows:

Step 1

Write the DATA LIST command (Chapter 3). The appropriate section of the Menu can be found by either (a) typing DATA LIST on the scratch pad and pressing **[Esc]**, or (b) moving down the MAIN MENU to **read or write data**, rightwards into the **read or write data menu**, down to **DATA LIST**, and pressing ↵ to paste DATA LIST on the scratch pad.

Since the data set is small, the scores can be entered in free-field format and included in the commands rather than being stored in a separate data file.

If the variables are *coordin* and *proficy*, the command is:

DATA LIST FREE / coordin proficy.

The data are then typed on the scratch pad after the BEGIN DATA command eg

BEGIN DATA.
4 4 4 5 5 6 2 2 10 6 4 2 7 5 8 6 9 9 5 3
END DATA.

Step 2

The rather cryptic variable names *coordin* and *proficy* can be expanded in a **VARIABLE LABELS** command eg

VARIABLE LABELS coordin 'Initial Co-ordination'
             proficy 'Final Tennis Proficiency'.

Step 3

Execute these data commands by moving the cursor to the DATA LIST command, pressing **[F10]** and ⏎. This will allow you to check that these commands have been correctly written and will enable SPSS/PC+ to generate a table of variable names for pasting into subsequent commands.

Step 4 (optional but highly recommended)

Construct a scatterplot. The command for obtaining a scatterplot of the paired data is **PLOT**, which is found under **graph data** in the **MAIN MENU**. Press ⏎ to paste PLOT on the scratch pad. (Alternatively, type PLOT on the scratch pad and press **[Esc]** key to display the **PLOT** menu in the upper window.)

Move down to **/PLOT** and press ⏎ to paste **/PLOT** on the scratch pad. Read the examples. Move down to **vertical axis**, press ⏎, select the appropriate variable name *coordin* from the variable table and paste it with ⏎. Press **[Esc]**, move down to **WITH**, press ⏎, and select the other variable *proficy*. Paste it with ⏎ and remove the variable table with the period (.).

(Alternatively, after pasting /PLOT, you may prefer to enter the rest of the command by pressing **[Alt]/E** and typing the required material.)

The command is:

PLOT/PLOT coordin WITH proficy.

Step 5

Find **CORRELATIONS** in the menu via **analyze data** and **correlation and regression**, and press ⏎ to paste **CORRELATIONS** on the scratch pad. (Alternatively, type **CORRELATIONS** on the scratchpad and press **[Esc]**.)

Read the examples, move down to **/VARIABLES** and press ⏎ to paste **/VARIABLES** on the scratch pad. Select the first variable (*coordin*) from the variable table, press ⏎, move down to **WITH**, press ⏎, select the second variable (*proficy*), press ⏎, and then **[Esc]** to remove the variable table.

(Alternatively, after pasting /VARIABLES, you may prefer to enter the rest of the command by pressing **[Alt]/E** and typing the required material.)

The command is:

CORRELATIONS /VARIABLES coordin WITH proficy.

Unless subcommands are being added, ensure that the command ends with a period (.).

Step 6 (optional)

Add suitable subcommands. Additional subcommands available in the **CORRELATIONS** menu include **/OPTIONS**, which offers the two-tailed (rather than the default one-tailed) p-value, and **/STATISTICS 1**, which displays the means and standard deviations of the variables. Here we shall choose the /STATISTICS 1 subcommand.

Return to the CORRELATIONS menu with two presses of the ← cursor key, move down to /STATISTICS and press ↵. Select 1 and press ↵ again. The command is then:

CORRELATIONS /VARIABLES coordin WITH proficy /STATISTICS 1.

Ensure that there is a period (.) after the final subcommand.

Step 7

Save the commands to a named file on the floppy disk by using **[F9]** (see Chapter 2) and then execute the PLOT and CORRELATIONS commands by moving the cursor to the PLOT command line, pressing **[F10]** and then ↵.

11.2.2 The listing for the Pearson correlation

The first item in the listing is the scatterplot requested with the PLOT/PLOT command:

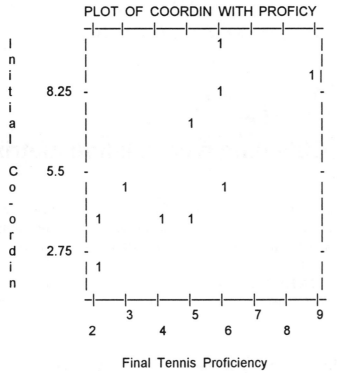

10 cases plotted.

This is followed by the statistics for the variables requested by the /STATISTICS 1 subcommand.

```
CORRELATIONS /VARIABLES coordin WITH proficy
              /STATISTICS 1.
```

Variable	Cases	Mean	Std Dev
COORDIN	10	5.8000	2.5734
PROFICY	10	4.8000	2.1499

Finally the correlation coefficient, together with an indication of its significance, is listed. One asterisk (*) means it is significant beyond the 1 per cent level, two asterisks (**) denote significance beyond the 0.1 per cent level. The correlation coefficient (0.7752) is significant beyond the 1 per cent level.

```
Correlations:      PROFICY

      COORDIN  .7752*

N of cases: 10        1-tailed Signif:    * - .01      ** - .001
```

11.2.2.1 SAVING THE LISTING TO A FILE

To save a copy of the listing to a file on the floppy disk (an essential preliminary to the obtaining of a hard copy), add a **SET/LISTING** command at the head of the commands and submit all the commands for execution again with **[F10]** and ⏎ .

11.2.2.2 PRINTING OUT THE LISTING AND COMMAND FILES

Detailed instructions for the printing of the listing and command files are given in Chapter 2, (section 2.6).

11.2.3 Obtaining a correlation matrix

When there are more than two variables, SPSS/PC+ can be commanded to construct a **correlation matrix**, a rectangular array whose entries are the correlations between each variable and every other variable. It is also possible to obtain only a specified column of the correlation matrix, however, that is, the set of correlations involving just one specified variable. Suppose that the DATA LIST command specifies the variables *spelling, spatial, number, generIQ,* and *clerical.* The following command will produce a complete correlation matrix:

```
CORRELATION/VARIABLES spelling spatial number generIQ clerical.
```

If, however, it is desired only to correlate *generIQ* with the other variables, the keyword **WITH** is used as follows:

CORRELATION/VARIABLES generIQ WITH spelling spatial number clerical.

11.3 OTHER MEASURES OF ASSOCIATION

The Pearson correlation is suitable only for **scalar** (interval) data. With other kinds of data (ordinal or nominal), other measures must be used. (**Ordinal** data are either ranks or records of **ordered** category membership; **nominal** data are records of **qualitative** category membership.)

When people's membership of two sets of mutually exclusive and exhaustive categories (such as sex or blood group) is recorded, it is possible to construct a **crosstabulation**, or **contingency table**. A crosstabulation is a table showing the joint frequency distribution of the two variables, that is, the numbers of individuals falling into each of the category combinations. For example, a crosstabulation of the variables sex and political group affiliation (category 1 or 2) would show the number of people who are female and group 1, female and group 2, male and group 1, and male and group 2. In the analysis of nominal data, the crosstabulation is the analogue of the scatterplot. Note that the categories of each variable must be mutually exclusive, ie no individual or case can fall into more than one combination of categories.

In SPSS/PC+ crosstabulations are handled with the **CROSSTABS** command. This command has several measures of association in its **/STATISTICS** subcommand. Many of these are based on the familiar **chi-square** statistic, which is used for determining the presence of an association between two variables. The rejection of H_0 by means of chi-square, however, only establishes the **existence** of a statistical association: it does not measure its **strength**. The chi-square statistic is unsuitable as a **measure** of association, because it is affected by the total frequency.

[A word of warning about the misuse of chi-square is in order here. It is important to realise that the calculated statistic is only **approximately** distributed as the theoretical chi-square distribution: the greater the expected frequencies, the better the approximation, hence the rule about minimum expected frequencies, which is stated in section 11.3.2 to follow. It is also important to note that the use of the chi-square statistic requires that each individual studied contributes to the frequency of only one cell in the crosstabulation. There are several other potential problems of which the user should be aware. A lucid account of the rationale and assumptions of the chi-square test is given by Howell (1992), and a survey of the errors and misconceptions about chi-square that abound in the research literature is given by Delucchi (1983).]

Several measures of strength of association have been proposed (see Reynolds, 1984). An ideal measure of association should mimic the correlation coefficient by having a maximum absolute value of 1 for perfect association, and a value of 0 for no association. The choice of the appropriate statistic depends on whether the variables are ordinal or nominal, and whether the contingency (crosstabulation) table is 2 x 2 (meaning that each variable has two categories) or larger. Guidance is given in the SPSS/PC+ menu. One such statistic, for example, is the **phi coefficient**, obtained by dividing the value of chi-square by the total frequency and taking the square root. For two-way contingency tables involving variables with more than two categories, however, another statistic, known as **Cramer's V**, is preferred because with more complex tables, Cramer's measure can still, as in the 2 x 2 case, achieve its maximum value of unity. Other measures of association, such as **Goodman & Kruskal's lambda**, record the proportional reduction in error achieved when membership of a category on one attribute is used to predict category membership on the other.

11.3.1 The analysis of 2 x 2 contingency tables

Suppose that boys and girls are individually asked to select toys from a cupboard. The available toys have previously been categorised as mechanical or non-mechanical. The hypothesis is that the boys should prefer mechanical toys, and the girls non-mechanical toys. There are two nominal variables here: *group* (boys or girls); and *children's choice* (mechanical or non-mechanical). The null hypothesis (H_0) is that there is no association between the variables. The contingency table is given below:

CHILDREN'S CHOICE

		Mechan-ical	Non-mechanical	Total
	Boys	30	20	50
GROUP	**Girls**	15	35	50
	Total	45	55	100

From inspection of this 2 by 2 contingency table, it would certainly appear that there is an association between the group and choice variables: the majority of the boys did, in fact, choose mechanical toys; whereas the majority of the girls chose non-mechanical toys.

11.3.2 The commands for crosstabulation and associated statistics (chi-square and phi)

The test for the presence of association in two-way contingency tables is performed by the SPSS/PC+ CROSSTABS command. The commands are prepared on the scratch pad in the following steps:

Step 1

Write the DATA LIST command (Chapter 3). The appropriate section of the Menu can be found by either (a) typing DATA LIST on the scratch pad and pressing **[Esc]**, or (b) moving down the MAIN MENU, rightwards into **read or write data**, down to **DATA LIST**, and pressing ⏎ to paste DATA LIST on the scratch pad.

Since the data set is small, they can be entered in free-field format and included in the commands rather than stored in a separate data file. In the experiment on the children's choice of toys, the independent variable was *group* and the dependent variable was *choice*. In the SPSS/PC+ analysis, however, the two classifying variables in the contingency table are regarded as the independent variables and the cell frequencies as the dependent variable. If the dependent variable is *count*, the number of children in a cell of the contingency table, and the independent variables are *group* and *choice*, the DATA LIST command is:

DATA LIST FREE/group choice count.

The data are then typed in triplets on the scratch pad after the BEGIN DATA command: the first value is 1 or 2 for *group*, the second value is 1 or 2 for *choice*, and the third value is the cell frequency variable *count* :

BEGIN DATA.
1 1 30 1 2 20 2 1 15 2 2 35
END DATA.

Step 2

To instruct SPSS/PC+ to read the values of *count* as frequencies, rather than values of a quantitative variable, type the command **WEIGHT BY** followed by the name of the variable carrying the cell frequencies:

WEIGHT BY count.

Step 3 (optional but highly recommended)

The contingency table in the listing is greatly improved if verbal labels, rather than numbers, appear in the row and column headings. This is accomplished by using the **VALUE LABELS** command:

```
VALUE LABELS group 1 'Boys' 2 'Girls'
         / choice 1 'Mechanical' 2 'Non-mechanical'.
```

Step 4

Execute these data commands by moving the cursor to the DATA LIST command, pressing **[F10]** and ↵. This will enable SPSS/PC+ to generate a table of variable names.

Step 5

Find the CROSSTABS command in the **analyze data** item of the **MAIN MENU** by moving into the **descriptive statistics** menu and down to **CROSSTABS**. Press ↵ to paste CROSSTABS on the scratch pad. (Alternatively, type CROSSTABS on the scratch pad and press **[Esc]** to display the CROSSTABS menu.)

Read the examples, move down to **/TABLES=**, press ↵ to paste this on the scratch pad and press ↵ again when **row variables** appears. Select the appropriate variable *group* from the variable table and press ↵. Press **[Esc]**, move down to **BY**, and press ↵. Move down to **column variables**, press ↵, select the appropriate variable (*choice*) and press ↵. Press **[Esc]**. This completes the basic part of the CROSSTABS command.

It is now necessary to add the subcommand for calculating chi-square and the phi coefficient. The **/STATISTICS=** subcommand gives both of these. The statistics can be pasted by using the cursor keys to move to the items concerned and pressing ↵.

(Alternatively, after pasting **/TABLES=**, the user may prefer to dispense with the menus by pressing **[Alt]/E** and typing in the material.)

The command is:

```
CROSSTABS /TABLES= group BY choice /STATISTICS= CHISQ PHI .
```

Ensure that there is a period (.) after the final subcommand, unless another subcommand is to be added.

Step 6 (optional)

We recommend an additional subcommand for computing the expected cell frequencies. This enables the user to check that the prescribed minimum requirements for the valid use of chi-square have been fulfilled. Although there has been debate about these, the practice of leading authorities has been to proscribe the use of chi-square as follows:

a)   in 2×2 tables, if any of the expected frequencies is less than 5;

b)   in larger tables, if any of the expected frequencies is less than 1 and if more than 20% are less than 5.

The subcommand is /CELLS, selecting the COUNT EXPECTED option. Thus the full command is:

```
CROSSTABS /TABLES= group BY choice /STATISTICS=  CHISQ  PHI
     /CELLS= COUNT EXPECTED.
```

Step 7

Save the commands to a named file on the floppy disk by using **[F9]** (see Chapter 2) and then execute the CROSSTABS command by pressing **[F10]** and then ⏎ .

11.3.3 The listing for crosstabulation and associated statistics (chi-square and phi)

The listing first displays the cross-tabulation (contingency) table, with the observed and expected frequencies, as requested with the /CELLS= COUNT EXPECTED subcommand. None of the expected frequencies is less than 5:

GROUP   by   CHOICE

		CHOICE		
	Count Exp Val	|Mechanic |al | 1.00 |	Non-mech anical 2.00 |	Row Total
GROUP				
Boys	1.00	| 30 | 22.5	| 20 | 27.5	| 50 | 50.0%
Girls	2.00	| 15 | 22.5	| 35 | 27.5	| 50 | 50.0%
	Column Total	45 45.0%	55 55.0%	100 100.0%

This is followed by the statistics requested with the **/STATISTICS= CHISQ PHI** subcommand. The first section is labelled Chi-square. The row labelled "Pearson" lists the conventional chi-square statistic, along with its tail probability under H_0 (labelled Significance). Ignore the Likelihood Ratio and the Mantel-Haenszel test for linear association. The remaining information confirms the information already found with the /CELLS COUNT EXPECTED subcommand.

Chi-Square	Value	D.F.	Significance
Pearson	9.09091	1	.00257
Likelihood Ratio	7.91919	1	.00489
Mantel-Haenszel test for linear association	9.00000	1	.00270

Minimum Expected Frequency -   22.500

The second section is labelled Statistic, and tabulates the Phi coefficient and Cramer's V. In a 2×2 table, these have the same value.

Statistic	Value	ASE1	T-value	Approximate Significance	
Phi	.30151			.00257	*1
Cramer's V	.30151			.00257	*1

*1 Pearson chi-square probability

Number of Missing Observations = 0

It can be concluded that there is a significant association between the variables *group* and *choice*, as shown by the p-value (less than 0.01) for chi-square. The phi coefficient provides a value similar to a correlation coefficient for the strength of the association.

11.3.3.1 SAVING THE LISTING TO A FILE

If it is desired to save a copy of the listing to a file on the floppy disk (essential if a printed version is needed), add a **SET/LISTING** command at the head of the commands and submit all the commands for re-execution with **[F10]** and ⏎ .

11.3.3.2 PRINTING THE LISTING FILE

Details are given in Chapter 2 (section 2.6) about how to print files from the floppy disk.

11.4 SUMMARY

1) The degree of association between quantitative variables can be measured by means of a correlation coefficient. The most well-known correlation coefficient is the **Pearson correlation**. If there are just two variables, the command is of the form

   CORRELATIONS/VARIABLES *variable name* **WITH** *variable name.*

   If there are several variables, it takes the form:

   CORRELATIONS/VARIABLES *variable names.*

   This will yield a **correlation matrix**, in which are arrayed the correlations between each variable and all the others.

   The command

   CORRELATIONS/VARIABLES *variable name* **WITH** *variable names.*

   will yield the correlations between the first named variable and each of those named after the keyword **WITH**.

   Additional subcommands for **CORRELATIONS** include **/OPTIONS**, for specifying two-tail rather than one-tail probabilities, and **/STATISTICS**, for displaying means and standard deviations.

2) It is recommended that a scatterplot should **always** be requested. The command is:

   PLOT/PLOT *variable name* **WITH** *variable name.*

3) Various coefficients for ranks and for nominal data are available in the **CROSSTABS** command, which analyses data in contingency tables. For contingency tables in which the data are in the form of counts of category membership, coding variables are needed to identify the cells of the table. Hence the data must be entered in triplets, according to the order of variables specified in the DATA LIST command:

   DATA LIST FREE/*row variable name   column variable name   cell frequency variable name .*

The following additional command is essential:

WEIGHT BY *dependent variable name*.

4)   The **CROSSTABS** command has the form:

CROSSTABS/TABLES *row variable name* **BY** *column variable name*.

The subcommand **/STATISTICS=** is used to select the required statistic(s). For example, the chi-square and phi coefficient statistics would be selected with

   /STATISTICS= CHISQ PHI.

A recommended optional subcommand for tabulating the expected cell frequencies is:

   /CELLS= COUNT EXPECTED.

CHAPTER 12

REGRESSION

12.1 INTRODUCTION

Much of Chapter 11 was devoted to the use of the Pearson correlation to measure the strength of the association between two quantitative variables, each of which has been measured on an interval scale.

But the associative coin has two sides. On the one hand, a single number can be calculated (a correlation coefficient) which expresses the **strength** of the association. On the other, however, there is a set of techniques, known as **regression methods**, which utilise the presence of an association between two variables to predict the values of one (the dependent variable) from those of another (the independent variable). It is with this predictive aspect that the present chapter is concerned.

To sum up, in **correlation**, the **degree of statistical association** between variables variables is expressed as a single number known as a **correlation coefficient**. In **regression**, on the other hand, the purpose is to **estimate** or **predict** some characteristic from a knowledge of others by constructing a **regression equation**.

12.1.1 Simple, two-variable regression

In **simple, two-variable regression**, the values of one variable (the dependent variable, y) are estimated from those of another (the independent variable, x) by a linear (straight line) equation of the general form

$$y' = b_1 (x) + b_0$$

where y' is the estimated value of y, b_1 is the slope (known as the **regression coefficient**), and b_0 is the intercept (known as the **regression constant**).

12.1.2 Multiple regression

In **multiple regression**, the values of one variable (the dependent variable y) are estimated from those of other variables (the independent variables x_1 , x_2 , ... , x_p). This is achieved by the construction of a linear equation of the general form

$$y' = b_1 (x_1) + b_2 (x_2) + ... + b_p (x_p) + b_0$$

where the parameters b_1 , b_2 , ..., b_p are the **regression coefficients** and the intercept (b_0) is the **regression constant**. This equation is known as the **multiple linear regression equation of y upon x_1 , ... , x_p** .

12.1.3 Residuals

When a regression equation is used to estimate the values of a variable (y) from those of one or more independent variables (x), the estimates (y') will usually fall short of complete accuracy. Geometrically speaking, the data points will not fall precisely upon the straight line, plane or hyperplane specified by the regression equation. The discrepancies ($y - y'$) on the predicted variable are known as **residuals**. When using regression methods, the study of the residuals is of great importance, because they form the basis of measures of the accuracy of the estimates and of the extent to which the **regression model** gives a good account of the data in question. (See Lovie, 1991, for an account of the analysis of residuals, a topic which is known as **regression diagnostics**.)

12.1.4 The multiple correlation coefficient (R)

One simple (though rather limited) measure of the efficacy of regression for the prediction of y is the Pearson correlation between the true values of the target variable (y) and the estimates (y') obtained from substituting the corresponding values of x into the regression equation. The correlation between y and y' is known as the **multiple correlation coefficient** (R). Notice that the upper case is used for the multiple correlation coefficient, to distinguish it from the correlation between the target variable and any one independent variable considered separately. In simple, two-variable regression, the multiple correlation coefficient takes the **absolute** value of the Pearson correlation between the target variable and the independent variable: so if r = -0.90, R = 0.90. It can be shown algebraically that the multiple correlation coefficient cannot have a negative value.

12.2 REGRESSION WITH ONE INDEPENDENT VARIABLE

Among university authorities, there is much concern about the methods used to select students for entry. The following example concerns a study of the association between students' marks on the initial academic selection examinations and performance in their university examinations.

Given data on people's final examination marks (y) and their performance on the entrance examinations (x), correlation coefficients can be used to measure the degree of statistical association between the former and the latter. It is also possible to use simple regression to predict examination performance at university from marks on the entrance examinations. It can be shown by mathematical proof, however, that when two or more independent variables are used to predict the target variable y, the predictions will, on average, be **at least as accurate** as when any one of the same independent variables is used: in other words, the multiple correlation coefficient (R) must be at least as great as any single Pearson correlation (r). For the moment, however, we shall be considering the simple regression of university examination performance upon the marks on one entrance examination.

12.2.1 The commands for regression with one independent variable

In the following table, the first score (x) in each (x, y) pair is a student's mark in the entrance examination, and the second (y) is the same student's mark in the university examination.

x	y	x	y	x	y	x	y	x	y
49	195	62	169	58	164	54	152	55	150
60	145	56	142	52	140	63	125	49	117
46	114	41	114	49	112	48	107	55	106
43	105	48	103	37	100	48	100	40	98
39	95	41	94	45	91	47	86	53	81
41	78	37	76	34	74	46	73	44	69
42	65	43	61	40	49	44	38		

Step 1

Write the DATA LIST command (Chapter 3). The appropriate section of the Menu can be found by either (a) typing DATA LIST on the scratch pad (after pressing **[Alt]/E** if still in the Menu and Help mode) and pressing **[Esc]**, or (b) moving down the MAIN MENU to **read or write data**, rightwards to expand this item into the **read or write data menu**, down to **DATA LIST**, and finally pressing ↵ to paste DATA LIST on the scratch pad.

Since the data set is small, the data can be entered in free-field format, and included in the commands rather than stored in a separate data file. No coding (grouping) variables are necessary.

If the variables are *finalex* and *selectex*, the command is:

DATA LIST FREE / finalex selectex.

The data are then typed on the scratch pad after the BEGIN DATA command:

BEGIN DATA.
195 49 169 62 . . . 38 44
END DATA.

Step 2

Execute these data commands by moving the cursor to the DATA LIST command, and pressing **[F10]**, then ↵ . This checks whether there have been any errors in the reading of the data, and enables SPSS/PC+ to generate a table of variable names which can be pasted into subsequent commands.

Step 3

Find **REGRESSION** in the menu via the **analyze data** and **correlation and regression** menus, and press ⌐ to paste REGRESSION on the scratch pad. (Alternatively, type REGRESSION on the scratchpad and press **[Esc]**).

Read the information about **/VARIABLES**, and press ⌐ again to paste /VARIABLES on the scratch pad. Move down to **ALL** and press ⌐ . (Note: If there are other variables in the DATA LIST command besides those being used for regression, then obviously ALL cannot be used: in that case select the appropriate variables from the table of variable names by pressing ⌐ on the **variable list** item and selecting the variables in the usual way.) Alternatively, the variable names can be typed directly on the scratch pad after pressing **[Alt]/E**. At this stage, the command is:

REGRESSION / VARIABLES ALL

Step 4 (optional)

It is useful to list the means and standard deviations of the variables, as well as the correlation coefficient. Return to the REGRESSION menu with the ← cursor key, and then down to the subcommand **/DESCRIPTIVES** and press ⌐ . The command is now:

REGRESSION /VARIABLES ALL /DESCRIPTIVES

Step 5

Return to the **REGRESSION** menu with the ← cursor key, and then down to **building an equation**. Read the information supplied. Move down to **/DEPENDENT**, read the information about it and press ⌐ to paste /DEPENDENT on the scratch pad. Select the dependent variable name (*finalex*) from the table of variable names, press ⌐ , and then **[Esc]**. Continue down the **REGRESSION** menu to **/METHOD**, read the information, press ⌐ , move down to **ENTER** and press ⌐ . (ENTER is the only suitable method for this example: the other methods refer to multiple regression, where there are several independent variables.) Select the independent variable name from the table of variable names (*selectex*), press ⌐ and **[Esc]**. The command is now:

REGRESSION /VARIABLES ALL /DESCRIPTIVES
       /DEPENDENT finalex /METHOD ENTER selectex.

This completes the essential components of the regression command, but the additional subcommands relating to residual analysis are strongly recommended. Ensure that there is a period (.) after the final subcommand.

Step 6 (optional)

It is strongly recommended that information about residuals be requested when using REGRESSION. A **residual** is the difference between the actual value of the dependent variable and its predicted value using the regression equation. Analysis of the residuals gives a measure of how good the prediction is and whether there are any cases which are so discrepant that they might be considered as outliers and so dropped from the analysis. Subcommands can obtain a listing of any exceptionally large residuals, a histogram of all the residuals, and a cumulative probability plot to show how well they lie along a straight line (as they should do if the relationship between the target and the independent variables is basically a linear one).

Move back to the **REGRESSION** menu with the ← cursor key, and down to **residual analysis**. Read the information, move down to **/RESIDUALS**, and press ↵ . Only the keyword RESIDUALS is required: ignore the options within RESIDUALS and return to the **residual analysis** menu with ← . Move down to **/CASEWISE** and press ↵ . Again, only the keyword CASEWISE is required: ignore the options within CASEWISE and return to the **residual analysis** menu with ← .

Finally, we recommend the following two plots. The first is a plot of the final examination marks against the selection examination marks, to show the nature of the original bivariate distribution. The second is a plot of the residuals against the predicted values. If the assumptions of linearity and homoscedasticity (homogeneity of variance) hold for the data, there should be no relationship between the predicted and residual values. SPSS/PC+ creates several temporary variables (prefaced with *) during execution of the REGRESSION command. The appropriate ones for this plot are ***pred** and ***resid**. Both plots can be requested in the /SCATTERPLOT subcommand.

Move down to **/SCATTERPLOT** and press ↵ . When **( )** appears, press ↵ , move down to ***PRED**, press ↵ , move down to ***RESID** and press ↵ again. Move up to **( )**, press ↵ , move down to **regression variables**, and press ↵ . Select the variables (*finalex* and *selectex*) from the table of variable names, pressing ↵ each time. Finally, remove the table of variable names with the period (.), which also terminates the command.

(Alternatively, after pasting /SCATTERPLOT, press **[Alt]/E** and type the names of the variables directly on the scratch pad, putting each pair in brackets.)

The command is now:

REGRESSION /VARIABLES ALL /DESCRIPTIVES
        /DEPENDENT finalex /METHOD ENTER selectex
        /RESIDUALS /CASEWISE
        /SCATTERPLOT (*PRED * RESID) (finalex selectex).

Ensure that there is a period (.) after the final subcommand.

Step 7

Save the commands to a named file on the floppy disk by using **[F9]** (see Chapter 2, section 2.5.3).

Step 8

Execute the REGRESSION command in the usual way by pressing **[F10]**, followed by ⏎ .

12.2.2 The listing for regression with one independent variable

The listing contains the following items:

1) Means and standard deviations

The means and standard deviations for the two variables and the correlation coefficient are presented as follows:

	Mean	Std Dev	Label
FINALEX	105.529	35.813	
SELECTEX	47.324	7.429	

N of Cases = 34

Correlation:

	FINALEX	SELECTEX
FINALEX	1.000	.671
SELECTEX	.671	1.000

2) Multiple R and ANOVA

The next section contains a value for Multiple R. There is also an ANOVA, which is intended to test whether there really is a linear relationship between the variables by forming an F ratio of the mean square for regression to the residual mean square. In this example, the value of F is highly significant. **It should be noted, however, that only an examination of the scatterplot can establish that the relationship between two variables is genuinely linear.**

Equation Number 1   Dependent Variable.. FINALEX
                           Method: Enter

Variable(s) Entered on Step Number
        1.. SELECTEX

Multiple R	.67096
R Square	.45019
Adjusted R Square	.43301
Standard Error	26.96662

Analysis of Variance

	DF	Sum of Squares	Mean Square
Regression	1	19054.12080	19054.12080
Residual	32	23270.34979	727.19843

F =   26.20209   Signif F =   .0000

3) Regression equation

The values of the regression coefficient and constant are given in column B of the table:

Equation Number 1   Dependent Variable.. FINALEX

------------------ Variables in the Equation ------------------

Variable	B	SE B	Beta	T	Sig T
SELECTEX	3.23435	.63186	.67096	5.119	.0000
(Constant)	-47.53140	30.25724		-1.571	.1260

The equation is, therefore,

Predicted Final Exam Mark = 3.23435(Selection Exam Mark) - 47.53140

Thus a person with a Selection Exam Mark of 60 would be predicted to score

$3.23435 \times 60 - 47.53140 = 146.5296$ ie 147.

Notice from the data that the person who did score 60 on the selection examination actually scored 145 on the final examination. The residual is, therefore, 147 - 145 = +2.

The remaining parts of the listing relate to the optional subcommands given in Step 6 concerning the analysis of residuals.

4) Casewise plot

A casewise plot shows any outliers ie standardised residuals greater than 3 or less than -3 (ie well beyond the conventional 1% level).

Casewise Plot of Standardized Residual

Outliers = 3.   *: Selected   M: Missing

```
                 -6. -3. 3.  6.
Case #           O:.......: :.......:O  FINALEX   *PRED      *RESID
        1          .      ..*      .     195.00   110.9517   84.0483
```

1 Outliers found.

This shows that the person with a mark of 195 on the final examination (FINALEX) is an outlier, because the predicted value (*PRED) is 110.9517, a difference (the residual *RESID) of 84.0483. The asterisk shows that this residual, when standardised, is greater than +3. A procedure to eliminate this case will be described later.

5) Statistics relating to the residuals

In the following table of statistics relating to the residuals, *PRED comprises the unstandardised predicted values, *RESID is the set of unstandardised residuals, *ZPRED contains the standardised predicted values (ie *PRED has been transformed to a scale with mean 0 and SD 1), and *ZRESID comprises the standardised residuals (ie *RESID standardised to a scale with mean 0 and SD 1).

Equation Number 1   Dependent Variable.. FINALEX

Residuals Statistics:

	Min	Max	Mean	Std Dev	N
*PRED	62.4365	156.2326	105.5294	24.0291	34
*RESID	-56.7800	84.0483	-.0000	26.5549	34
*ZPRED	-1.7934	2.1101	.0000	1.0000	34
*ZRESID	-2.1056	3.1168	-.0000	.9847	34

6) The most extreme cases

The table below shows the ten most extreme cases based on *ZRESID including, of course, the outlier who was identified in the casewise plot (ie case 1).

Outliers - Standardized Residual

Case #	*ZRESID
1	3.11675
34	-2.10556
25	-1.59045
33	-1.21790
9	-1.15819
32	-1.13272
12	1.07255
29	-1.04754
18	1.03315
30	-.95600

7) Histogram of *ZRESID

Below is a histogram of *ZRESID with * showing actual cases and . showing the normal curve. Ideally, the residuals should be normally distributed. Notice the * for the outlier at the top of the histogram.

```
Histogram - Standardized Residual
N     Exp N (* = 1 Cases, . : = Normal Curve)
0     .03   Out
1     .05   3.00  *
0     .13   2.67
0     .30   2.33
0     .62   2.00 .
0    1.14   1.67 .
0    1.87   1.33   .
4    2.74   1.00 **:*
5    3.61    .67 ***:*
6    4.26    .33 ***:**
4    4.50    .00 ****.
4    4.26   -.33 ***:
1    3.61  - .67 * .
6    2.74  -1.00 **:***
1    1.87  -1.33 *.
1    1.14  -1.67 :
1     .62  -2.00 :
0     .30  -2.33
0     .13  -2.67
0     .05  -3.00
0     .03   Out
```

8) Cumulative probability plot of *ZRESID

Below is a cumulative probability plot of *ZRESID. Ideally, the asterisks (*) should lie along the diagonal. If they do not, the residuals are not normally distributed and it may be necessary to apply a transformation to the data. (For a discussion of the rationale of transformations, see Howell, 1992, Chapter 11.)

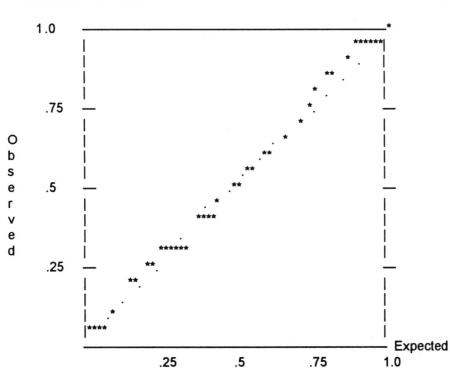

Normal Probability (P-P) Plot
Standardized Residual

9) Scatterplot of the original bivariate data and a plot of the residuals against predicted marks

The final two plots are those requested in the /SCATTERPLOT subcommand, namely a plot of the bivariate distribution with standard scores, and a plot of the standardised residuals against the standardised predicted marks. Can you spot the principal outlier in the first plot? A method of eliminating outliers will be illustrated later.

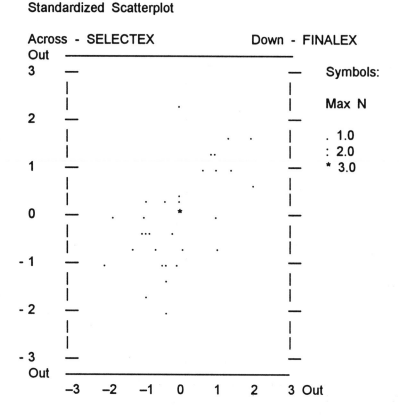

The second plot (overleaf) shows no pattern, thereby confirming that the assumptions of linearity and homogeneity of variance have been met. If the cloud of points were crescent-shaped or formed a funnel-shaped cloud, further screening of the data (or abandonment of the analysis) would be necessary.

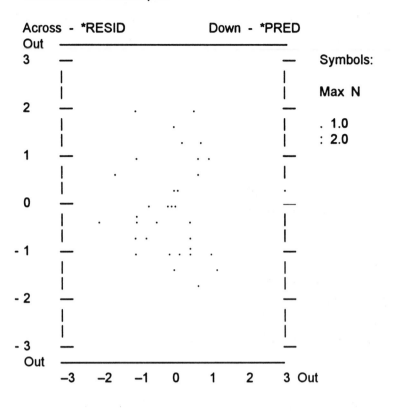

Standardized Scatterplot

12.2.2.1 SAVING THE LISTING TO A FILE

To save a copy of the listing to a file on the floppy disk (an essential operation if a printed version is needed), add a **SET/LISTING** command at the head of the commands, and submit all the commands for re-execution (Chapter 2).

12.2.2.2 PRINTING OUT THE LISTING AND COMMAND FILES

Details are given in Chapter 2, (section 2.6) .

12.2.3 Eliminating outliers

The listing included a regression equation for predicting a person's mark on the Final Examination *finalex*, given the same person's mark on the Selection Examination *selectex*. The listing also showed that there is just one pair of discrepant marks (an **outlier**) and that the basic assumptions for performing a regression analysis have not been violated.

A more reliable analysis, however, can be obtained by eliminating any outliers. This is easily achieved by making use of the **SELECT IF** command described in Chapter 4. Return to the scratch pad and write the following command after END DATA to eliminate the outlier with a Final Examination mark of 195 (this is achieved by selecting *finalex* values that are **not** equal to 195):

```
. . .
END DATA.
SELECT IF (finalex NE 195).
REGRESSION/VARIABLES ALL
. . .
```

Alternatively, the **/SELECT** subcommand of REGRESSION can be used. Examples and instructions are found within the **other global specs** item in the REGRESSION menu. The REGRESSION command would be:

```
REGRESSION /VARIABLES ALL
        /DESCRIPTIVES /SELECT finalex NE 195
        /DEPENDENT finalex /METHOD ENTER selectex
        /RESIDUALS /CASEWISE
        /SCATTERPLOT (*PRED *RESID) (finalex selectex).
```

Either way, the commands can be executed again and a more reliable equation constructed.

The effects of the two procedures are slightly different. In the case of the SELECT IF command, the regression program does not process the unselected case(s), whereas for the /SELECT subcommand within REGRESSION, the residuals and predicted values are calculated separately for both the selected and unselected case(s).

12.3 MULTIPLE REGRESSION (REGRESSION WITH MORE THAN ONE INDEPENDENT VARIABLE)

The foregoing procedure is easily extended to situations where one is regressing a target variable on two or more independent variables.

Suppose that data are also available on other characteristics of the candidates, such as their ages, IQs and their scores on a project completed at the time of the selection examination.

Would the inclusion of these extra variables in the regression equation appreciably improve the prediction of the final examination mark?

In the following data set, scores on three extra variables have been added: the students' ages, their IQs and their project marks:

Finalex	Selectex	Age	IQ	Project
195	49	21.5	151	81
169	62	21.2	150	85
.	.	.	.	.
.	.	.	.	.
38	44	21.9	116	50

For illustrative purposes, the data have been chosen such that ages are randomly assigned among all the subjects, IQ decreases systematically from the first to the last subject, and the project mark has a high but imperfect correlation with the Final Examination mark.

12.3.1 The commands for multiple regression

The commands are similar to those for simple regression; but more variable names must be listed and a different METHOD is required.

Step 1

Write the DATA LIST command. If the variables are named *finalex selectex age iq project*, the command is:

DATA LIST FREE / finalex selectex age iq project.

The data are then typed on the scratch pad after the BEGIN DATA command:

BEGIN DATA.
195 49 21.5 151 81
169 62 21.2 150 85

 .   .   .   .   .
 38 44 21.9 116 50
END DATA.

Step 2

Execute these data commands with **[F10]** and ↵ . This will enable SPSS/PC+ to generate a table of variable names for pasting in subsequent commands.

Step 3

Write the REGRESSION command. Include the extra variable names. The two subcommands are as before:

REGRESSION/VARIABLES finalex selectex age iq project
    /DESCRIPTIVES
    /DEPENDENT finalex

The /METHOD subcommand is handled differently in multiple regression. The recommended method is **STEPWISE**. Read about it on the menu by moving down the **REGRESSION** menu to **/METHOD**, and press ↵ to paste /METHOD on the scratch pad. Move down the **/METHOD** menu to **stepwise methods**. Read the additional information, go down to STEPWISE, and press ↵ to paste it on the scratch pad. The command is now:

REGRESSION/VARIABLES finalex selectex age iq project
    /DESCRIPTIVES
    /DEPENDENT finalex
    /METHOD STEPWISE

Step 4 (optional, but highly recommended)

Request the analysis of the residuals with the same subcommands as before:

    /RESIDUALS
    /CASEWISE
    /SCATTERPLOT (*pred *resid).

Ensure that there is a period (.) after the final subcommand.

Step 5

Save the commands to the floppy disk by using **[F9]** and a suitable filename (Chapter 2).

Step 6

Execute the REGRESSION command in the usual way by pressing **[F10]** and ↵ .

12.3.2 The listing for multiple regression

An examination of the correlations of the dependent variable (*finalex*) with the independent variables (these correlations can be found in the first row and column of the correlation table) shows that *iq* is more highly correlated with *finalex* than is any of the other variables. Not surprisingly, *iq* turns out to be the only predicting variable included in the regression equation reproduced below the correlation table:

Correlation:

	FINALEX	SELECTEX	AGE	IQ	PROJECT
FINALEX	1.000	.672	-.058	.967	.909
SELECTEX	.672	1.000	-.273	.697	.562
AGE	-.058	-.273	1.000	-.026	.100
IQ	.967	.697	-.026	1.000	.913
PROJECT	.909	.562	.100	.913	1.000

* * * * M U L T I P L E   R E G R E S S I O N * * * *

Equation Number 1   Dependent Variable.. FINALEX

Beginning Block Number 1.   Method: Stepwise

Variable(s) Entered on Step Number
            1..   IQ

------------------ Variables in the Equation ------------------

Variable	B	SE B	Beta	T	Sig T
IQ	3.31334	.15763	.96666	2.020	.0000
(Constant)	- 338.49079	21.19583		-15.970	.0000

------------- Variables not in the Equation -------------

Variable	Beta In	Partial	Min Toler	T	Sig T
SELECTEX	- 3.826 E-03	-.01071	.51427	-.059	.9536
AGE	-.03237	-.12636	.99932	-.698	.4907
PROJECT	.16261	.25950	.16698	1.472	.1515

The regression analysis has shown that only *iq* is worth including for maximum accuracy of prediction.

Suppose, however, for illustrative purposes, that *iq* is omitted from the list of variables by changing the list of variables in the REGRESSION command to:

REGRESSION/VARIABLES finalex selectex age project

and executing this along with the other subcommands. Now a different regression equation emerges:

Equation Number 1   Dependent Variable.. FINALEX

Beginning Block Number 1.   Method: Stepwise

Variable(s) Entered on Step Number
        1.. PROJECT

------------------ Variables in the Equation ------------------

Variable	B	SE B	Beta	T	Sig T
PROJECT	3.93946	.32355	.90943	12.176	.0000
(Constant)	-168.51318	22.67914		-7.430	.0000

------------- Variables not in the Equation -------------

Variable	Beta In	Partial	Min Toler	T	Sig T
SELECTEX	.23462	.46658	.68394	2.889	.0071
AGE	-.14987	-.35858	.99002	-2.104	.0439

Variable(s) Entered on Step Number
        2.. SELECTEX

------------------ Variables in the Equation ------------------

Variable	B	SE B	Beta	T	Sig T
PROJECT	3.36808	.35175	.77752	9.575	.0000
SELECTEX	1.13071	.39134	.23462	2.889	.0071
(Constant)	-182.22801	20.93600		-8.704	.0000

------------- Variables not in the Equation -------------

Variable	Beta In	Partial	Min Toler	T	Sig T
AGE	-.08564	-.21237	.57481	-1.170	.2514

End Block Number 1 PIN = .050 Limits reached.

The stepwise analysis stops at this stage, with *project* and *selectex* included, and *age* excluded. PIN means Probability IN and is a criterion tail probability of F-to-enter for the inclusion of a variable in the regression equation.

In this regression analysis with *selectex age project* as the independent variables, the variable *age* is excluded from the final regression equation for the predicted final exam mark:

Mark = 3.36808(Project mark) + 1.13071(Selection Exam mark) - 182.22801

[Many years ago, Darlington (1968) drew attention to some widespread misunderstandings and abuses of multiple regression. Darlington's paper did for regression what Lewis and Burke's (1949) paper had done for chi-square analysis. He placed special emphasis upon the thorny problem of how to say which of the independent variables in a regression equation are the most important. Despite the ease with which modern packages can perform stepwise regressions, the problem of relative importance has no unequivocal solution. The satisfactory interpretation of regression data requires a **psychological**, **causal** model, as well as a **statistical** model. For a lucid discussion, see Cohen and Cohen (1983).]

12.3.2.1 SAVING THE LISTING TO A FILE

Save the listing to a file on the floppy disk in the usual way by adding a **SET/LISTING** command at the head of the commands, and re-submitting all the commands again for execution (Chapter 2).

12.3.2.2 PRINTING OUT THE LISTING AND COMMAND FILES

For details of the procedure, see Chapter 2 (section 2.6).

12.4 SUMMARY

1) Regression generates an equation for predicting a value on a target variable from specified values of one or more other variables (the independent variables). In **simple regression**, there is only one independent variable; in **multiple regression**, there may be many.

2) The command is of the form

REGRESSION/VARIABLES *all the variable names*

> **/DEPENDENT** *dependent variable name*
> **/METHOD** *name of method*

When there is only one independent variable, the method is **ENTER**. When there are two or more independent variables, the recommended method is **STEPWISE**.

3)   Optional subcommands include the following:

> **/DESCRIPTIVES**

which lists the means and standard deviations of all the variables;

> **/RESIDUALS**
> **/CASEWISE**
> **/SCATTERPLOT** *(names of variables for one plot)*
>   *(names of variables for next plot)*

which provide extra information about outliers and checks for violation of the assumptions of the linear regression model.

4)   In the listing of the output, the regression equation appears in column B of the section subheaded **Variables in the Equation.** In multiple regression, there may be more than one equation, in which case the final equation is the appropriate one.

5)   Outliers can be omitted from a second execution of the commands by using **either**

i) **SELECT IF** (*variable name* **NE** *value*)**.**

(This command is placed after the data but before the **REGRESSION** command.)

or

ii) **/SELECT** *variable name* **NE** *value*

(This subcommand of REGRESSION is placed immediately after the **/VARIABLES** subcommand.)

CHAPTER 13

LOGLINEAR ANALYSIS

13.1 INTRODUCTION

From the point of view of this book, **all** data are numerical, and in this sense the statistical analyses described here are all "quantitative". In much psychological research, however, an individual observation is not a measurement on a scale indicating that the person has so-many units of the variable in question: instead, it is a record of the person's category membership, with respect to variables such as gender or political affiliation. Since these variables are possessed **in kind**, rather than **in degree**, they are known as **qualitative** (or **nominal**) variables, and the data are referred to collectively as **nominal data.** Often the purpose of gathering nominal data is to explore the possibility of relationships among qualitative variables: to ask whether females are more conservative than males, for example, is to ask whether there is an association between the qualitative variables of gender and political affiliation.

The starting point for the analysis of nominal data is a **contingency table**, each cell of which is the **frequency of occurrence** of individuals in various combinations of categories. In an earlier chapter (Chapter 11), we described the use of the chi-square test to test for the presence of an association between qualitative variables in a **two-way** contingency table.

In a two-way contingency table, the presence (or absence) of an association between the attributes is often very apparent from inspection alone: the formal statistical analysis merely confirms (or fails to confirm) a readily discernible pattern. It is quite possible, however, to have very complex contingency tables, in which individuals are classified with respect to many qualitative variables. In such multi-way contingency tables, it is often very difficult to discern associations; and indeed, it is only too easy to misinterpret what one does see. Recent years have seen great advances in the analysis of multi-way contingency tables, and these new methods, collectively known as **loglinear analysis**, are now available in computing packages such as SPSS/PC+.

13.1.1 Comparison with ANOVA

To understand how loglinear analysis works, it may be helpful to recall some aspects of the completely randomised factorial analysis of variance, because there are some striking parallels between the two sets of techniques. In the ANOVA, it is possible to test for **main effects** and for **interactions**. Suppose that, following a three-factor experiment, all systematic sources are found to be significant. That would imply that the correct model for the experimental data must contain a term for each and every possible effect thus:

score = systematic effects* + error effects

(* 3 main effect terms + 3 two-way interaction terms + 1 three-way
  interaction term)

If, on the other hand, only one main effect and one of the possible two-way interactions were to prove significant, a much simpler model would account for a subject's score. This simplified model would contain, in addition to the error term, only one main effect term and one two-way interaction term thus:

score = systematic effects* + error effects

(* 1 main effect term + 1 two-way interaction term)

In the analysis of variance, the presence of an interaction often necessitates the re-interpretation of a significant main effect. Examination of the interaction may show that an experimental treatment has a strong effect at some levels (or combinations of levels) of other factors in the experiment, but no effect at other levels.

Graphs of two-way tables of means are often very illuminating: if the factor profiles are non-parallel, a two-way interaction is indicated. Graphs of three-way tables, however, are more difficult to interpret visually, because, just as graphs of two-way tables reflect the presence of main effects as well as the two-way interaction, graphs of three-way tables reflect two-way interactions as well as the three-way interaction.

There are many parallels between the foregoing considerations and the loglinear analysis of multi-way contingency tables. Just as in the context of ANOVA, it is meaningful to speak of "main effects" and of "interactions". Moreover, in interpreting multi-way tables by inspection alone, it is only too easy to confuse one effect for another. Loglinear analysis, however, like ANOVA, offers methods of testing the various effects separately. As in ANOVA, the presence of an interaction often necessitates the re-interpretation of a main effect; indeed, main effects, when considered on their own, can be highly misleading. That is why the common procedure of "collapsing", ie combining the frequencies at all levels of some factors to exclude those factors from the classification, can produce very misleading patterns in the data. As with ANOVA, a loglinear analysis tries to find the model that best accounts for the data available. It contains both main effect terms and interaction terms, so that the values in the contingency table are expressed as the sum of main effects and interaction components.

There are also important differences between loglinear and ANOVA models, however. In the ANOVA, the "target" of the model is the **individual score** of a subject in the experiment. In loglinear analysis, the target is the **total frequency of observations in a cell.** The ANOVA model cannot possibly predict the individual scores with perfect accuracy, because of the inevitable presence of error: errors of measurement, individual differences and experimental error. In contrast, as we shall see, it is **always** possible, by including all the possible terms in the loglinear model, to predict perfectly the cell frequencies in a contingency table. A model that contains all the possible effect terms is known as a **saturated model**. The purpose of a loglinear analysis is to see whether the cell frequencies may be adequately approximated by a model that contains **fewer** than the full set of possible treatment effects.

13.1.2 Why 'loglinear' analysis?

Recall that in the simple chi-square test of association in a two-by-two contingency table, the **expected frequencies** are obtained by **multiplying** marginal total frequencies and dividing the product by the total frequency. This is because the null hypothesis of independence of the variables implies that the probability of an individual occupying a cell of the classification is the **product** of the relevant main effect probabilities, the latter being estimated from the marginal totals. (Recall that in elementary probability, the probability of the joint occurrence of independent events is the **product** of their separate probabilities.) Loglinear analysis exploits the fact that the logarithm (log) of a product is the **sum** of the logs of the terms in the product. Thus the **log** of the cell frequencies may be expressed as a **linear** (ie additive) function of the **logs** of the components. If one were to work directly with the cell frequencies, rather than their logs, one would require a **multiplicative** model for the data. While that is feasible, however, the simplicity of a summative, ANOVA-type model would be lost.

13.1.3 Constructing a loglinear model

The purpose of a loglinear analysis is to construct a model such that the cell frequencies in a contingency table are accounted for with a minimum number of terms. Several strategies can be followed in the construction of such a model, but the **backward hierarchical method** is perhaps the easiest to understand. The first step is to construct a saturated model for the cell frequencies, in which all the component effects are present. This model, as we have seen, will predict the cell frequencies perfectly. The next step is to remove the highest-order interaction, to determine the effect this would have upon the closeness with which the model predicts the cell frequencies. It may be that this interaction can be removed without affecting appreciably the accuracy of estimation of the target frequencies. The process of progressive elimination is continued, and each time a term is removed, a statistical test is carried out to determine whether the accuracy of prediction falls to a sufficient extent to show that the component most recently excluded should indeed be one of the components in the final model. The assessment of the goodness-of-fit at each stage of the procedure is made by means of a statistic known as the **likelihood ratio** (called **L.R. Chisq** by SPSS/PC+), which has a known distribution.

The evaluation of the final model is made by comparing the observed and expected frequencies for each cell using the likelihood ratio as described above; but it is also prudent to examine the distribution of **residuals** (the differences between the observed and expected frequencies), or more conveniently, the **standardised residuals** (the residuals expressed in standardised form) in a manner similar to that described for regression in the last chapter.

13.1.4 Small expected frequencies

Just as in the case of the Chi-square test, the size of the **expected frequency** (not the observed frequency) in each cell must be adequate for the analysis to be worthwhile. Small expected frequencies can lead to a drastic loss of power. Problems with low expected cell frequencies should not arise provided:

i)   there are not too many variables in comparison with the size of the sample, and
ii)   there are no categories with very few cases.

Tabachnick and Fidell (1989) recommend examining the expected cell frequencies for all **two-way associations** to ensure that all **expected frequencies** are greater than 1 and that no more than 20% are less than 5. If there is any doubt about the assumption of adequate expected cell frequencies, they can be checked out by using the CROSSTABS command.

13.2 AN EXAMPLE OF A LOGLINEAR ANALYSIS

In an investigation of the relationships between success on a second year university psychology statistics course and a number of possibly relevant background variables, the researchers collected a body of information on a number of students, including whether or not they had taken an advanced school mathematics course and whether they had passed a data-processing examination in their first year at university. On each student's record, it was also noted whether he or she had passed the second year psychology statistics examination. (It will be noted that these "yes/no" variables are not true dichotomies, but artificial ones created from true measurements; for present purposes, however, we shall assume that they are true qualitative variables.)   The data are presented in the following three-way contingency table:

Advanced Maths	Yes				No			
Data Processing	Pass		Fail		Pass		Fail	
Psychology Statistics	Pass	Fail	Pass	Fail	Pass	Fail	Pass	Fail
CELL FREQUENCIES	47	10	4	10	58	17	10	20

It is useful to summarise the cell frequencies for categories of single variables as shown below:

Advanced Maths	Yes: 71	No: 105	Total: 176
Data Processing	Pass: 132	Fail: 44	Total: 176
Psych Statistics	Pass: 119	Fail: 57	Total: 176

It can be seen that of the 176 students in the study, 71 had taken advanced mathematics, and 105 had not.   Of those who had taken advanced mathematics, 57 passed first year data-processing and 14 did not, compared with 75 passes and 30 failures in the non-mathematical group. Relatively speaking, therefore, more of the mathematical group passed first year data-processing. Turning now to the statistics examination, it can be seen that of the mathematical group, the pass ratio was 51:20, compared with 68:37 in the non-mathematical group; and among those who had passed data-processing, the success ratio was 105:27, compared with 14:30 in the group that had failed data processing.

First, let us consider the (very unlikely) null hypothesis that there are **no links whatsoever** among the three variables studied: there is no tendency for those who have taken school mathematics to pass first year data-processing, no tendency for those who have passed data-processing to pass second year statistics and so on. It is a simple matter, using a pocket calculator, to use the appropriate marginal totals to obtain the expected cell frequencies in a calculation similar to that appropriate for a two-way contingency table. Since there are three dichotomous (or pseudo-dichotomous) variables, there are 8 expected cell frequencies, the values of which are as follows:

$$36.00 \ 17.25 \ 12.00 \ 5.75 \qquad 53.25 \ 25.50 \ 17.75 \ 8.50$$

These values are in some cases markedly different from the corresponding observed cell frequencies in the table at the top of the page, suggesting that the complete independence model gives a poor account of the data. Clearly at least some associations are present among the three variables; but where exactly are they?

A loglinear analysis on SPSS/PC+ can answer that question very easily. SPSS/PC+ offers the program **HILOGLINEAR**, this label being a conflation of the words **hierarchical** and

loglinear. This program begins by constructing a fully saturated model for the cell frequencies, and works "backwards" in the manner described above, in order to arrive at a model with a minimum number of terms. Some of these are of little interest: for example, there are fewer subjects in the advanced mathematics group than there are in the non-mathematical group, so we can expect a main effect term for this variable in the final model. Main effects are often unimportant in loglinear analysis. In the terms of ANOVA, we are seeking **interactions**, rather than **main effects**: the presence of associations among the three variables will necessitate the inclusion of interaction terms in the model.

13.2.1 The commands for a loglinear analysis

The commands for analysing the data with the HILOGLINEAR program are prepared on the scratch pad in the following steps:

Step 1

Write out the **DATA LIST** command (Chapter 3). The appropriate section of the menu can be found by either (a) typing **DATA LIST** on the scratch pad and pressing **[Esc]**, or (b) moving down the menu to **read or write data**, rightwards to obtain the **read or write data menu**, down to **DATA LIST**, and pressing ⌐ to paste DATA LIST on the scratch pad.

Since the data set is small, the data can be entered in free-field format and included in the commands, rather than stored in a separate file. It will be necessary to construct code (grouping) variables to identify the categories of the three independent variables.

If the coding variables are labelled *maths*, *dataproc* and *psystats*, and the dependent variable of cell frequency is labelled *count*, the command is:

DATA LIST FREE/maths dataproc psystats count.

The data are then typed on the scratch pad after the **BEGIN DATA** command, as described in Chapter 3, thus:

```
BEGIN DATA.
1 1 1 47
1 1 2 10
1 2 1 4
1 2 2 10
2 1 1 58
2 1 2 17
2 2 1 10
2 2 2 20
END DATA.
```

Step 2 (optional but strongly recommended)

Add clarificatory labels. The cryptic variable names can be amplified with a **VARIABLE LABELS** command, and the numbers making up the code variables can be decoded by a **VALUE LABELS** command:

VARIABLE LABELS maths 'Advanced Maths Course' dataproc 'Data Processing
    Exam' psystats 'Psych Stats Exam'.
VALUE LABELS maths 1 'Yes' 2 'No' / dataproc 1 'Pass' 2 'Fail'
    /psystats 1 'Pass' 2 'Fail'.

Details and examples of the **VARIABLE LABELS** and **VALUE LABELS** commands can be found under **labels and formatting**, in the **read or write data** option in the MAIN MENU.

Step 3

The next command is essential, because it ensures that SPSS/PC+ reads the cell data as **counts**, rather than scores. Type the command **WEIGHT BY** on the scratch pad, followed by the name of the dependent variable (*count*) :

WEIGHT BY count.

Step 4

Execute these commands by moving the cursor up to DATA LIST, pressing **[F10]** and ↵ . This checks that these commands have been written correctly and allows SPSS/PC+ to generate a table of variable names for pasting into subsequent commands.

Step 5   (optional)

If there is any doubt about whether the expected frequencies are sufficiently large, these can be checked by using the **CROSSTABS** command (for details, type CROSSTABS and press **[Esc]** to obtain the CROSSTABS menu) and specifying the expected frequencies option in the **/CELLS** subcommand:

CROSSTABS/TABLES dataproc BY psystats BY maths/CELLS EXPECTED.

This presents the two-way contingency tables for each level of *maths*.

Step 6

Find the **HILOGLINEAR** command in the menu by moving the cursor down the **MAIN MENU** to **analyze data**, and then down the **analyze data** menu to **other**. Move rightwards, into the **other** menu, to **HILOGLINEAR**, read the information, and press ↵ to paste HILOGLINEAR on the scratch pad. (Alternatively, type HILOGLINEAR on the scratch pad and press [Esc] to display the HILOGLINEAR menu.)

Press ↵ and read the information about **variables**. Press ↵ again and select each of the coding variables (*maths dataproc psystats*) in turn from the table of variables (pressing ↵ each time), and then [Esc] to remove the table of variables. Move down to ( ), press ↵ , type in the lowest and highest values of the coding variables (in this example they are 1, 2), and press ↵ .

(Note: In this example, all three coding variables have two levels; if this were not so, it would be necessary to insert the appropriate numbers in brackets after each variable name.)

Return to the HILOGLINEAR menu with the ← cursor key, move down to **/METHOD BACKWARD** and press ↵ . (If plots of the residuals are desired, add the subcommand **/PLOT** for which details are available in the menu.)

The command is now:

HILOGLINEAR maths dataproc psystats(1,2)
    /METHOD BACKWARD.

Step 7

Save the commands to a named file on the floppy disk by using [F9] (see Chapter 2).

Step 8

Execute the HILOGLINEAR command by pressing [F10] and ↵ .

13.2.2 The listing for a loglinear analysis

The listing will begin with a note stating that the **LAST COMMAND ON HILOGLINEAR IS NOT A DESIGN SUBCOMMAND - A saturated model is generated.** This is not indicative of a mistake and can be ignored.

The listing continues with the following tables and items:

1) **Information about the DATA and the FACTORS**

* * * * * * * * H I E R A R C H I C A L   L O G   L I N E A R * * * * * * * *

DATA Information
    8   unweighted cases accepted.
    0   cases rejected because of out-of-range factor values.
    0   cases rejected because of missing data.
    176 weighted cases will be used in the analysis.

FACTOR Information

Factor	Level	Label
MATHS	2	Taken Maths Course
DATAPROC	2	Data Processing Exam
PSYSTATS	2	Psych Stats Exam

2) A table of counts

A table listing the counts (OBS count) for the combinations of the three factors is reproduced below. At this point, SPSS/PC+ is fitting a **saturated model**, MATHS × DATAPROC × PSYSTATS, to the cell frequencies. This table is useful for checking the accuracy of the data transcription.

DESIGN 1 has generating class

MATHS*DATAPROC*PSYSTATS

Note: For saturated models .500 has been added to all observed cells.

Observed, Expected Frequencies and Residuals.

Factor	Code	OBS count	EXP count	Residual	Std Resid
MATHS	Yes				
DATAPROC	Pass				
PSYSTATS	Pass	47.5	47.5	.00	.00
PSYSTATS	Fail	10.5	10.5	.00	.00
DATAPROC	Fail				
PSYSTATS	Pass	4.5	4.5	.00	.00
PSYSTATS	Pass	10.5	10.5	.00	.00
MATHS	No				
DATAPROC	Pass				
PSYSTATS	Pass	58.5	58.5	.00	.00
PSYSTATS	Fail	17.5	17.5	.00	.00
DATAPROC	Fail				
PSYSTATS	Pass	10.5	10.5	.00	.00
PSYSTATS	Pass	20.5	20.5	.00	.00

3) Tests of effects

In this section, are reported tests that K-way and higher order effects are zero, and that the K-way effects themselves are zero. These items give the tail probabilities for the effects of specified order and (where appropriate) a statement that an effect is significant. In this example, all effects are significant up to and including the 2-way level of complexity. The three-way effect, however, is not significant.

Tests that K-way and higher order effects are zero.

K	DF	L.R. Chisq	Prob	Pearson Chisq	Prob	Iteration
3	1	.431	.5115	.425	.5143	4
2	4	35.310	.0000	37.077	.0000	2
1	7	110.282	.0000	123.000	.0000	0

Tests that K-way effects are zero.

K	DF	L.R. Chisq	Prob	Pearson Chisq	Prob	Iteration
1	3	74.972	.0000	85.923	.0000	0
2	3	34.879	.0000	36.651	.0000	0
3	1	.431	.5115	.425	.5143	0

4) Table of parameter estimates

These are the lambda parameters of the loglinear model equation. Those with significant z values (ie z greater than 1.96) give a foretaste of which main effects and interactions will feature in the final loglinear model.

(When a variable comprises m categories (m > 2), (m - 1) parameters will be listed for main effects. For an interaction between variables with m and n categories, there will be (m-1)(n-1) parameters.)

Estimates for Parameters.

Parameter	Coeff.	Std. Err.	Z-Value	Lower 95 CI	Upper 95 CI
MATHS*DATAPROC*PSYSTATS					
1	.0600971015	.10093	.59541	- .13773	.25793
MATHS*DATAPROC					
1	.0996531028	.10093	.98731	- .09818	.29748
MATHS*PSYSTATS					
1	.0155350436	.10093	.15391	- .18229	.21337
DATAPROC*PSYSTATS					
1	.5290659771	.10093	5.24172	.33124	.72690
MATHS					
1	- .2794337695	.10093	-2.76849	- .47726	-.08160
DATAPROC					
1	.4895099758	.10093	4.84982	.29168	.68734
PSYSTATS					
1	.1499791047	.10093	1.48592	-.04785	.34781

In this example, DATAPROC*PSYSTATS, MATHS, and DATAPROC have significant z values.

5) Backward elimination

This section contains the most interesting part of the listing:

Backward Elimination for Design 1 with generating class

The purpose of the analysis is to find the model that gives the best fit to the observed data. This is achieved by checking that the model currently being tested does not give a significantly worse fit than its predecessor in the hierarchy.

Recall that in the hierarchical backward elimination method, the procedure starts with the most complex model (which in the present case contains all three factors, together with all their possible interactions), and progresses down the hierarchy of complexity, eliminating each effect from the model in turn and determining which decrement in accuracy is less than the **least-significant change in the chi-square value.** At each step, such an effect would be eliminated, leaving the remaining effects for inclusion: "The best model has generating class ....".

The procedure continues until no elimination produces a decrement with a probability greater than 0.05. The model containing the remaining effects is then adopted as "The final model". In this example, the final model is reached after four steps.

Backward Elimination for DESIGN 1 with generating class

    MATHS*DATAPROC*PSYSTATS

Likelihood ratio chi square =   .00000   DF = 0   P = 1.000

If Deleted Simple Effect is	DF	L.R. Chisq Change	Prob	Iter
MATHS*DATAPROC*PSYSTATS	1	.431	.5115	4

Step 1

The best model has generating class
MATHS*DATAPROC
MATHS*PSYSTATS
DATAPROC*PSYSTATS
Likelihood ratio chi square =   .43090   DF = 1   P = .512

If Deleted Simple Effect is	DF	L.R. Chisq Change	Prob	Iter
MATHS*DATAPROC	1	1.029	.3104	2
MATHS*PSYSTATS	1	.198	.6564	2
DATAPROC*PSYSTATS	1	32.098	.0000	2

At this stage MATHS*PSYSTATS is eliminated, because it has the largest probability (.6564).

Step 2

The best model has generating class
MATHS*DATAPROC
DATAPROC*PSYSTATS

Likelihood ratio chi square =		.62884	DF = 2	P = .730	
If Deleted Simple Effect is	DF	L.R. Chisq Change		Prob	Iter
MATHS*DATAPROC	1	1.806		.1790	2
DATAPROC*PSYSTATS	1	32.875		.0000	2

At this stage MATHS*DATAPROC is eliminated, because it has the larger probability (and it is greater than the criterion level of 0.05). The next step introduces any main effect which is not part of the remaining 2-way interaction. In this case, MATHS is such a variable.

Step 3

The best model has generating class
DATAPROC*PSYSTATS
MATHS

Likelihood ratio chi square =   2.43511   DF = 3   P = .487

If Deleted Simple Effect is	DF	L.R. Chisq Change	Prob	Iter
DATAPROC*PSYSTATS	1	32.875	.0000	2
MATHS	1	6.610	.0101	2

Neither of these effects can be eliminated, because both probabilities are less than 0.05.

Step 4

The best model has generating class
DATAPROC*PSYSTATS
MATHS

Likelihood ratio chi square =   2.43511   DF = 3   P = .487

The final model has generating class
DATAPROC*PSYSTATS
MATHS

The final model, therefore, includes the interaction between the variables representing the data processing exam and the psychology statistics exam, plus a main effect of maths. Note that there are no interactions involving the maths variable. Thus the most interesting finding is the interaction between the two examinations.

6) Table of frequencies

Finally, the computer lists the table of observed frequencies and the expected frequencies **as estimated by the final model**. The final chi-square test shows that these expected frequencies do **not** differ significantly from the observed frequencies (chi-square is not significant).

This Table also lists the residuals and standardised residuals. If the **/PLOT** subcommand is included in the commands, the standardised residuals will be used in the plots.

Observed, Expected Frequencies and Residuals.

Factor	Code	OBS count	EXP count	Residual	Std Resid
MATHS	Yes				
DATAPROC	Pass				
PSYSTATS	Pass	47.0	42.4	4.64	.71
PSYSTATS	Fail	10.0	10.9	-.89	-.27
DATAPROC	Fail				
PSYSTATS	Pass	4.0	5.6	-1.65	-.69
PSYSTATS	Fail	10.0	12.1	-2.10	-.60
MATHS	No				
DATAPROC	Pass				
PSYSTATS	Pass	58.0	62.6	-4.64	-.59
PSYSTATS	Fail	17.0	16.1	.89	.22
DATAPROC	Fail				
PSYSTATS	Pass	10.0	8.4	1.65	.57
PSYSTATS	Fail	20.0	17.9	2.10	.50

Goodness-of-fit test statistics

Likelihood ratio chi square	= 2.43511 DF = 3	P = .487
Pearson chi square	= 2.39308 DF = 3	P = .495

13.2.2.1 SAVING THE LISTING TO A FILE

To save the listing to a file on the floppy disk (an essential step, if you require a hard copy of the output), add a SET/LISTING command at the head of the commands, and submit all the commands for re-execution (Chapter 2).

13.2.2.2 PRINTING THE LISTING AND COMMAND FILES

For details of these procedures, see Chapter 2 (section 2.6).

13.2.3 Comparison with the total independence model

Notice that the expected frequencies estimated by the final model are much closer to the observed counts than those for the total independence model, whose values were listed earlier in the chapter.

[The reader might wish to use the HILOGLINEAR program to check these values. Replace the /**METHOD BACKWARD** subcommand with /**DESIGN maths dataproc psystats** and execute the command again. A table of observed and expected frequencies will be listed for this total independence design.]

A table contrasting the observed and expected cell frequencies under the assumptions of the "best model" generated by HILOGLINEAR with the corresponding discrepancies under the total independence model is shown below:

Advanced Maths	"Yes"				"No"			
Data Processing	Pass		Fail		Pass		Fail	
Psychology Statistics	Pass	Fail	Pass	Fail	Pass	Fail	Pass	Fail
Observed Counts	47	10	4	10	58	17	10	20
Expected Counts assuming the DATAPROC*PSYSTATS and MATHS model	42.4	10.9	5.6	12.1	62.6	16.1	8.4	17.9
Expected Counts assuming the total independence model	36.0	17.3	12.0	5.7	53.2	25.5	17.8	8.5

13.3 SUMMARY

1) When data are in the form of counts in the cells of a **multi-way contingency table**, loglinear analysis provides a means of constructing the model that gives the best approximation to the values of the cell frequencies.

2) The appropriate SPSS/PC+ command is **HILOGLINEAR** (hierarchical loglinear), which is of the form:

    HILOGLINEAR *independent variable names*
    /METHOD BACKWARD.

3) Plots of the standardised residuals can be obtained by including the **/PLOT** subcommand.

4) If there is any doubt about the sizes of the expected frequencies, they can be scrutinised by using the **CROSSTABS** command to construct the two-way crosstabulations among all the variables. For example, in the case of three variables, the command would be:

    CROSSTABS/TABLES *variable* **BY** *variable* **BY** *variable*
    /CELLS EXPECTED.

5) The listing includes tables indicating the level of complexity of interaction at which the effects are significant, a table of parameter estimates, and the various steps of the backward elimination of insignificant effects, culminating in the identification of the optimal model. Finally, there is a table contrasting the observed frequencies with the expected frequencies, assuming the optimal model.

CHAPTER 14

PREDICTION OF GROUP MEMBERSHIP: DISCRIMINANT ANALYSIS

14.1 INTRODUCTION

In the various analyses of variance (ANOVA) that we have considered so far in this book, the purpose was to determine the effects of one or more independent variables (IVs) upon **one** dependent variable (DV). Because only one DV is involved, these methods are known as **univariate** analyses of variance. The situation often arises, however, in which measurements are available on **more than one** DV. For example, in an experiment designed to test the effects upon memorability of certain characteristics of written passages, memorability might be tested in more than one way: the number of items correctly recalled by the subject could be recorded; but so also could the number of errors in the recall. In that case, there would be **two** dependent variables, not one, as in all previous examples.

In analysing such data, one obvious (and popular) approach is to perform an ANOVA on each DV separately. Thus, in the present example, two ANOVAs could be carried out; one with the recall scores, the other with the errors. Such an analysis, however, invariably leaves the researcher with a feeling of unease, because the two DVs are often highly correlated, and it is obvious that the two analyses are not independent. Correct recall, for example, can be expected to correlate negatively with the number of errors. There is therefore dubiety about the interpretation of the tail probabilities (p-values) yielded by the separate analyses.

The methods of ANOVA, however, have been extended to situations where there are two or more DVs. Such **multivariate analyses of variance (MANOVAs)** permit a direct test of the null hypothesis with respect to **all** the DVs in an experiment. In the present example, where memorability is measured by number of items correctly recalled and by the number of errors, MANOVA offers a direct test of the null hypothesis that the different types of passage are equally memorable. In MANOVA, a linear function (y) of the dependent variables in the analysis is constructed, so that inter-group differences on y are maximised. The composite variable y is then treated in a manner somewhat similar to the DV in a univariate ANOVA, and the null hypothesis accepted or rejected accordingly.

14.1.1 What is discriminant analysis?

Essentially, the multivariate technique known as **discriminant analysis** is the obverse of MANOVA. In the MANOVA situation, you know which categories the subjects belong to and you want to explore the possibility of identifying a composite variable (y) which shows up differences among the groups. In other circumstances, however, one might wish to ascertain **category membership** on the basis of subjects' performance on the DVs. It would be of considerable value, for example, on the basis of records of children on a number of variables recorded during the earlier school years, to predict which children go on to further education, which secure immediate employment on leaving school, and which join the ranks of the unemployed. Discriminant analysis offers an answer to such a question.

The composite variable y obtained in MANOVA is known as a **discriminant function**, because it is a weighted sum of the DVs, with the weightings chosen such that the distributions of y for the various groups are separated to the greatest possible extent. In discriminant analysis, the very same composite variable y is constructed, so that category membership can be predicted to the greatest possible extent. Mathematically, therefore, the techniques of MANOVA and discriminant analysis have much in common. In the latter, however, the attempt is made to predict category membership using the discriminant function. There are other important differences between MANOVA and discriminant analysis (see Tabachnick & Fidell, 1989). For present purposes, however, their similarities are more notable than their differences, and it is worth noting that MANOVA computing programs can be used to perform discriminant analyses.

It is important to note that in performing a discriminant analysis on data from an experiment with two or more DVs, the true DVs now become the **independent variables**, and the group variable is now the **dependent variable**.

14.1.2 Types of discriminant analysis

There are three types of discriminant analysis: **direct, hierarchical,** and **stepwise**. In **direct** analysis, all the variables enter the equations at once; in **hierarchical**, they enter according to a schedule set by the researcher; and in **stepwise**, statistical criteria alone determine the order of entry. In most analyses, the researcher has no reason for assigning some predictors higher priority than others. The third (stepwise) method, therefore, is the most generally applicable and is the only one discussed in this chapter.

14.1.3 The process of stepwise discriminant analysis

The statistical procedure for stepwise discriminant analysis is similar to that for multiple regression, in that the effect of the addition or removal of a IV is monitored by a statistical test and the result used as a basis for the inclusion of that IV in the final analysis. When there are only two groups, there is just one discriminant function. With more than two groups, however, there can be several functions; though it is unusual for more than the first three to be useful.

Various statistics are available for weighing up the addition or removal of variables from the analysis, but the most commonly used is **Wilks' Lambda**. The significance of the change in Lambda when a variable is entered or removed is obtained from an **F test**. At each step of adding a variable to the analysis, the variable with the largest F (**F TO ENTER**) is included. This process is repeated until there are no further variables with an F value greater than the threshold value of 1.0. At the same time any variable which had been added earlier, but which no longer contributes to maximising the assignment of cases to the correct groups because other variables in concert have taken over its role, is removed when its F value (**F TO REMOVE**) drops below the threshold of 1.

Eventually, the process of adding and subtracting variables is completed, and a summary table is listed showing which variables were added or subtracted at each step. The variables remaining in the analysis are those used in the discriminant function(s). The first table thereafter shows which functions are statistically reliable. The first function provides the best means of predicting membership of the groups: later functions may or may not contribute reliably to the prediction process. Additional tables for listing the functions and their success rate for correct prediction can be requested with further subcommands. Plots can also be specified.

14.2 ANALYSIS OF DATA USING
DISCRIMINANT ANALYSIS

A school's vocational guidance officer is trying to help a pupil to choose which subjects to study at university. Fortunately, some data (modified in this example from some actual research data) are available from a project on the background interests and school-leaving examination results of samples of architectural, engineering and psychology students. The students also filled in a questionnaire about their extra-curricular interests, including outdoor pursuits, drawing, painting, computing, and kit construction.

14.2.1 The commands for discriminant analysis

The commands for analysing the data using the DSCRIMINANT program are prepared on the scratch pad in the following steps:

Step 1

Write the **DATA LIST** command (Chapter 3). The appropriate section of the Menu can be found by either (a) typing DATA LIST on the scratch pad and pressing **[Esc]**, or (b) moving down the MAIN MENU to **read or write data**, rightwards to expand this item into the **read or write data menu**, down to the **DATA LIST** item, and pressing ↵ to paste DATA LIST on the scratch pad.

Since the data are extensive, it is not practical to reproduce them here. The best procedure with a large data set is to store them in **fixed-column** format in a separate **data file**. The data file often contains all the data from the research, including many variables that may not be used for a particular analysis. The DATA LIST command must include all the variable names for the data included in the data file. Later commands (eg for discriminant analysis) can call up whichever variables are desired at that stage.

If the data file is called ARENGPSY.DAT (**AR**chitects, **ENG**ineers, **PSY**chologists) and is located on a disk in drive A, the DATA LIST command is as follows:

DATA LIST FILE 'A:ARENGPSY.DAT' /caseno 1-3 sust 5 age 7-8 sex 10 etc etc.

where the values of the variable *caseno* occupy columns 1-3, those of *sust* (subject studied) occupy column 5, *age* occupies columns 7-8 . . . and so on.

Step 2 (optional but highly recommended)

Add clarificatory labels. The cryptic variable names and numerical codes can be amplified with the **VARIABLE LABELS** and **VALUE LABELS** commands eg

VARIABLE LABELS caseno 'case number' sust 'subject studied'
        age 'age of student' sex 'sex of student'   etc.
VALUE LABELS sust 1 'Architects' 2 'Engineers' 3 'Psychologists'
        /sex 1 'Male' 2 'Female'/   etc.

Details and examples of **VARIABLE LABELS** and **VALUE LABELS** commands are contained in **labels and formatting**, in the **read or write data** item of the MAIN MENU.

Step 3

Execute these commands by moving the cursor up to DATA LIST, pressing **[F10]** and ↵ . This checks that these commands have been correctly written, that the data file has been located and accessed, and allows SPSS/PC+ to generate a table of variable names for pasting into later commands.

Step 4 (optional)

Before performing a discriminant analysis, one should check the distributions of the variables in each category for outliers by using the **EXAMINE** command (see Chapter 4):

EXAMINE *variable names* BY *grouping variable* /PLOT BOXPLOT.

If necessary, an outlier (or outliers) can be removed.

[This command is not included in this example, since the resulting listing would be very large.]

Step 5

Find the **DSCRIMINANT** command in the menu by moving the cursor down the MAIN MENU to **analyze data**, and thence to **classification & clustering**. Move rightwards into **classification & clustering** to find **DSCRIMINANT**, read the information, and then press ↵ to paste DSCRIMINANT on the scratch pad.

(Alternatively, type DSCRIMINANT on the scratch pad and press **[Esc]** to display the DSCRIMINANT menu.)

Read the information about **/GROUPS**, press ↵ to paste /GROUPS on the scratch pad, and read about the **grouping variable**. Press ↵ , select the grouping variable (*sust*) from the table of variable names, press ↵ and then **[Esc]** to remove the table. Move down to ( ), press ↵ , type in the lowest and highest values of the grouping variable (in this example they are 1, 3), and press ↵ .

Return to the DSCRIMINANT menu with the ← cursor key, move down to **/VARIABLES**, press ↵ , and select each variable in turn from the table of variable names (pressing ↵ each time to paste the name on to the scratch pad). Remove the table with **[Esc]**. At this stage, the command is:

DSCRIMINANT/GROUPS sust(1, 3) /VARIABLES draw1 paint1 vismod quals model1
    sex conkit1 comp1 out1.

Next, the method of analysis is chosen by moving down to **/METHOD** and pressing ↵ . We recommend the use of the **stepwise method**, using the **Wilks** criterion. Move down to **stepwise methods** and read the information. Continue down to **WILKS** and press ↵ . The command is now:

DSCRIMINANT/GROUPS sust(1, 3) /VARIABLES draw1 paint1 vismod quals model1
sex conkit1 comp1 out1 /METHOD WILKS.

Step 6 (optional)

Obtain some extra statistics. We recommend selecting some of the statistics available in the **/STATISTICS** subcommand. Move back to the DSCRIMINANT menu, down to **/STATISTICS**, and press ↵ . Not all the available statistics are listed in the ordinary menu: it is necessary to type **[Alt]/X** to obtain the extended menus.

Select 6 for listing the univariate F ratios for each variable, and 13 for listing a table showing the group membership prediction success rates. The final version of the command is:

DSCRIMINANT/GROUPS sust(1, 3) /VARIABLES draw1 paint1 vismod quals model1
sex conkit1 comp1 out1 /METHOD WILKS /STATISTICS 6 13.

Ensure that there is a period (.) at the end of the final subcommand.

Step 7

Save the commands to a named file on the floppy disk by using **[F9]** (see Chapter 2) and then execute the DSCRIMINANT command by pressing **[F10]** followed by ↵ .

14.2.2 The listing for discriminant analysis

The listing begins with a note stating **Since ANALYSIS= was omitted for the first analysis, all variables on the VARIABLES= list will be entered at level 1.** This does not indicate an error and can therefore be ignored.

The listing contains the following items:

1) Information about the DATA and the number of cases in each category of the grouping variable

- - - - - - - - D I S C R I M I N A N T   A N A L Y S I S - - - - - - - -

On groups defined by SUST   study subject

          118 (unweighted) cases were processed.
          15 of these were excluded from the analysis.
               0 had missing or out-of-range group codes.
               15 had at least one missing discriminating variable.
          103 (unweighted) cases will be used in the analysis.

185

Number of Cases by Group

SUST	Number of Cases Unweighted	Weighted	Label
1	27	27.0	architects
2	37	37.0	psychologists
3	39	39.0	engineers
Total	103	103.0	

2) Statistics

Under the STATISTICS 6 option, a table of univariate F-ratios is listed, showing whether there is a statistically significant difference among the group category means for each variable.

Wilks' Lambda (U-statistic) and univariate F-ratio
with   2 and   100 degrees of freedom

Variable	Wilks' Lambda	F	Significance
SEX	.77218	14.75	.0000
CONKIT1	.83945	9.563	.0002
MODEL1	.94645	2.829	.0638
DRAW1	.85218	8.673	.0003
PAINT1	.78559	13.65	.0000
OUT1	.94358	2.990	.0548
COMP1	.99949	.2536E-01	.9750
VISMOD	.84176	9.399	.0002
QUALS	.89647	5.774	.0042

All these are significant except *model1 out1 comp1* .

3) Selection of variables

The stepwise variable selection begins with the variable with the highest **F-to-enter** value, namely *sex*, and continues adding (and possibly removing) variables until no remaining variable exceeds the minimum F-to-enter level of 1.0:

- - - - - - - - D I S C R I M I N A N T   A N A L Y S I S - - - - - - - -

On groups defined by SUST   study subject

Analysis number 1

Stepwise variable selection

```
        Selection rule: Minimize Wilks' Lambda
        Maximum number of steps................     18
        Minimum Tolerance Level................    .00100
        Minimum F to enter.....................    1.0000
        Maximum F to remove....................    1.0000
```

Canonical Discriminant Functions

     Maximum number of functions.............. 2
     Minimum cumulative percent of variance... 100.00
     Maximum significance of Wilks' Lambda.... 1.0000

Prior probability for each group is .33333

---------------- Variables not in the analysis after step 0 ----------------

Variable	Tolerance	Minimum Tolerance	F to enter	Wilks' Lambda
DRAW1	1.0000000	1.0000000	8.6729	.85218
PAINT1	1.0000000	1.0000000	13.647	.78559
VISMOD	1.0000000	1.0000000	9.3992	.84176
QUALS	1.0000000	1.0000000	5.7741	.89647
MODEL1	1.0000000	1.0000000	2.8291	.94645
SEX	1.0000000	1.0000000	14.752	.77218
CONKIT1	1.0000000	1.0000000	9.5630	.83945
COMP1	1.0000000	1.0000000	.25358E-01	.99949
OUT1	1.0000000	1.0000000	2.9897	.94358

At step 1, SEX   was included in the analysis.

		Degrees of Freedom			Signif. Between Groups
Wilks' Lambda	.77218	1	2	100.0	
Equivalent F	14.7519	2		100.0	.0000

---------------- Variables in the analysis after step 1 ----------------

Variable	Tolerance	F to remove	Wilks' Lambda
SEX	1.0000000	14.752	

---------------- Variables not in the analysis after step 1 ----------------

Variable	Tolerance	Minimum Tolerance	F to enter	Wilks' Lambda
DRAW1	.9977950	.9977950	8.5096	.65890
PAINT1	.8945768	.8945768	13.252	.60911
VISMOD	.9984814	.9984814	8.7719	.65594
QUALS	.9855300	.9855300	6.1019	.68744
MODEL1	.9475987	.9475987	2.8054	.73076
CONKIT1	.9192815	.9192815	3.3784	.72284
COMP1	.7374811	.7374811	4.4376	.70865
OUT1	.9829148	.9829148	1.3997	.75094

At step 2, PAINT1   was included in the analysis.

		Degrees of Freedom			Signif. Between Groups
Wilks' Lambda	.60911	2	2	100.0	
Equivalent F	13.9245		4	198.0	.0000

---------------- Variables in the analysis after step 2 ----------------

Variable	Tolerance	F to remove	Wilks' Lambda
PAINT1	.8945768	13.252	.77218
SEX	.8945768	14.341	.78559

---------------- Variables not in the analysis after step 2 ----------------

Variable	Tolerance	Minimum Tolerance	F to enter	Wilks' Lambda
DRAW1	.6780717	.6079278	.85543	.59866
VISMOD	.9615869	.8615217	4.4920	.55796
QUALS	.9542126	.8661496	7.8466	.52503
MODEL1	.8521314	.8044513	.34133	.60490
CONKIT1	.8247377	.7680776	4.3086	.55988
COMP1	.7366425	.6846854	4.3830	.55910
OUT1	.9424490	.8577478	2.6177	.57822

This continues for a further six steps until

At step 8, DRAW1   was included in the analysis.

		Degrees of Freedom			Signif. Between Groups
Wilks' Lambda	.35206	8	2	100.0	
Equivalent F	7.96739		16	186.0	.0000

---------------- Variables in the analysis after step 8 ----------------

Variable	Tolerance	F to remove	Wilks' Lambda
DRAW1	.6436316	1.8607	.36614
PAINT1	.5454206	4.0805	.38295
VISMOD	.8783740	7.2891	.40724
QUALS	.8979781	10.059	.42821
SEX	.5866828	6.8394	.40384
CONKIT1	.7802993	4.3280	.38482
COMP1	.6971706	3.6083	.37937
OUT1	.8515705	3.5869	.37921

--------------- Variables not in the analysis after step 8 ---------------

		Minimum		
Variable	Tolerance	Tolerance	F to enter	Wilks' Lambda
MODEL1	.7273899	.5361777	.33547	.34951

F level or tolerance or VIN insufficient for further computation.

The stepwise variable selection section concludes with a Summary Table showing the order in which the variables were entered or removed (though in this analysis none was removed), along with values of the Wilks' Lambda and the associated probability levels.

Summary Table

	Action		Vars	Wilks'		
Step	Entered	Removed	In	Lambda	Sig.	Label
1	SEX		1	.77218	.0000	sex of student
2	PAINT1		2	.60911	.0000	previous interest in painting
3	QUALS		3	.52503	.0000	total point count for highers
4	VISMOD		4	.47227	.0000	ability to visualise model
5	COMP1		5	.43059	.0000	previous interest in computing
6	CONKIT1		6	.39577	.0000	previous interest in construction kits
7	OUT1		7	.36614	.0000	previous interest in outdoor pursuit
8	DRAW1		8	.35206	.0000	previous interest in drawing

4) Statistics of the discriminant functions

The table shows the percentage (pct) of the variance accounted for by each discriminant function and how many of them (if any) are significant. It also shows that both functions (fcn) are highly significant (see the **Sig** column on the right).

Canonical Discriminant Functions

		Pct of	Cum	Canonical		After	Wilks'			
Fcn	Eigenvalue	Variance	Pct	Corr		Fcn	Lambda	Chisquare	DF	Sig
					:	0	.3521	100.743	16	.0000
1*	.8080	58.59	58.59	.6685	:	1	.6365	43.592	7	.0000
2*	.5710	41.41	100.00	.6029	:					

* marks the 2 canonical discriminant functions remaining in the analysis.

5) Standardised coefficients and within-groups correlations with discriminants

Two tables follow in the listing, the first (not reproduced here) being the standardised function coefficients, and the second being the pooled within-groups correlations between the discriminating variables and the functions. Both tables show which variables contribute the most to each function but the second table is the more useful. It indicates that the first function is based on subjects' interests in painting, drawing, and visualising models, while the second function is essentially based on the sex of the subjects and their interest in kit construction.

The asterisks mark the correlation with the higher value for each variable.

Pooled-within-groups correlations between discriminating variables
    and canonical discriminant functions
(Variables ordered by size of correlation within function)

	FUNC 1	FUNC 2
PAINT1	.55598*	.20143
DRAW1	.46266*	.02964
VISMOD	.43478*	-.24842
QUALS	-.37795*	-.01008
MODEL1	.15806*	.02458
SEX	.03755	.71741*
CONKIT1	.01678	-.57839*
OUT1	-.09463	.30338*
COMP1	-.01900	.01943*

6) Success of predictions of group membership

Under the STATISTICS 13 option, the final table overleaf shows the success rate of predicting membership of the grouping variable's categories using the discriminant functions developed in the analysis. It indicates that the engineers are the most successfully predicted and the psychologists the least. The overall success rate, however, is 74%:

Classification Results -

Actual	Group	No. of Cases	Predicted Group Membership 1	2	3
Group architects	1	29	21 72.4%	2 6.9%	6 20.7%
Group psychologists	2	37	4 10.8%	26 70.3%	7 18.9%
Group engineers	3	41	4 9.8%	5 12.2%	32 78.0%

Percent of "grouped" cases correctly classified: 73.83%

Classification Processing Summary
    118 Cases were processed.
    0   Cases were excluded for missing or out-of-range group codes.
    11 Cases had at least one missing discriminating variable.
    107 Cases were used for printed output.

14.2.2.1 SAVING THE LISTING TO A FILE

To save a copy of the listing to a file on the floppy disk (essential if a print of the output is needed), add a **SET/LISTING** command at the head of the commands, and submit all the commands for re-execution (Chapter 2).

14.2.2.2 PRINTING OUT THE LISTING AND COMMAND FILES

Details are given about the printing of files in Chapter 2 (section 2.6).

14.3 SUMMARY

1) Discriminant analysis is used to predict **category membership** (the DV) from data on several other variables (the IVs). The procedure generates **discriminant functions**, which are weighted sums of IVs, in which the weightings are chosen to maximise the differences, on the new variable, among the categories.

2) The independent variables (IVs) should generally be quantitative and satisfy the usual assumption of normality of distribution, though some authorities allow qualitative binary IVs to be included.

3) The command is of the form

DSCRIMINANT /GROUPS *grouping variable name* (m, n)
  /VARIABLES *predictor variable names*
  /METHOD WILKS
  /STATISTICS *choice of statistics.*

where m and n are the lowest and highest code numbers of the grouping variable. The /STATISTICS subcommand is optional; however, statistics 6 and 13 are recommended.

4) The listing includes details of which variables are included in the functions, and which functions are significant. There is also an option for listing the weighting coefficients in the discriminant functions.

CHAPTER 15

THE SEARCH FOR LATENT VARIABLES: FACTOR ANALYSIS

15.1 INTRODUCTION

Suppose that the subjects in a sample are each tested on several variables, perhaps an assortment of tests of intellectual ability, such as vocabulary, short term memory, reaction speed and so on. The correlations between performance on each of the tests and that on every other test in the battery can be arranged in a rectangular array known as a **correlation matrix**, or **R-matrix**. Each row (or column) of R would contain all the correlations involving one particular test in the battery. The cells along the **principal diagonal** (running from the top left to the bottom right of the matrix) would remain empty, since each cell on that diagonal represents the combination of a particular test with itself; but each off-diagonal cell would be occupied by the correlation between the tests whose row and column intersect at that particular cell. The R-matrix is the starting point for several statistical procedures, but in this chapter we shall consider just one: **factor analysis.**

The presence, in the R-matrix, of clusters of sizeable correlations among subsets of the tests in the battery would suggest that the tests in a subset may be measuring the same underlying psychological dimension, or ability. If the traditional British theories in the psychology of intelligence are correct, there should be fewer (far fewer) dimensions than there are tests in the battery. The purpose of factor analysis is to discern and to quantify the dimensions supposed to underlie performance on a variety of tasks. The **factors** produced by factor analysis are mathematical entities, which can be thought of as classificatory axes, with respect to which the tests in a battery can be "plotted". The assumption, however, is that the mathematical factors

192

represent **latent variables**, ie psychological dimensions, the nature of which can only be guessed at by examining the nature of tests that have sizeable coordinates on any particular axis. It should perhaps be said at the outset that this claim is controversial, and there are notable psychologists who hold that the factors of factor analysis are statistical realities, but psychological fictions.

The topic of factor analysis is not elementary, and the SPSS/PC+ output bristles with highly technical terms. If you are unfamiliar with factor analysis, we suggest you read the lucid texts by Kim and Mueller (1978a, 1978b) and by Tabachnick and Fidell (1989), which contain relatively painless introductions to most of the technical jargon.

15.1.1 Stages in factor analysis

A factor analysis usually takes place in three stages:

1)   A **matrix of correlation coefficients** is generated for all the variable combinations.

2)   From the correlation matrix, **factors** are extracted. The most common method is called **principal factors** (often wrongly referred to as **principal components** extraction, hence the abbreviation **PC**).

3)   The factors (or axes) are **rotated** to maximise the relationships between the variables and some of the factors. The most common method is **varimax**, which is a rotation method which maintains independence among the mathematical factors. Geometrically, this means that the axes remain **orthogonal**, ie they are kept at right angles, during rotation.

A fourth stage can be added at which the scores of each subject on each of the factors emerging from the analysis are calculated. It should be stressed that these **factor scores** are not the results of any actual test taken by the subjects: they are estimates of the subjects' standing on the **supposed** latent variables that have emerged as mathematical axes from the factor analysis of the data set. Factor scores are very useful, however, because they can subsequently be used as input for further statistical analysis.

It is advisable to carry out only stage 1 initially, in order to be able to examine the correlation coefficients in the correlation matrix R. Since the purpose of the analysis is to link variables together into factors, those variables must be related to one another and therefore have correlation coefficients larger than about 0.3. Should any variables show no substantial correlation with any of the others, they would be removed from R in subsequent analysis. It is also prudent to check that the correlation matrix does not possess the highly undesirable properties of **multicollinearity** and **singularity**. The former is the condition where the variables are very highly (though imperfectly) correlated; the latter arises when some of the variables are exact linear functions of others in the battery, as when the variable C is constructed by adding together the subjects' scores on variables A and B. Should either multicollinearity or singularity be present, it would be necessary to drop some of the variables from the analysis.

15.2 A FACTOR ANALYSIS OF DATA ON SEVEN VARIABLES

Suppose a researcher has available the scores, on seven variables, of 120 applicants for a place on a course on cartography. In order to identify the psychological dimensions tapped by the seven variables, it is decided to perform a factor analysis on the correlation matrix. The variable set comprised the following tests: Mapping; Engineering; Spatial ability; Mathematics; English; Art; Intelligence.

15.2.1 The commands for the correlation matrix

Factor analysis operates upon the values in a correlation matrix. If a matrix is already available, move to section 15.2.5, headed **Using a correlation matrix as input for factor analysis**. If a matrix has not yet been constructed, the command begins with the correlation program.

Step 1

Write the **DATA LIST** command (Chapter 3). The appropriate section of the menu can be found by either (a) typing DATA LIST on the scratch pad and pressing **[Esc]**, or (b) moving down the MAIN MENU to **read or write data**, rightwards into the **read or write data menu**, down to **DATA LIST**, and pressing ↵ to paste DATA LIST on the scratch pad.

Since the data are extensive, it is advisable to use the fixed-column format and to store the data in a separate data file (see **Entering Data from a Data File** in Chapter 3, section 3.6).

The command for reading the data file (assuming that the data are in a file called A:APPLICNT.DAT) and printing the column locations of the subjects (case numbers) and the values of the variables is as follows:

DATA LIST FILE 'A:APPLICNT.DAT' TABLE / caseno 1-3 mapping 5-6 engineer 8-9
    spacerel 11-12 maths 14-15 english 17-18 artwork 19-20 intellig 22-24.

The variable names can be amplified, if desired, by means of the **VARIABLE LABELS** command.

Step 2 (optional)

Enter the **missing values** code. Any missing values can be identified by including the **MISSING VALUES** command. When the data were transcribed into the data file, any missing values were entered as -9 to distinguish them from the actual data, which were all positive. The MISSING VALUES command thus specifies the value of -9:

MISSING VALUES mapping engineer spacerel maths english artwork intellig (-9).

Step 3

Execute these data commands by moving the cursor up to DATA LIST, pressing **[F10]** and ⌐ . This provides a check that the commands have been correctly written and that the data can be found. It also allows SPSS/PC+ to generate a table of variable names for pasting into subsequent commands.

Step 4

Save the R matrix. In order to save the matrix of correlation coefficients to a named file (A:CORRMATR.MAT) for subsequent input to the factor analysis part of the exercise, give the **SET/RESULTS** command thus:

SET/RESULTS 'A:CORRMATR.MAT'.

Step 5 (optional)

Obtain some statistics. It is useful to display the means, standard deviations, largest and smallest values, and the number of cases used for each variable by means of the **DESCRIPTIVES** command, in the **descriptive statistics** menu:

DESCRIPTIVES VARIABLES mapping TO intellig.

Step 6

Find **CORRELATIONS** in the menu via **analyze data** and **correlation and regression**, and press ⌐ to paste CORRELATIONS on the scratch pad. (Alternatively, type CORRELATIONS on the scratch pad and press **[Esc]** to obtain the CORRELATIONS menu.)

Read the examples, move down to /**VARIABLES**, press ⌐ , and either select each variable in turn from the table of variable names, or select *mapping* followed by TO followed by *intellig*, pressing ⌐ each time, to paste them on the scratch pad. Press **[Esc]** to remove the table of variable names.

Finally, move down to **/OPTIONS**, press ↵ , and then select 4 (if 4 is not available in the menu, press **[Alt]/X** to turn on the extended menus, which include option 4). This option writes the matrix of correlation coefficients into the file previously named in the SET/RESULTS command:

CORRELATIONS/VARIABLES mapping TO intellig /OPTIONS 4.

Step 7

Save the commands on the scratch pad to a named file on the floppy disk by using **[F9]** (Chapter 2, section 2.5.3) and then execute the remaining commands by moving the cursor up to **SET/RESULTS**, pressing **[F10]**, and then ↵ .

15.2.2 The listing of the correlation matrix

The listing on the screen will include the descriptive statistics for each variable as, requested in the DESCRIPTIVES command, followed by a table of correlations with the significant ones flagged by either one or two asterisks, indicating the 0.01 (1%) and 0.001 (0.1%) levels of significance respectively (not the more usual 0.05 and 0.01).

	MAPPING	ENGINEER	SPACEREL	MATHS	ENGLISH	ARTWORK	INTELLIG
MAPPING	1.0000	.3823**	.6502**	.5175**	.2384*	.5432**	.4554**
ENGINEER	.3823	1.0000	.4083**	.6556**	.3587*	.3530*	.6220**
SPACEREL	.6502	.4083**	1.0000	.4419**	.1554	.7222**	.5444**
MATHS	.5175	.6556**	.4419**	1.0000	.4117**	.2302*	.6572**
ENGLISH	.2384	.3587*	.1554	.4117**	1.0000	.1990	.5435**
ARTWORK	.5432	.3530*	.7222**	.2302*	.1990	1.0000	.3555*
INTELLIG	.4554	.6220**	.5444**	.6572**	.5435**	.3555*	1.0000

N of cases: 106   1-tailed Signif: * - .01   ** - .001

Since most of correlation coefficients are larger than 0.3, it is reasonable to continue directly to the factor analysis stage by adding further commands, as described overleaf.

15.2.3 The commands for factor analysis

Step 1

Write a DATA LIST command. Another **DATA LIST** command has to be prepared in order to read the correlation coefficient matrix from the file A:CORRMATR.MAT, nominated in the **SET/RESULTS** command of Step 4. Details are found in the DATA LIST menu when in the extended menu mode - press **[Alt]/X** if necessary. Both the file name and the keyword **MATRIX** are essential. The number of variable names must be identical to the number used in the CORRELATIONS command: it is easiest just to use the same variable names:

DATA LIST FILE 'A:CORRMATR.MAT' MATRIX /mapping engineer spacerel maths
     english artwork intellig.

Step 2

Execute this command with **[F10]** and ⏎ to check that the correlation matrix has been found and that the command has been correctly written. It also enables SPSS/PC+ to generate a table of variable names for pasting into subsequent commands.

Step 3

Find **FACTOR** in the **classification & clustering** menu (in **analyze data**) and press ⏎ to paste FACTOR on to the scratch pad. (Alternatively, type FACTOR on the scratch pad and press **[Esc]** to obtain the **FACTOR** menu in the upper window.)

Press ⏎ to paste **/VARIABLES** on the scratch pad, press ⏎ to select **ALL** from the table of variable names, and then **[Esc]** to remove the table.

The next subcommand ensures that SPSS/PC+ reads the data from the correlation matrix identified in the DATA LIST command. Details are only available in the extended menus: press **[Alt]/X** if you are not already in the extended menu mode. Move down to **overall specification**, press ⏎, move down to **/READ** and press ⏎. Ignore the next menu and return to the FACTOR menu with the ← cursor key. The command is thus:

FACTOR /VARIABLES ALL /READ.

Step 4 (optional subcommands)

If not all the variables specified in the DATA LIST command are needed for the factor analysis, the **/ANALYSIS** subcommand can be added, to specify the names of the variables to be included.

Other optional subcommands can be added but in default of those, the computer will perform a principal factors (or "principal components") analysis, followed by an orthogonal **varimax** rotation. Rotation is a procedure for transforming the original output of a factor analysis so that it is easier to interpret. Varimax is the most commonly used of the various methods available. For an explanation of rotation, see Kim & Mueller (1978a). Basically, varimax works by transforming the factor matrix so that the variables have higher loadings on some factors and lower loadings on others. As a result, each test can be accounted for in terms of fewer psychological dimensions.

A highly recommended subcommand is **/FORMAT SORT BLANK(.5)**, which has the effect of ordering the factor loadings by magnitude and of suppressing coefficients with values less than 0.5. It is explained in the **analysis details** item. The command is thus:

FACTOR /VARIABLES ALL /READ /FORMAT SORT BLANK(.5).

There are further subcommands which provide useful information : eg **/PRINT ALL** directs the computer to print all the optional statistics, including those testing for multicollinearity and singularity in the R matrix (see above); **/PLOT EIGEN** prints a special graph called a **scree plot**, showing the variance (expressed as an **eigenvalue**) associated with each factor. The syntax is as follows:

FACTOR /VARIABLES ALL /READ /FORMAT SORT BLANK (.05)
      /PRINT ALL/PLOT EIGEN .

Step 5

Save these commands to a named file on the floppy disk by using **[F9]** (Chapter 2) and then execute the FACTOR command by pressing **[F10]**, followed by ↵ .

15.2.4 The listing for factor analysis

If the FACTOR command does not include the optional subcommands /PLOT EIGEN and /PRINT ALL, the listing on the screen will include the following:

1) **A Table of Initial Statistics for Principal-Components Analysis**

Ignore the left side of the Table overleaf, which lists the variables and communalities and inspect the side to the right of the asterisks, which tabulates factors, their eigenvalues, the percent of variance attributable to each factor, and the cumulative variance for the factor and the previous factors. The program subsequently drops any factors with an eigenvalue of less than 1. (An **eigenvalue** is a measure of standardised variance with a mean of 0 and a standard deviation of 1. Because the variance that each standardised variable contributes to a principal components extraction is 1, a component with an eigenvalue of less than 1 is less important than an observed variable, and can therefore be ignored.)

Notice that the first factor accounts for 53.5% of the variance and the second factor for the next 17.8% of the variance. The remaining factors are insignificant.

- - - - F A C T O R   A N A L Y S I S - - - -

Analysis Number 1 Matrix input

Extraction 1 for Analysis 1, Principal-Components Analysis (PC)

Initial Statistics:

Variable	Communality	*	Factor	Eigenvalue	Pct of Var	Cum Pct
		*				
MAPPING	1.00000	*	1	3.74729	53.5	53.5
ENGINEER	1.00000	*	2	1.24631	17.8	71.3
SPACEREL	1.00000	*	3	.69026	9.9	81.2
MATHS	1.00000	*	4	.51557	7.4	88.6
ENGLISH	1.00000	*	5	.37527	5.4	93.9
ARTWORK	1.00000	*	6	.25189	3.6	97.5
INTELLIG	1.00000	*	7	.17341	2.5	100.0

2) A Table of Factor Loadings (called the Factor Matrix)

This table shows the relative importance of the various factors in accounting for the variance shared by each test with others in the battery. When the factors are orthogonal (ie uncorrelated with each other), these factor loadings are the correlation coefficients between the variables and the factors. Thus the higher the absolute value of the loading (which can never exceed a maximum of 1), the more the variable contributes to the factor.

Note that the gaps in the Table represent factor loadings with values less than 0.5, because the subcommand /FORMAT SORT BLANK(.5) suppresses these numbers, thereby making the table easier to read.

Factor Matrix:

	FACTOR 1	FACTOR 2
INTELLIG	.82646	
SPACEREL	.78189	
MATHS	.77898	
MAPPING	.75011	
ENGINEER	.74841	
ARTWORK	.66100	-.57320
ENGLISH	.53515	.53820

3) A Table of Final Statistics.

This table (below and overleaf) contains the **communalities**, which show how much of the variance in the variables has been accounted for by the two factors that have been extracted: for example, nearly 85% of the variance in Space Relations is accounted for, whereas only 57% of the variance in English is accounted for. The right side shows the two factors and their associated variances.

Final Statistics:

Variable	Communality	*	Factor	Eigenvalue	Pct of Var	Cum Pct
		*				
MAPPING	.67227	*	1	3.74729	53.5	53.5
ENGINEER	.64116	*	2	1.24631	17.8	71.3
SPACEREL	.84796	*				

Variable	Communality	
MATHS	.72114	*
ENGLISH	.57605	*
ARTWORK	.76549	*
INTELLIG	.76954	*

4) The Rotated Factor Matrix

This shows the effect of trying to simplify the previous Factor Matrix by minimising the number of factors on which variables have high loadings.

Now that Space Relations, Artwork, and Mapping are loaded substantially only on Factor 2 and Maths, English, and Engineering are loaded only on Factor 1, the matrix is much easier to interpret psychologically.

Varimax Rotation 1, Extraction 1,   Analysis 1 - Kaiser Normalization.

Varimax converged in 3 iterations.

Rotated Factor Matrix:

	FACTOR 1	FACTOR 2
INTELLIG	.80331	
MATHS	.79891	
ENGLISH	.75857	
ENGINEER	.74002	
SPACEREL		.89016
ARTWORK		.87046
MAPPING		.75527

5) A Factor Transformation Matrix

This matrix, not reproduced here, specifies the rotation applied to the factors, and for most purposes can be ignored.

If a fuller listing is requested with the optional subcommands /PLOT EIGEN and /PRINT ALL, a plot of the variances associated with each factor is drawn and extra tables printed, many of which are of a technical nature, and of little interest. However, some of the information conveyed can be of importance for deciding the efficacy and legitimacy of the analysis, as will be pointed out at the appropriate places.

6) Scree plot

The first extra item is the graph plotting the eigenvalues of all the factors. It is useful for deciding how many factors to retain. The point of interest is where the curve connecting the asterisks starts to flatten out. This region of the curve has been likened to the rubble or scree on a mountain side. The **scree test** halts factor extraction beyond the point at which the scree begins.

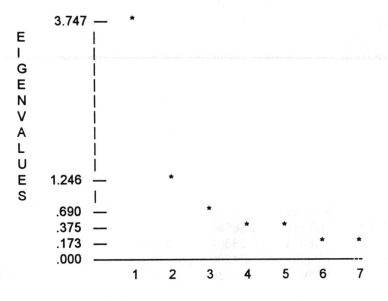

PC Extracted 2 factors.

It can be seen that the curve begins to flatten out between the second and third factors. Note also that Factor 3 has an eignevalue of less than 1. Only two factors should be retained.

7) Correlation matrix

The second extra item, which appears at the start of the listing, is a copy of the **correlation matrix** that was read in (though this time it is in lower triangular form), together with the value of its **determinant**. Provided the determinant is larger than 0.00001, the matrix can be assumed not to suffer from multicollinearity or singularity.

Analysis Number 1 Matrix input

Correlation Matrix:

	MAPPING	ENGINEER	SPACEREL	MATHS	ENGLISH	ARTWORK	INTELLIG
MAPPING	1.00000						
ENGINEER	.38235	1.00000					
SPACEREL	.65021	.40834	1.00000				
MATHS	.51753	.65564	.44193	1.00000			
ENGLISH	.23843	.35865	.15543	.41173	1.00000		
ARTWORK	.54324	.35296	.72224	.23023	.19899	1.00000	
INTELLIG	.45544	.62197	.54439	.65720	.54347	.35546	1 .00000

Determinant of Correlation Matrix = .0272442

8) Inverse of the correlation matrix and a measure of sampling adequacy

The third extra item is the **inverse of the correlation matrix**, followed by the **Kaiser-Meyer-Olkin (KMO) measure of sampling adequacy** (which should be greater than about 0.5 for a satisfactory factor analysis to proceed) and the **Bartlett test of sphericity**. If the Bartlett test is **not** significant (ie its associated probability is greater than 0.05), then there is the danger that the correlation matrix is an identity matrix (ie the diagonal elements are 1 and the off-diagonal elements are 0) and is therefore unsuitable for further analysis.

Inverse of Correlation Matrix:

	MAPPING	ENGINEER	SPACEREL	MATHS	ENGLISH	ARTWORK	INTEL-LIG
MAPPING	2.05713						
ENGINEER	.15270	2.10110					
SPACEREL	-.77680	.24257	3.29999				
MATHS	-.73726	-1.01779	-.37164	2.56993			
ENGLISH	-.07193	.07202	.68334	-.25864	1.57567		
ARTWORK	-.45324	-.53503	-1.70067	.71202	-.40451	2.45791	
INTELLIG	.07574	-.68849	-1.11618	-.63036	-.92661	.34323	2.79222

Kaiser-Meyer-Olkin Measure of Sampling Adequacy = .75155

Bartlett Test of Sphericity = 7.737E+09, Significance = .00000

9) Reproduced correlation matrix and residuals

The fourth extra item is the **reproduced correlation matrix** of coefficients, computed from the extracted factors. The elements of this matrix are subtracted from those of the original correlation matrix to produce a matrix of **residuals**, the properties of which indicate the adequacy of the factor model.

This table lists both the correlations and the residuals as explained beneath it. A good factor analysis should be a good fit; the computer lists the number of residuals (ie the differences) that are greater than 0.05.

Reproduced Correlation Matrix:

	MAPPING	ENGINEER	SPACEREL	MATHS	ENGLISH	ARTWORK	INTELLIG
MAPPING	.67227*	-.08479	-.09733	.04514	.01519	-.14235	-.06712
ENGINEER	.46714	.64116*	-.03835	-.02361	-.19508	.02145	-.08029
SPACEREL	.74754	.44669	.84796*	-.00269	-.00121	-.07341	.04126
MATHS	.47239	.67925	.44462	.72114*	-.18712	-.09087	-.08604
ENGLISH	.22324	.55373	.15664	.59885	.57605*	.15375	-.05711
ARTWORK	.68559	.33151	.79565	.32110	.04524	.76549*	-.02224
INTELLIG	.52256	.70226	.50313	.74324	.60058	.37770	.76954*

The lower left triangle contains the reproduced correlation matrix, with the communalities, marked with asterisks, along the principal diagonal. The upper right triangle contains the **residuals**, ie the differences between the observed correlations and the reproduced correlations.

There are 12 (57.0%) residuals (above diagonal) that are > 0.05

Sometimes what appears to be an unsatisfactory factor analysis can be saved by dropping a variable that correlates too highly with the others. A new analysis without the offending variable can easily be performed by inserting an /ANALYSIS subcommand specifying only the variables to be included. For example, *artwork* could be dropped by excluding it from the list of variables thus:

FACTOR /VARIABLES ALL /READ /FORMAT SORT BLANK (.05)
    /ANALYSIS mapping engineer spacerel maths english intellig
    /PRINT ALL /PLOT EIGEN.

15.2.4.1 SAVING THE LISTING TO A FILE

To save the listing to a named file on the floppy disk (essential if a print of the output is needed), add a **SET/LISTING** command at the head of the commands, and submit all the commands for re-execution (Chapter 2).

15.2.4.2 PRINTING THE LISTING AND COMMAND FILES

The instructions are given in Chapter 2 (section 2.6).

15.2.5 Typing in a correlation matrix as input for factor analysis

Sometimes it may be more convenient to type in correlation coefficients, rather than use a matrix generated by the **CORRELATIONS** program. This is easily done in the following steps:

Step 1

Write the **DATA LIST** command:

DATA LIST MATRIX FREE/*all the variable names*.

Step 2

Type on the scratch pad the value of n (ie the number of cases), using the following syntax (eg if n = 120):

n 120.

Step 3

Type on the scratch pad, in lower triangular form, the matrix of coefficients between the **BEGIN DATA** and **END DATA** commands. Note that each row must end with 1.0 :

BEGIN DATA.
1.0
.3824 1.0
.6502 .4083 1.0
.5175 .6556 .4419 1.0
END DATA.

Step 4

Write the FRACTOR command. This must include a subcommand directing SPSS/PC+ to read the data from a triangular correlation matrix:

FACTOR /VARIABLES ALL /READ CORRELATION TRIANGLE

Then other subcommands can be added, such as **/FORMAT SORT BLANK (.5)**, **/PRINT ALL**, and **/PLOT EIGEN**.

15.3 SUMMARY

1) **Factor analysis** is a set of techniques designed to account for the correlations among a set of variables in terms of relatively few underlying dimensions, or **factors**.

2) Several different kinds of factor analysis have been devised. The SPSS/PC+ package uses the **principal factors** method (which it terms **principal components** (PC)). The starting-point for a factor analysis is the **correlation matrix.**

3) The relationships between the variables and **some** of the factors are maximised by a process called **rotation**. The most common method of rotation is **varimax.**

4)   The command for factor analysis is of the form

        FACTOR/VARIABLES *variable names*

5)   Optional subcommands include **/ANALYSIS** for specifying a subset of variables to be used in the current analysis, **/PLOT EIGEN** for plotting the "scree slope" showing the variance accounted for by each factor, **/FORMAT SORT BLANK (.5)** for ordering the factor loadings by size and suppressing loadings with a value of less than 0.5 (thereby making the tables of factor loadings easier to read), and **/PRINT ALL** which lists a much fuller set of tables and includes various statistics for checking the advisability of conducting a factor analysis on the available data set.

EXERCISES

EXERCISE 1

INTRODUCTION TO SPSS/PC+

Those readers who are unfamiliar with a PC should read Chapter 1, in order to understand the underlined terms below. Often the user of a PC computer network must store, or <u>save</u> files on portable <u>floppy disks</u>, rather than the <u>hard disk</u> of the computer or the network's <u>file server</u>. The information in the files can then be recalled for use during later sessions on any PC. To be usable, a floppy disk must first be <u>formatted</u> (Section 1.4.2). From time to time, a disk becomes damaged or <u>corrupted</u> and the files on it cannot then be accessed. We suggest, therefore, that the user have available two formatted disks, so that files can be duplicated, or <u>backed up</u>, on a second disk. We assure you, this precaution is well worth the trouble: to lose several hours of painstaking work because a disk has become corrupted is a very nasty experience!

Whether or not you are familiar with a PC, it is essential that you read Chapter 2 of this book before you proceed with this practical.

<u>Starting up</u>

Since computers vary enormously in their start-up procedures, it is impossible to provide a set of details that would apply to any and every possible computing system. A general outline of a typical drill, however, is given in Section 1.4.1.

<u>Accessing SPSS/PC+</u>

Having entered the computer network, the user must now access the SPSS/PC+ package itself. Do this by following the instructions in Section 2.1.

<u>Getting acquainted with the menu and scratch pad</u>

Explore the menu and experiment with the scratch pad, as described in Sections 2.2 and 2.3.

<u>Using SPSS/PC+ : a short exercise</u>

Work through the miniature exercise in Section 2.4. This will give you the opportunity, before you finish this practical session, to see SPSS/PC+ actually doing something with a set of data.

<u>Terminating the SPSS/PC+ session</u>

Having completed the miniature data-processing exercise, move down the main menu to FINISH. Paste FINISH into the scratch pad by pressing ⏎ and leave SPSS/PC+ by pressing [F10], then ⏎ .

EXERCISE 2

DESCRIBING DATA AND SAVING THEM TO A FILE

There is the danger, now that it is so easy to command a computing package to perform all manner of statistical tests, that the user may be tempted to rush into formal testing straight away and fail to check for errors in data transcription or omit to ascertain whether the distribution of the data is such as to permit the use of the chosen tests. Several years ago, Tukey (1977) wrote a seminal book on the description and depiction of data sets by means of a series of techniques known as exploratory data analysis (EDA). These methods have now found their way into most good modern statistical computing packages, and the purpose of the present exercise is to demonstrate some of SPSS/PC+'s facilities for describing and exploring data. It is very important not to omit this preliminary exploratory phase from the processing of data, because the common practice of launching directly into a formal statistical analysis is fraught with pitfalls. Since the set of data for this exercise will also be used for Exercise 3, it is essential, before ending this session on SPSS/PC+, to save the data to a file on floppy disk: this move will save you much tedious re-typing of the same numbers when you come to Exercise 3.

The data

The data we are going to explore in this exercise might have been yielded by the following project. A team of investigators has good reason to believe that a small dosage of a certain drug increases the speed with which people can make decisions. They decide to try to confirm this by carrying out an experiment in which the decision times of 14 people who have ingested the drug are compared with those of a comparison, or control, group of 14 other people who have performed the task under a placebo condition. The experimenters expect that the decision times of the experimental group will tend to be shorter than those of the control group.

DRUG GROUP

Subject	Time	Subject	Time
1	471	2	494
3	386	4	323
5	660	6	406
7	345	8	425
9	421	10	407
11	386	12	550
13	470	14	393

CONTROL (PLACEBO) GROUP

Subject	Time	Subject	Time
15	446	16	749
17	599	18	460
19	390	20	477
21	556	22	440
23	471	24	501
25	492	26	392
27	578	28	398

Procedure

1) Getting started

Enter your network and access SPSS/PC+ in the manner appropriate for your local set-up (see Exercise 1).

2) Entering data into SPSS/PC+

At this point, it is essential to be clear about the terms variable and value. A variable is some characteristic or property of a person or a situation. It may be a set of related categories or conditions: in the present exercise, the Drug and Control conditions comprise what could be called the Treatment variable. It may also be the set of possible values for a measurement, such as height, weight or IQ. A particular condition, category or measurement is a value of the variable concerned: the category Control is a value of the variable Treatment; the value 75 kg is a value of the variable Weight. When a variable comprises a number of categories, it is useful to denote these by code numbers. In the present study, the code number 1 could denote the Drug condition and 2 could be the Control. The entire set of code numbers is a grouping variable.

In psychological research, one variable, known as the independent variable, is hypothesised to affect the values of another, known as dependent variable. Usually, grouping variables are codes for independent variables and the dependent variable is a set of measurements, or scores, of some kind. In the present example, the independent variable is the Treatment, comprising the values Drug and Control; and the dependent variable is the time taken by a subject to perform the task.

It is important to note that an SPSS/PC+ data set does not take quite the same form as a typical table of experimental results, such as those of the imaginary experiment of the present exercise. An SPSS/PC+ data set must always take the form of a set of columns of values (usually these are numbers, but sometimes they can be letters), each column representing a variable and each row representing only one subject, or case.

Thus in this experiment, the first column of the data set will represent the grouping variable (ie the type of treatment - drug or placebo) and might be given the variable name group. The second column will represent all the subjects' scores on the dependent variable and might be given the variable name score. Notice that this second column will include the scores for both treatments - the first column, which represents the type of treatment, will be used by the computer to distinguish whether a score in the second column belongs to the drug group or to the placebo group.

The reconstructed data for entering into SPSS/PC+ will be of the form shown on the next page:

group	score
1	471
1	494
1	386
.	.
1	393
2	446
2	749
.	.
2	398

The value for *group* changes to 2 from subject 15 onwards.

You will also have to decide upon the arrangement, or format, that the data will take when entered into the system. Will the numbers be typed in freefield format or in fixed-column format (Section 3.2.3)? In this series of exercises, all of which involve miniature data sets, we recommend that you use freefield format; but with larger data sets, especially when some of the numbers are given to several places of decimals, it is much safer to use fixed-column format.

These (and other points) are illustrated by the example in Section 3.5.1, which should serve as a model when you come to prepare the present data set.

3) Writing the DATA LIST command

The next step is to prepare the DATA LIST command (Sections 3.3 and 3.4). Find DATA LIST in the Menu and paste the words DATA LIST on the scratch pad by highlighting them and pressing ↵.

As a general rule when working with SPSS/PC+, it is good practice to store the data in a separate file on floppy disk, as described in Section 2.5.3. In that procedure, before anything else is written, the data are typed into the empty scratch pad and saved to a named data file (such as A:scores.DAT). Once this has been done, there is no need to type the data into the scratch pad again: it will only be necessary to name the file in the DATA LIST command, as shown in Section 3.6. For this exercise, however, we think it may clarify some aspects of the DATA LIST command if the data are included among the data commands, rather than being stored away in their own file.

Accordingly, the next step in preparing the DATA LIST command is to highlight FREE/ in the menu and press ↵ to paste the beginning of the DATA LIST command into the scratch pad. The DATA LIST command now reads

DATA LIST FREE/

Read about variables by moving the cursor down through each of the items in the FREE/ menu, then move back up the menu to **variables** and press ↵. A box will appear in the middle of the screen: type in the variable names you have chosen, and press ↵ again. The command is now (depending on the variable names you selected)

DATA LIST FREE/ group score.

Ensure that there is a full stop at the end to indicate that the command has been completed. The full stop is essential. If there is no stop, return to the scratch pad with [Alt]/E and type one in.

4) Typing in the data

Before the data are typed in, they must be preceded by the command BEGIN DATA and followed by the command END DATA, each of these ending (as in all commands except FINISH) with a full stop. Type in the data, as described in Section 3.5, by returning to the **read or write data** menu with two presses of the ← cursor key, moving down to BEGIN DATA, and pressing ↵. This will result in BEGIN DATA and END DATA appearing on the scratch pad separated by an empty line, in which the cursor is blinking to indicate where the data have to be typed in. Type in the data, remembering that they must be entered in the order in which the variables are named in the DATA LIST command. Hence if the order of the variables in the DATA LIST command was *group score*, SPSS/PC+ will assume that the first number given is a value for *group* (the grouping variable), and the second is a *score* (the dependent variable). The data are therefore typed in the scratch pad in pairs, pressing ⏎ to move the cursor to the next row until the end of the final pair of data, when [Esc] is pressed. The cursor will then jump to just beyond the END DATA command. The beginning and end of the data will be:

```
BEGIN DATA.
1 471
1 494
1 386
   .   .

   .   .
 2  398
END DATA.
```

{Although we have referred to two columns of values for two variables, it is permissible to type the data across rows in pairs, starting a new row with ⏎ when necessary. This saves space, but it makes the data less easy to check against the original experimental data.}

5)   Using the VARIABLE LABELS and VALUE LABELS commands to clarify the output

There are two useful commands, whose purpose is to clarify the output, or listing, that results from the execution of SPSS/PC+ commands. The two commands are VARIABLE LABELS and VALUE LABELS. Both are fully described in Section 3.7, which we recommend you to review now. Compare the syntaxes of the two commands, noting that in VALUE LABELS (but not in VARIABLE LABELS) the information about different variables is separated by a slash (/).

However self-explanatory the names *score* and *group* might appear just now, while the experiment is still fresh in your mind, such labels can seem very opaque indeed when an output listing is reviewed later. Accordingly, the VARIABLE LABELS command should always be used to amplify the rather cryptic variable names given in DATA LIST.

Usually we recommend that, rather than writing commands into the scratch pad directly, you use the menus to paste them in. With the commands VARIABLE LABELS and VALUE LABELS, however, the pasting procedure is extremely tiresome and we strongly recommend that you get into write mode with [Alt]/E and type them into the scratch pad directly. In the present exercise, an appropriate wording of the VARIABLE LABELS command is as follows, assuming that the variable names *group* and *score* were used in the DATA LIST command:

VARIABLE LABELS group 'Treatment Condition' score 'Decision Time'.

The VALUE LABELS command will enable you, at a later point, to identify which results were obtained under the Drug condition and which under the Placebo. The command will appear as follows, assuming that the variable name *group* was used in the DATA LIST command:

VALUE LABELS group 1 'Drug' 2 'Placebo'.

(Note that had the values been letters, rather than numbers, they too would have required quotes. Note also that had the experiment been more complex, with another grouping variable, the instructions to assign labels to the values of the second variable would have been preceded by a slash (/).)

6)   Saving the data commands to a file on floppy disk

We strongly recommend that, before continuing, you save the data commands, which include DATA LIST, BEGIN DATA, the data themselves, END DATA, VARIABLE LABELS and VALUE LABELS and, possibly, a MISSING VALUES command also. This ensures that if for any reason you should lose everything that was written on the scratch pad (which is quite possible), you would have a back-up copy of its contents which you could quickly restore. Store the data commands to a named file by using the [F9] function key and type in a file name, as described in Section 2.5.3.

7)   Executing the data commands

Execute the data commands (Section 2.4.2 or 4.2.1) by moving the cursor up to the first line, pressing [F10] and then ⏎. This allows you to check for any errors in syntax. But it has the additional advantage of enabling

SPSS/PC+ to create a table of variable names, from which selected items can be pasted into subsequent commands merely by highlighting them in the list and pressing ↵. If there are no errors, the screen will eventually return to the original display, with the Menu in the upper half of the screen and the scratch pad below. Should there be any errors, (and most people make at least one or two when they first attempt to write commands), correct them as described in Section 4.2.2, resave the corrected commands to the same file using [F9], and re-execute them to ensure that all the errors have been corrected.

The practice of executing the data commands first has a third advantage. When further commands are added to the list on the scratchpad, they can be executed by placing the cursor on the line of the latest command, pressing [F10] and then ↵. This has the effect of obtaining the output listing for that command alone, rather than the unwanted listing from all previous commands.

8) Exploring the data: the MEANS and EXAMINE commands

When presented with a set of experimental results, the first thing we shall want is a table of means and standard deviations. This is readily obtained by giving the MEANS command. The MEANS command is in the **descriptive statistics** menu. Note, however, that this command cannot be used with variables that have not been categorised by a grouping variable. Here we do have a grouping variable (*group*), so the MEANS command can be used.

Press [Alt]/E and type MEANS on the scratch pad. Press [Esc] to get the MEANS menu to appear. Press ↵ to paste /TABLES. Read the examples, move down to **dependent variable**, press ↵, move along the table of variables to *score* (or whatever name you used), press ↵, and then [Esc]. Move down to the keyword **BY**, press ↵, move down to **independent variable**, press ↵, select *group* (or whatever name you used), press ↵ and finally press the period (.). This completes the MEANS command. If you have followed the foregoing procedure correctly, the MEANS command should appear similar to the following:

MEANS/TABLES score BY group.

Save the new command to the command file on floppy disk (using the [F9] procedure), move the cursor to the MEANS command and execute with [F10], then ↵.

- Examine the table of means and SDs. Write down their values. Do the results confirm the researchers' hypothesis?

Useful as it is, the MEANS output listing omits much important information. For example, it gives no indication of the manner in which the data are distributed; nor does it warn of the presence of outliers. What is needed is a command that will yield more detailed information, permitting a much closer inspection of the data. The EXAMINE command will achieve this.

Type EXAMINE into the scratch pad and press [Esc]. Read the examples, move down to /VARIABLES and press ↵. Press ↵ again when **variable(s)** appears. Notice that the table of variable names appears at the top of the screen. At the right hand end should be the names that you specified in the DATA LIST command: *score* and *group*. Move the highlighting along to the dependent variable *score*, press ↵ and then [Esc] to remove the table of variables.

Move down the menu to the keyword **BY**, press ↵, move the highlighting along to the independent variable *group* in the table of variables, press ↵, and then [Esc]. This concludes the entry of variables for the EXAMINE command.

You will now need to fine-tune the EXAMINE command by selecting appropriate subcommands. A percentile is the value below which a specified proportion of the distribution lies: for example, 50% lies below the 50th percentile; and 75% lies below the 75th percentile. (The median is the 50th percentile.) We suggest you use subcommands to request percentiles and various plotting options. Return to the EXAMINE menu with the ← cursor key and then down to /PERCENTILES. Press ↵ and when ( ) appears, press ↵ again and type the percentiles you want in the box (do not use any punctuation). We suggest you type 25 50 75 (thus requesting the 25th, 50th and 75th percentiles) and then press ↵ to paste these numbers into the scratch pad.

Return to the EXAMINE menu with the ← cursor key and move down to /PLOT. Press ↵ and when STEMLEAF appears, press ↵ again. Move down to BOXPLOT and press ↵. Move down to HISTOGRAM and press ↵. These subcommands will produce stem-and-leaf diagrams, boxplots and a horizontal histogram (further details are given in Section 4.4.1). This completes the EXAMINE command. Make sure there is a full stop at the end (if necessary, press [Alt]/E and type one in).

If you have responded correctly to the prompts from the menu, the EXAMINE command will appear as follows:

EXAMINE/VARIABLES score BY group /PERCENTILES (25 50 75) /PLOT STEMLEAF BOXPLOT HISTOGRAM.

Resave the extended set of commands by using [F9] and the same file name, and then execute the new command by entering the scratch pad using [Alt]/E, moving the cursor up to the EXAMINE command, pressing [F10] and then ↵. Correct any errors if necessary, and resave.

The listing starts with descriptive statistics, the various plots and percentiles for all the cases combined across all the categories of the independent variable. It then examines the dependent variable split into each group specified by the independent variable - ie the drug group and the placebo group - concluding with side-by-side box plots comparing the groups. Further details about the plots are given in Section 4.4.1.

When there is a marked discrepancy between the mean and median of a set of scores, it may be that the distribution is skewed or otherwise asymmetrical. Atypical scores, or outliers can also pull the value of the mean away from that of the median. The listing from EXAMINE includes the mean and median.

- In the output listing for the EXAMINE command, is there any indication that the mean is unrepresentative of the general level in either group of scores?

9) Printing the listing

If you want to print out the listing, you must re-execute all the commands after inserting a SET/LISTING command on the very first line (see Section 2.5.6). The printing routine will depend upon your local set-up.

10) Finishing the session

Terminate the SPSS/PC+ session by running the FINISH command.

Appendix to Exercise 2

When data have not been categorised by a grouping variable (or you want to ignore the categorisation), the means and standard deviations of dependent variables are most easily found with the DESCRIPTIVES command - see Section 4.4. For example, the following command would list the mean and standard deviation for the dependent variable *score* in this exercise across both categories of the coding variable:

DESCRIPTIVES/VARIABLES score.

EXERCISE 3

COMPARING THE AVERAGES OF TWO INDEPENDENT SAMPLES

Before proceeding with this exercise, we suggest you read Sections 6.1 and 6.2 carefully, noting especially the table at the top of page 75. This exercise concerns the independent samples t-test (Section 6.4) and the non-parametric alternative known as the Mann-Whitney test.

The data from Exercise 2 will be used again for the present exercise. In Experiment 2, the subjects were randomly assigned to either the Drug or the Placebo condition. Their scores, therefore, are two independent samples of true measurements on a scale with units. Provided the distributions of the scores are appropriate, the independent samples t-test can be used to test the null hypothesis of no difference (in the population) between the means of the Drug and Control groups.

The t-test is an example of a <u>parametric test</u>: that is, it makes certain assumptions about the populations from which the samples have supposedly been drawn. It is assumed, for example, that the populations are normal, and that they have the same variance. When a data set is examined (by the methods of Exercise 2), it is often quite clear that neither the assumption of normality of distribution nor that of homogeneity of variance is tenable. This can mean that the tail probability, or p-value, given in the t-test output is misleading. One solution to this problem is to use a non-parametric test, a method which makes fewer assumptions about the population distributions. Later in this exercise, we shall use a non-parametric text, the Mann-Whitney, to compare the averages (medians) of the Drug and Placebo groups.

Procedure

1)   Entering the data

If you worked through Exercise 2 and stored the data commands (and the data themselves) to a file on floppy disk, the data (and the commands) can easily be restored to SPSS/PC+. Otherwise, the data of Exercise 2 must be typed into the scratch pad as described in Exercise 2.

2)   Exploring the data

Before any formal statistical tests are carried out, it is essential to explore the data to examine their distribution. Markedly atypical scores, or <u>outliers</u>, can also be detected at this stage. In this case, however, the data have already been thoroughly explored. In the previous exercise, it was found that both samples had practically identical variances (ie their standard deviations had very similar values) and the various plots (boxplots, stem-and-leaf diagrams, and histograms) indicated that the distributions were such as to permit the use of a parametric test. The only untoward finding was that one of the subjects in the Placebo group had a score of 749, which is highly atypical of the group as a whole.

3)   Reading the command file from Exercise 2 into the scratch pad

Full instructions for restoring a file's contents to the scratch pad are given Section 2.5.5. The sequence is: press [F1]; press ↵; press [F3]; select the **Insert file** option by pressing I; in the box after **File to insert**, type the file name under which you saved the commands you wrote in Exercise 2 (eg A: examine.CMD); press ↵ and the commands (and data) should then appear on the screen in the scratch pad.

Among the commands now in the scratch pad, however, are several that will not be required for the present exercise. These must now be deleted. Move the cursor down to the MEANS command and delete all the remaining lines of the file from there down, using the [F7] and [F8] keys, as described in Sections 2.3.1 and 2.3.2. You should then have only the data commands (DATA LIST, BEGIN DATA, the data themselves, END DATA, VARIABLE LABELS, VALUE LABELS), and possibly a SET/LISTING command as well, remaining on the scratch pad. If you do have a SET/LISTING command at the top of the file, remove it now.

4)   Executing the data commands

Move the cursor up to the first line of the commands, press [F10], and then ↵. Later, this will make available a list of variable names for pasting and allow subsequent commands to be executed independently.

5)   Preparing and executing the T-TEST command

When preparing commands by using the menu to paste them into the scratch pad, you may find the following tip helpful: When, in the SPSS/PC+ menus, you come across an item in upper case, paste the word (or words) into the scratch pad by pressing the ↵ key. Some items, however, as well as being printed in upper case, are preceded by an exclamation mark (!). This is an indication that you are about to be requested to supply variable names or values. When the ↵ key is pressed, an appropriate prompt will appear. To make sure that you respond to such prompts correctly, always study the examples given in the opposite panel of the menu.

Full details of the preparation of the independent t-test are given in Section 6.4.1. Start at Step 4 to prepare the

T-TEST command, and then follow Step 5, thereby performing the t-test and saving all the commands to a file on floppy disk. The command is:

T-TEST/GROUPS group(1,2) /VARIABLES score.

6) The listing for the independent samples t-test

Guidance on how to interpret the listing is given in Section 6.4.2. We suggest you study that section and try to answer the following questions.

- Write down the value of t and its tail probability. Is the p-value evidence against the null hypothesis? Remember that if the result is sufficiently unlikely (ie $p < 0.05$) under the null hypothesis, it is regarded as evidence against the null hypothesis and hence in favour of the experimental hypothesis. Write down your interpretation of the result of the test: has the t-test confirmed the pattern shown by the means of the two groups?

7) A non-parametric method: The Mann-Whitney test

When there are serious violations of the distribution assumptions of the t-test, a non-parametric test should be considered. When there are two independent samples of scores, the Mann-Whitney test can be used to compare the averages of the two groups. It should be noted, however, that whereas in the parametric test the null hypothesis stated that the two population means are equal, the non-parametric test concerns medians, not means: specifically, in the Mann-Whitney test, the null hypothesis states that the population medians are equal.

To prepare the command for the Mann-Whitney test, return to the **analyze data** menu (by pressing [Esc] several times to get back to the MAIN MENU and then moving down to **analyze data**). In the **analyze data** menu, find the item labelled **other,** move rightwards to obtain the menu, select NPAR TESTS and press ↵ to paste NPAR TESTS into the scratch pad.

Going through the above procedure helps familiarise the user with the menus. Later, however, it will be found much simpler to get into write mode with [Alt]/E, type in the command NPAR TESTS and press [Esc]. This will obtain the NPAR TESTS menu directly.

Find /MANN-WHITNEY by moving down the NPAR TESTS menu. (Since the MANN-WHITNEY item is near the bottom of the list, it will be out of sight initially.) Press ↵ to paste /MANN-WHITNEY into the scratch pad. Complete the details about the (dependent) variable name and the grouping variable. The command is:

NPAR TESTS/MANN-WHITNEY score BY group(1,2).

Execute the command in the usual manner. The Mann-Whitney listing tabulates values for the statistics U and W (the W statistic belongs to a test by Wilcoxon which is the exact equivalent of the Mann-Whitney), followed by an exact 2-tailed probability value, and then a standard normal deviate score Z and a 2-tailed probability value corrected for ties. If this p-value is less than 0.05, the null hypothesis can be rejected and the groups declared to differ significantly.

- Write down the results of the Mann-Whitney test, including the value of U and its p-value. State whether the result is significant. (If so, you could write, 'The Mann-Whitney test showed a significant difference between the two medians (U = so-&-so; p = so-&-so)' .) State whether the Mann-Whitney test confirms the result of the t-test. In what circumstances would you expect the p-values of U and t to differ? Compare the results of the Mann-Whitney and t-tests in the present example and comment on your findings.

8) Saving the listing and finishing the session

If a printed listing is required, add a SET/LISTING command at the head of the other commands on the scratch pad. The command is:

SET/LISTING 'A:indttest.LIS'.

Execute all the commands again. Finish the session by running the FINISH command and logging out of the network in the usual way.

EXERCISE 4

COMPARING THE AVERAGES OF TWO SAMPLES: PAIRED DATA

The methods described in the previous exercise, ie the independent t-test and the Mann-Whitney test, are appropriate for data from a <u>between subjects experiment</u>, that is, one with independent samples of subjects in the two groups. Suppose, however, that the data had come from an experiment in which the same subjects had been tested under both the experimental and control conditions. Such a <u>within subjects experiment</u> would yield a set of paired (or correlated) data. In this exercise, we shall consider some methods for comparing the averages of the scores obtained under the experimental and control conditions when we have a set of paired data, rather than independent samples. Before proceeding with this exercise, the reader may wish to review the material in Section 6.2.2.

The data

In an experiment investigating the relative ease with which words presented in the left and right visual fields are recognised, subjects were instructed to fixate a spot in the centre of the field and were told that, after a short interval, a word would appear to the left or the right of the spot and they were to press a key as soon as they recognised it. In the trials that followed, each word was presented an equal number of times in each field, though the order of presentation of the words was, of course, randomised. From the results, the following table of median decision times was constructed from the subjects' reactions to presentations of 40 words in each of the two visual fields:

Subject	Right visual field	Left visual field
1	323	324
2	493	512
3	502	503
4	376	385
5	428	453
6	343	345
7	523	543
8	439	442
9	682	683
10	703	998
11	598	600
12	456	462
13	653	704
14	652	653

Do these data support the experimental hypothesis that there is a difference between the response times for words in the left and right visual fields?

In the paired t-test, the strategy is to subtract (consistently) either the first or the second member of each pair of scores from the other, producing a single column of <u>difference scores</u>. If there is, in the population, no difference between the mean scores for the right and left visual fields, the mean difference will also be zero. The null hypothesis to be tested states that our 14 difference scores are a sample from a population with a mean of zero and a variance which can be estimated from the difference scores in the sample. If we can assume that the population of differences is normally distributed, the null hypothesis can be tested with the statistic t, where

t = [mean difference] / [standard error of the difference]

and

[standard error of the difference] = [standard deviation of the differences] / $\sqrt{n}$,

where n is the number of subjects. This t statistic has (n-1) degrees of freedom. (In the present example, df = 13.)

The making of a one-sample t-test presupposes that the difference scores are normally distributed. Should it turn out from preliminary inspection of the data, however, that the differences are far from being normally distributed, or that there are huge outliers, the user must beware of the t-test, especially with a small data set, such as the present one, and should consider using a test that makes fewer assumptions about the data. For sets of paired data showing contraindications against the use of the related t-test, there are two non-parametric tests, neither of which assumes normality of the population distribution:

(1)   the Wilcoxon matched pairs test;
(2)   the Sign test.

The latter is the more resistant to the leverage exerted by outliers; but, provided there are no outliers, the Wilcoxon is the more powerful test. (On the other hand, there are those who would say that if the data are good enough for the Wilcoxon, they are good enough for the related t-test.)

Procedure

Before proceeding with this exercise, we strongly urge you to read Section 6.3, which describes the procedure for a paired t-test.

1)   Preparating the data for entry

SPSS/PC+ expects a column of values for each variable in the data set. In the data set for the independent t-test, one of the variables must be a grouping variable, showing which subjects performed under which conditions. With the related samples t-test, however, since the data are paired, there is no need for a grouping variable. It is convenient to think of the paired data being stored in SPSS/PC+ as two columns, one headed, say, *rvf* (Right Visual Field), the other *lvf* (Left Visual Field). Since, however, this would take up many rows in the scratch pad, it is more practical to enter several pairs of data on each line, taking a new line when necessary. As usual, we suggest that free format will suffice for the miniature data set of the present exercise.

2)   Preparing the DATA LIST command

The next step is to prepare the DATA LIST command (Sections 3.3 and 3.4). The command is:

DATA LIST FREE/ rvf lvf.

3)   Entering the data

Type in the data between the BEGIN DATA and END DATA commands, as described in Section 3.5. Remember that the data must be entered in pairs, in the order in which the chosen variable names appear in the DATA LIST command. So of the first four numbers typed, SPSS/PC+ will assume that the first and the third are values of *rvf* and the second and fourth are values of *lvf*, assuming the DATA LIST command is as shown in 2.

4)   Clarifying the output: the VARIABLE LABELS command

Always include a VARIABLE LABELS command (Section 3.7). In this case, the command is:

VARIABLE LABELS rvf 'Right Visual Field' lvf 'Left Visual Field'.

Since, in this case, there are no grouping variables, the question of a VALUE LABELS command does not arise.

5)   Saving and executing the data commands

Save the data commands to a file on floppy disk in the usual way by using [F9]. Check for errors by pressing [F10] and ⏎ to execute the commands, if necessary correcting their wording until an error-free run is achieved. This will also have the advantage of making available at a later point a list of variable names for pasting operations.

6)   Exploring the data

Since the null hypothesis concerns only the population of differences (rather than the separate *rvf* and *lvf* populations), we first calculate the differences and see how those are distributed. It is a very simple matter to obtain the differences by using the COMPUTE command and following that with LIST, to have the differences displayed on the screen. Let *diffs* be the difference between *rvf* and *lvf*. The commands are as follows:

COMPUTE diffs=lvf - rvf.
LIST/ VARIABLES diffs.

Execute these new commands by moving the cursor up to COMPUTE, pressing [F10] and then ↵.

From inspection of the column of differences produced by the LIST command, it is quite clear that there is a glaring outlier. It is instructive to ascertain the effect of its presence upon the results of the one-sample t-test, in comparison with the non-parametric Wilcoxon and Sign tests.

7)   Preparing the related T-TEST command and plot

The details of the preparation of the command for a related t-test are given in Section 6.3.1. In the present example, the command is:

T-TEST/PAIRS rvf lvf.

Although, in the related samples t-test, the interest centres on the column of differences rather than the original scores, it is nevertheless of interest to see the scatterplot of *rvf* against *lvf*, which, ideally, should show an elliptical cloud of points indicating a bivariate normal distribution. The command for the scatterplot is:

PLOT/PLOT lvf WITH rvf.

Save and execute both commands in the usual way, with [F9] and [F10].

In Section 6.3.2, the interpretation of the listing for the related sample t-test is discussed at some length. We suggest that the reader study that section before proceeding.

From the details given in the listing, it is clear that there are contraindications against the use of the related-samples t-test for the data in the present experiment. There is marked discrepancy between the standard deviations of the scores obtained under the *rvf* and *lvf* conditions. This arises from the presence of a glaring outlier, which shows up dramatically in the scatterplot.

- • From the listing, write down the value of t and its p-value. Is t significant? Write down, in terms of the research hypothesis, the import of the result of the t-test. Have you any qualifications to add to your interpretation of t?

What has happened here? You should find the t-test result paradoxical to say the least. Each of the fourteen pairs of data (one pair from each subject) shows a difference in the same direction: the *rvf* time is always lower than the *lvf* time. Moreover, in the case of the outlying pair of scores, the difference is even greater. Surely this should strengthen the evidence against the null hypothesis? Yet, in fact, the t-test does not show significance. The reason is that the outlier has exerted more leverage upon the denominator of the t statistic than it has upon the numerator, thus reducing the value of t. The vulnerability of the standard deviation to the leverage exerted by outliers derives from the fact that the elements of the variance are the squares of deviations from the mean, and large deviations continue to exert disproportionate influence, even after the square root operation by which the standard deviation is derived from the variance.

As was mentioned at the end of item 6, one solution to the outlier problem is to use non-parametric tests. Another, which will be discussed later, is to eliminate the outlier (or outliers) altogether.

10)   Non-parametric tests for paired data

a)   The Sign test

This test is based very simply on how many positive and negative differences there are between pairs of data, assuming that the value of one variable is consistently subtracted from the value of the other. Thus in this example, if there is, in the population, no difference between the speeds with which people process words in the right and left visual fields, and we subtract the right column from the left (or vice versa), preserving only the sign of the difference (+ or -), then, as we progress down the column of signs, there should be as many pluses as minuses. If the pluses and minuses are thought of as the heads and tails in a series of coin tosses (with the probability (p) of a plus being 1/2 each time), it is clear that we have a set of Bernoulli trials, to which the binomial probability model is applicable with p = 1/2. The meanings of *Bernoulli trial* and *binomial probability model* are explained below.

Suppose a coin is tossed ten times. This can be viewed as a sequence of experiments of chance, that is, procedures with uncertain outcomes. At each stage, there are the same two mutually exclusive and exhaustive possibilities: Heads or Tails. The 10 trials are independent: that is, the outcome of no trial affects, or is affected by, the outcomes of any of the others. Finally, the probability of one of the dichotomous outcomes (and therefore that of the other) is fixed from trial to trial: if the coin is fair, the probability of Heads is 1/2 and remains so throughout the sequence. Trials with all these characteristics are known as Bernoulli trials. As another example, suppose a die is rolled ten times. If A is 'a six' and B is 'not a six', A and B are mutually exclusive and exhaustive events and the probability of A, which is 1/6, remains constant across the ten rolls of the die. The ten rolls of the die, therefore, like the ten tosses of the coin, qualify as a sequence of Bernoulli trials. The binomial probability model is applicable to a situation in which there are to be n Bernoulli trials. Let X be the number of heads in ten tosses of a coin. So X can have any of the values 0, 1, . . ., 10. The binomial model generates a formula which gives the probability of any of these values. It also enables one to obtain the probability of, say, 'at least 8 heads' (that is, 8, 9 or 10 heads), 'no heads' (all tails) and so on.

The Sign test is a straightforward application of the binomial model to paired data, such as the results of the visual field experiment above. To merely record the signs (rather than the magnitudes) of the differences between the times for the left and right visual fields is certainly to lose a considerable amount of information. Indeed, when paired data show no contraindications, the related t-test is preferable to the Sign test, for to use the latter in such circumstances would be to make a needless sacrifice of power. The great advantage of the Sign test, however, is its robustness to the influence of outliers. It makes only the assumption of Bernoulli trials and there are no requirements about bivariate normality or outliers in the original paired data.

Some information about the preparation of the command for the Sign test is given in Section 6.5. Get into write mode with [Alt]/E, type NPAR TESTS and press [Esc] to obtain the NPAR TESTS menu. Select the /SIGN item, and follow the prompts. The command on the scratch pad should appear as follows:

NPAR TESTS/SIGN=rvf lvf.

Save and execute this command in the usual way.

- Write down the results of the Sign test, including the p-value. Is the result significant? Compare this with the result of the paired-samples t-test and explain any discrepancy. What are the implications for the results of the experiment and the experimenter's hypothesis?

b)   The Wilcoxon matched pairs test

Now carry out the Wilcoxon matched pairs test. The command is as follows:

NPAR TESTS/WILCOXON rvf lvf.

- From the output for the /WILCOXON subcommand, write down the value of the statistic and its p-value. Compare the p-value with those for the t and Sign tests. Relate the result of the Wilcoxon test to the experimenter's scientific hypothesis.

You may have noticed that the p-value for the Wilcoxon test, though small, is not as small as the p-value for the Sign test. This is because although the Wilcoxon test is less sensitive to the presence of outliers than is the t-test, it is still affected by them to some extent.

10)   Eliminating the outliers

When there are contraindications for the paired t-test, the use of a non-parametric test is not the only alternative available. Another approach is to consider the possibility of eliminating some of the data. In the present set of paired data, there is one (lvf-rvf) difference which is much larger than all the others. This may have arisen because subject 10 had special difficulty in recognising words in the left visual field. At any rate, that subject's performance is quite atypical of this sample of participants and certainly calls into question the claim that he or she was drawn from the same population as the others. It is instructive to reanalyse the data after excluding the scores of Subject 10. This is done by using the SELECT IF command (see Section 4.5.2).

Move the cursor up the scratch pad to just under the E of END DATA and press ↵. Type in the following on the blank line created there:

SELECT IF (rvf NE 703).

This command selects all the data except the case whose *rvf* score is 703 (NE means *not equal to*).

Save all the commands as usual. Now execute SELECT IF and all subsequent commands to see what happens to the results of the t-test and the Sign test when the data from subject 10 have been omitted.

- • Examine the listing for the related samples t-test that has just been carried out on a data set from which the scores of subject 10 have been eliminated. Write down the value of t and its tail probability. Write down your interpretation of this new result. Similarly, give the statistics and their p-values for the Sign and Wilcoxon tests, commenting on the relative sizes of the p-values.

11) Storing and printing the listing

If a printed copy of the listing is required, add a SET/LISTING command (such as SET/LISTING 'A:ttestrel.LIS') at the top of all the commands and re-execute them all. Terminate the session in the usual way, with the FINISH command.

Appendix to Exercise 4

Some further uses of one-sample parametric and non-parametric tests

(Experience shows that the foregoing material is sufficient for one practical session. The following tests, however, are often useful and we recommend that you experiment with them in the near future.)

So far, we have been concerned with tests of the null hypothesis that, in the population, there is no difference between the averages of two correlated samples of data. There can arise, however, situations where one has a single sample of scores and wishes to test the null hypothesis that the sample has been drawn from a population with a specified mean, which may be other than zero.

The one-sample t-test

For example, suppose it is known that, over the years, the mean performance on a spelling test of children in a particular class at school is 51. One year, however, following the introduction of a new teaching method, there is reason to hope the standard of spelling may now be higher. The mean and standard deviation of the spelling scores of the children in that year's class are 60 and 11, respectively. Has the expectation of better spelling performance been borne out? The command for the one-sample t-test of the null hypothesis that the population mean has value 51 can be tested with the following commands, inserting the scores of the children as the data and using the COMPUTE command to specify the population mean as 51 for the new variable *mean*:

```
DATA LIST FREE/ spelling.
BEGIN DATA.
52 80 45 ... 61
END DATA.
COMPUTE mean = 51.
T-TEST /PAIRS spelling mean.
```

The binomial test on a single sequence of outcomes

So far the binomial model has been considered only in the context of the Sign test for a difference between the medians of correlated columns of paired data. The question also arises as to whether, given the outcomes of a series of Bernoulli trials, there is reason to reject the null hypothesis of chance performance.

There are two ways of entering the data for the binomial test: you can decide upon a code for right and wrong guesses, eg 1 for a correct answer, 0 for a wrong one and enter the person's performance as a series such as:

1 1 0 1 1 0 0 0 . . .

If we assume that there were only two choices for each question (ie the probability of a correct guess is 1/2 each time), the commands for the first method are as follows:

DATA LIST FREE/ fred.
BEGIN DATA.
1 1 0 1 1 0 0 0 . . .
END DATA.
NPAR TESTS/BINOMIAL=fred(0,1).

Alternatively, the data can be entered as the numbers of correct and incorrect answers that Fred produced (assuming he got 24 right and 21 wrong), and adding the **WEIGHT BY** command to instruct SPSS/PC+ to treat the values 24 and 21 as frequencies rather than scores:

DATA LIST FREE/ freq.
BEGIN DATA.
24 21
END DATA.
WEIGHT BY freq.
NPAR TESTS/BINOMIAL freq.

So far, the binomial test has assumed the default value of 0.5 for the proportion of cases expected in the first category (ie the probability p of a case falling into the first category). In most multiple-choice examinations, however, there are more than two choices per question. We need to be able to cope with situations where p is not 0.5. We need the general form of the /BINOMIAL subcommand, which is:

NPAR TESTS/BINOMIAL(*specified value of p*)=fred(0,1).

If there were four choices for each question, for example, the command would be:

NPAR TESTS/BINOMIAL(0.25)=fred(0,1).

If we want to use the WEIGHT BY method, the command is

NPAR TESTS/BINOMIAL(0.25)=freq.
WEIGHT BY freq.

In the former case, however, where the code numbers are given in the command, the data set is a series of coded outcomes of a number of Bernoulli trials; whereas in the latter, the data variable contains only two values, interpreted as frequencies.

EXERCISE 5

THE ANALYSIS OF NOMINAL DATA: THE CHI-SQUARE TEST

In the exercises so far, the data have related to characteristics that can be possessed in degree: one person may be taller than another; one day may be hotter than the next; one person may be slower than another. Height, temperature and time are all quantitative variables.

There are two kinds of data arising from research with quantitative variables: <u>scalar or interval data</u>, which are 'measurements' on an independent scale with units, such as a ruler, weighing scales or a clock; and <u>ranks</u>, or <u>ordinal data</u> as they are known. The latter, though relating to quantitative variables, do not comprise measurements on an independent scale: a group of people can be arranged in order of height; but the rank each person receives depends upon who else is in the group, which is not the case if their heights had been measured with a tape or a ruler.

Suppose, however, that a researcher, interested in children's preferences, suspects a spatial response bias towards the right hand side. Thirty children enter a room containing three identically-marked doors: one to the right; another to the left; and a third straight ahead. They are told they can go through any of the three doors. Their choices are as follows:

	DOOR	
Left	Middle	Right
5	8	17

The variable of 'Position' is <u>qualitative</u>, not quantitative: it cannot be possessed in degree. Position is a set of three qualitatively different categories, and the data in the table are tallies of the distribution of the 30 children among those three categories. Data relating to qualitative variables are known as <u>nominal</u> data.

It looks as if there is indeed a preference for the rightmost door, at least among the children sampled. Had the children been choosing at random, we should have expected about 10 in each category: that is, the theoretical, or <u>expected distribution</u> (E), of the tallies is a <u>uniform</u> one. The <u>observed frequencies</u> (O), on the other hand, have a distribution which is far from uniform.

In psychological terms, we want to know whether children tend to prefer the rightmost door. In statistical terms, we want to see whether the <u>theoretical distribution</u> is a <u>good fit</u> to the <u>observed distribution</u>: that is, are the discrepancies between the observed frequencies (O) and the expected frequencies (E) so great as to constitute evidence against the null hypothesis of uniformity of distribution?

Pearson's <u>chi-square test</u> can be used to test for the <u>goodness-of-fit</u> of the expected to the observed distribution. Its rationale is lucidly discussed in any good statistical textbook (eg Howell, 1992). Here, we shall merely describe how to command SPSS/PC+ to carry out the test.

5A) CHI-SQUARE TEST OF GOODNESS-OF-FIT

Procedure

1) <u>The DATA LIST command</u>

The data set must include a column containing code numbers for the categories and another containing the frequencies of children in each category. The DATA LIST command should appear similar to the following:

DATA LIST FREE/position freq.

2) <u>Entering the data</u>

Let us assign the code numbers 1, 2 and 3 to the categories Left, Centre and Right, respectively. Type in the data between the BEGIN DATA and END DATA commands, using a value for the coding variable followed by the frequency for each of the categories thus:

BEGIN DATA.
1 5 2 8 3 17
END DATA.

3)   The WEIGHT BY command

The WEIGHT BY command instructs SPSS/PC+ to read the values of the variable it names as category frequencies. In the present example, the command is:

WEIGHT BY freq.

4)   The VALUE LABELS command

Always include a VALUE LABELS command to allow the user to decode grouping variables in the listing. In the present example, the command is:

VALUE LABELS position 1 'Left' 2 'Centre' 3 'Right'.

Now save and execute the data commands.

5)   The NPAR TESTS command

Type NPAR TESTS on the scratch pad and press [Esc]. Find /CHISQUARE and press ⌐. Find the appropriate variable name in the table of variables (it is the name you used for the coding variable, not the frequencies, so it might be *position*) and press ⌐. This completes the command when the expected frequencies are equal, as they are in this example. (It is possible to enter unequal values of expected frequencies in the /EXPECTED subcommand.) Ensure that the command concludes with a period (.). The command is:

NPAR TESTS /CHISQUARE position.

Save all the commands to a file on floppy disk and execute the NPAR TESTS command.

- Write down the value of the chi-square statistic and its p-value. Does the test show significance, ie is the p-value sufficiently small to constitute evidence against the null hypothesis? Write down the implications for the experimenter's research hypothesis.

Appendix to Exercise 5A

When the researcher carried out the experiment, the door that each child chose was noted at the time. In terms of the code numbers, their choices might have been:

1 1 3 2 1 1 3 3 3 . . . and so on.

In that case, the variable *position* could contain the codes for the 30 choices that the children made, and the /CHISQUARE subcommand would be:

NPAR TESTS/CHISQUARE position.

When the data are entered like this, there is no need for a WEIGHT BY command.

5B) CHI-SQUARE TEST OF ASSOCIATION BETWEEN TWO QUALITATIVE VARIABLES

Suppose that a researcher, having watched a number of children enter a room and recorded each child's choice between two objects, wants to know whether there is a tendency for boys and girls to choose different objects. This question concerns two variables: gender and choice. In statistical terms, the researcher is asking whether they are associated: do more girls than boys choose object A and more boys than girls choose object B? Suppose that the children's choices are as in the following table:

	BOYS	GIRLS
OBJECT A	20	5
OBJECT B	6	19

A two-way table of nominal data of this kind is known as a <u>contingency table</u> or <u>cross-tabulation</u>. A contingency table is constructed with a view to ascertaining the presence of an association between <u>qualitative variables</u> such as gender and choice.

In statistics, the analysis of nominal data in the form of contingency tables has progressed enormously in recent years. In this exercise, however, we shall consider only the traditional, 'Pearsonian' chi-square test for association, as applied to nominal data in two-way contingency tables like the present one. (Multi-way contingency tables are better analysed by modern loglinear methods.)

In the present exercise, we shall be concerned only with ascertaining the <u>presence</u> of an association, not with measuring its <u>strength</u>. We shall return to that problem later (see Exercise 14).

Procedure

1) The DATA LIST command

(Guidance on the preparation of the DATA LIST command for two-way contingency tables is given in Section 11.3.2.)

The data set must contain <u>three variables</u>: one variable will contain the <u>cell frequencies</u>; but in addition there must be <u>two</u> grouping variables, one for each qualitative variable. We can call these *gender* (Girl, Boy) and *object* (A, B). The categories of these variables will be denoted by code numbers as follows: for *gender*, 1 = 'Boy' and 2 = 'Girl'; for *object*, 1 = 'A', 2 = 'B'.

The DATA LIST command is:

DATA LIST FREE/ gender object count.

The data are entered as follows:

BEGIN DATA.
1 1 20 1 2 6 2 1 5 2 2 19
END DATA.

2) The WEIGHT BY command

Add this command so that SPSS/PC+ reads the values of the frequency variable as frequencies:

WEIGHT BY count.

3) The VALUE LABELS command

This is absolutely essential. The command is:

VALUE LABELS gender 1 'Boys' 2 'Girls' / object 1 'A' 2 'B'.

Note the slash (/) separating the information about the two grouping variables.

Save and execute these data commands to ensure that all is well and to obtain the list of variables for pasting.

4) Preparing the CROSSTABS command

The command for the analysis of a two-way contingency table is CROSSTABS (short for crosstabulations). This command is to be found in the **descriptive statistics** menu, but it can be accessed immediately by getting into write mode with [Alt]/E, typing CROSSTABS and pressing [Esc]. Move down to /TABLES and press ↵. When **row variables** appears, press ↵, select *gender* from the variable table, press ↵, and then [Esc]. Move down to **BY**, press ↵, move down to **column variables**, and press ↵. Select *object* from the variable table, press ↵, and then [Esc]. Use the ← cursor key to move back to the CROSSTABS menu.

We suggest that you include some subcommands. The most important is the subcommand /STATISTICS CHISQ, which obtains the value of the chi-square statistic and its associated p-value. The subcommand /CELLS COUNT EXPECTED obtains the expected frequencies. This will enable you to check for the presence of cells with unacceptably low expected frequencies (see Section 11.3.2 for details). It is possible, though somewhat tedious, to paste these subcommands in from the menu; but it is easier just to type them in the scratch pad. The complete command is:

CROSSTABS /TABLES gender BY object/STATISTICS CHISQ/CELLS COUNT EXPECTED.

Save and execute this command.

The listing is discussed in Section 11.3.3. First, a crosstabulation table is listed showing the observed and expected frequencies in each cell, along with row and column totals. Second, a table of various chi-square statistics, together with their associated significance levels, is listed.

- Write down the value of the Pearson chi-square and its associated tail probability (p-value). Is it significant? In terms of the experimental hypothesis, what has this test shown?

5) <u>Terminating the session</u>

If a printed listing is required, add a SET/LISTING command and execute all the commands again. Terminate the session with the FINISH command.

EXERCISE 6
ONE-WAY ANALYSIS OF VARIANCE

We suggest that you may find it helpful to review the material in Chapter 7 before working through this practical exercise (see especially Section 7.1). The one-way analysis of variance (ANOVA) is potentially applicable to a situation in which a set of experimental results comprises several independent samples of scores, the samples having been obtained under a set of distinct but conceptually related conditions collectively known as a <u>factor</u>. (In ANOVA, the term <u>factor</u> is equivalent to <u>independent variable</u> elsewhere.) For instance, one sample might be the scores of participants under a control condition and the other samples might be the scores of other groups who have ingested small quantities of different drugs. The control and drug conditions might be referred to collectively as the 'Drug' factor. For such data, there is available on SPSS/PC+ the program ONEWAY. Note carefully that ONEWAY assumes that there are no repeated measures on the Drug factor, as would have been the case if each subject had been tested under all conditions, including the control. In that case, however, we could not have claimed to have independent samples of subjects at the various levels of the Drugs factor.

In the one-way ANOVA, the F ratio compares the spread among the treatment means with the (supposedly uniform) spread of the scores within groups about their group means. The purpose of this exercise is to help clarify the rationale of the F ratio by showing how its value is affected by various manipulations of some (or all) of the data. Before proceeding with this exercise, we ask you to suppose that a one-way ANOVA has been carried out upon a set of data and yields an F value of, say, 7.23. Now suppose that we were to multiply every score in the experimental results by a constant, say 10. What would happen to the value of F: would it still be 7.23? Or would it increase? Or decrease?

We also invite you to speculate upon the effect that adding a constant (say 10) to all the scores in just one of the groups would have upon F: suppose, for example, we were to add 10 to all the scores in the group with the largest mean. Would F stay the same, increase or decrease in value? Would the effect be the same if the constant were added to the scores of the group with the smallest mean?

As a first approach to answering these questions, we shall command SPSS/PC+ to carry out an ANOVA on a set of data. Then we shall see what happens to the value of F when the data are transformed as described in the previous paragraph.

The data

Suppose a researcher is interested in how well non Chinese-speaking students can learn Chinese characters using different kinds of mnemonics. Independent groups of participants are tested under three conditions: No Mnemonic, Mnemonic 1 and Mnemonic 2. The dependent variable is the number of Chinese characters that are correctly recalled.

The data are as follows:

No Mnemonic	3 5 3 2 4 6 9 3 8 10	(scores of 10 control subjects)
Mnemonic 1	10 8 15 9 11 16 17 15 7 10	(scores of 10 subjects trained in Mnemonic 1)
Mnemonic 2	20 15 14 15 17 10 8 11 18 19	(scores of 10 subjects trained in Mnemonic 2)

Procedure

1)   Preparing the DATA LIST command and entering the data

There will be two variables in the data set:

(1)   a grouping variable (*group*), comprising code numbers indicating the condition under which each score was achieved;

(2)   a variable (*score*), containing the score of every subject in the experiment.

Let us assign the code numbers 1, 2 and 3 to the No Mnemonic, Mnemonic 1 and Mnemonic 2 groups, respectively. The details of the preparation of the DATA LIST command are given in Section 7.2.1. The command is:

DATA LIST FREE/ group score.

Type in the data between the BEGIN DATA and END DATA commands (Section 3.5), remembering that each datum must be preceded by the code number in the grouping (independent) variable, as determined by the order in which these variables appear in the DATA LIST command. It is convenient to start a new row for each group (ie subjects 1 to 10 in the first row, subjects 11 to 20 in the second row and subjects 21 to 30 in the third row).

```
BEGIN DATA.
1 3  1 5 . . .  1 10
2 10  2 8 . . .  2 10
3 20  3 15 . . .  3 19
END DATA.
```

2)   Preparing the VARIABLE LABELS and VALUE LABELS commands.

Where, as in the present example, grouping variables have been used to assign code numbers to the conditions, it is a very good ideas to provide a key to the meanings of the (arbitrary) numbers, so that the listing is comprehensible. The command for providing the key is VALUE LABELS. It is also good practice, however, to use the VARIABLE LABELS command to amplify the often cryptic variable names given in DATA LIST.

When preparing the VARIABLE LABELS and VALUE LABELS commands, don't bother with the menu. Get into the scratch pad with [Alt]/E and type in the commands directly, taking the examples in Section 3.7 as a model. The commands are:

VARIABLE LABELS group 'Memory-Training History'.

VALUE LABELS group 1 'No Mnemonic' 2 'Mnemonic 1' 3 'Mnemonic 2'.

Save and excute the data commands to check for errors and to obtain, at a later point, the list of variables for pasting operations.

3)   Exploring the data

Before proceeding with the one-factor ANOVA, it is important to examine the data to see whether there are any contraindications for the use of ANOVA. Start with a MEANS command to obtain a table of means and standard deviations, and follow this up with EXAMINE as follows:

MEANS/TABLES score BY group.
EXAMINE/VARIABLES score BY group/PLOT STEMLEAF BOXPLOT/STATISTICS NONE.

The subcommand /STATISTICS NONE suppresses some of the otherwise rather copious descriptive statistics that are given by the EXAMINE command.

Save and execute these commands. Of the boxplots yielded by the EXAMINE command, the first depicts the entire set of experimental results; whereas the second displays the three groups side-by-side for comparison.

- Draw your own table showing the means and standard deviations of the scores in the three groups. Is there obvious heterogeneity of variance? Do the stem-and-leaf and boxplot displays suggest anomalies in the distributions of the data in any (or all) of the three groups? Write a statement assessing, purely from inspection, the suitability of the data for ANOVA.

4)   Adding a SUBTITLE command

In an exercise of this kind, in which a succession of similar analyses is to be carried out on a data set which is to be subjected to progressive modification, there is the danger that the output listing will be all but incomprehensible. What is needed is the appearance, at appropriate points, of captions that remind the reader of the stage reached by the analysis. This is accomplished by use of the SUBTITLE command. Since the first part of the analysis involves the original data set, an appropriate SUBTITLE command would be:

SUBTITLE Using the original data set.

The explanatory caption 'Using the original data set' will appear before the first section of the ANOVA listing.

5)   Writing the ONEWAY command

See Step 4 in Section 7.2.1. The command is:

ONEWAY/ score BY group(1, 3).

Note the brackets containing, in that order, the lowest and highest of the code numbers assigned.

Save all the commands and execute those from SUBTITLE onwards.

- Construct your own ANOVA summary table, including the value of F, its associated p-value, the mean squares of the treatment and error terms and their degrees of freedom. Is F significant? What are the implications of this result for the experimental hypothesis?

6)   Multiplying all the data by a constant

Next we shall demonstrate what happens to the mean squares and the F ratio when we alter (or transform) the data by multiplying each value by a constant of 10. But first, add a new subtitle:

SUBTITLE Multiplying all data by 10.

Next, type a COMPUTE command on the scratch pad (see Section 4.5.3) to create a new variable *allten*, containing the products of 10 with each of the original scores:

Exercises

COMPUTE allten=score*10.

Now write another ONEWAY command, this time using as the dependent variable the new variable you have just created (*allten*). The command is:

ONEWAY/VARIABLES allten BY group(1, 3).

Save the commands and execute the three new commands.

- From the listing, construct your own ANOVA summary table giving the new value of F and its associated p-value. Note also the mean squares for the treatment and error terms. Compare these with the corresponding values from the first analysis. Comment on what you find.

Both the between groups and within groups variance estimates have increased by a factor of 100. This is not at all surprising, since it is easy to show algebraically that when each of a set of scores is multiplied by a constant, the new variance is the old variance times the square of the constant. Since the factors of 100 in the numerator and denominator of the F ratio cancel out, the value of the F ratio remains unchanged.

7)   Adding a constant to the scores in only one group

Return once more to the scratch pad and add another subtitle:

SUBTITLE Adding a constant to just one group.

Prepare an IF command (see Section 4.5.5) that will add 10 to each datum in the third (Mnemonic 2) group only. In the present case, the command is:

IF (group = 3) score=score + 10.

Finally write another ONEWAY command:

ONEWAY/VARIABLES score BY group(1,3).

Save and execute these new commands.

- From the listing, construct your own ANOVA summary table. Compare the value of F, its p-value, the treatment mean square and the error mean square with the corresponding values from the previous analyses. Comment on your findings.

You will see that the effect of adding a constant of 10 to all scores in the Mnemonic 2 group has no effect at all upon the within groups variance estimate, which is not surprising, since adding the same constant to all the scores in a set has no effect upon the spread of the scores - it merely shifts the mean.

You will also see, however, that the between groups mean square has increased its value considerably. The between groups mean square is computed from the values of the treatment means alone. The within groups mean square, on the other hand, is the average of the variance estimates of the scores within groups and is quite independent of the spread among the group means. Consequently, it is quite possible to change the value of the former without affecting that of the latter and vice versa.

The effect of increasing the mean of the Mnemonic 2 group is to increase the spread of the three treatment means and hence the value of the numerator of the F ratio.

8)   Terminating the session

If a printed listing is required, add a SET/LISTING command, execute all the commands again, and exit from SPSS/PC+ with FINISH.

EXERCISE 7

ONEWAY ANOVA AND THE TUKEY TEST FOR PAIRWISE MULTIPLE COMPARISONS

In the one-way ANOVA, the F test is, in fact, an 'omnibus' test, in the sense that it tests the null hypothesis that, in the population, all the treatment means have the same value. That test is sensitive to differences anywhere among the array of treatment means. While this omnibus test overcomes the dangers inherent in proceeding to carry out a series of pairwise t-tests among the treatment means, there remains a very considerable problem: you may have a significant F value; but you will probably have more specific questions: for example, is the mean for the control group significantly different from the means of both Mnemonic groups, or just one? Is there a significant difference between the performance means of the two mnemonically-trained groups? The ANOVA F test cannot answer such questions: to obtain a significant value of F implies only that there is a difference somewhere among the means. To find the exact loci of the differences among the array of treatment means, further analysis is necessary.

In Section 7.1, it was pointed out that if pairwise t-tests are used to make comparisons among an array of treatment means, the probability of at least one test showing significance, even when the ANOVA null hypothesis is true (ie all treatment means have the same value in the population), can be considerably greater than the significance level (say, 0.05) set for each test. In other words, while the type I error rate per comparison may be set at 0.05, the type I error rate for the whole family of comparisons (the per family type I error rate) is greater. The purpose of this exercise is to make pairwise comparisons among an array of treatment means, while at the same time controlling the per family type I error rate.

In this context, it makes a considerable difference whether the comparisons are planned or unplanned. For the purposes of this exercise, we shall assume that the desired comparisons are unplanned. In other words, we are looking for a data-snooping technique for making unplanned pairwise comparisons among an array of treatment means, while at the same time controlling the per family type 1 error rate. The method we shall use is Tukey's Honestly Significant Difference test (HSD). While many other tests are used to make multiple pairwise comparisons, the HSD is known to be especially effective in controlling the per family type I error rate. The use of the HSD test will be illustrated with the same data that we used in Exercise 5.

The rationale of Tukey's HSD is this: if the treatment means are arranged in order of magnitude, and the smallest is subtracted from the largest, the probability of obtaining a large difference increases with the size of the array of means. The Studentised range statistic (q) expresses the difference between a pair of means in any array as so-many standard errors of the mean, the latter being estimated with $\sqrt{(MS_{ERROR}/n)}$, where n is the number of subjects in each treatment condition and (MS_{ERROR}) is the ANOVA error mean square. The Tukey HSD test requires that, to achieve significance, any pairwise difference must exceed a critical value which depends partly upon a critical value of q, the latter being fixed by the values of two parameters:

    (1)   the number of means in the array;

    (2)   the degrees of freedom of the ANOVA error term
              {in the one-way ANOVA, if there are k treatment means and n subjects in each
              treatment group, df(error term) = k(n-1)}.

Note that in Tukey's HSD test, the critical value for the significance of any of the pairwise comparisons is determined partly by the size of the entire array of means. There are other tests (such as the Newman-Keuls) which adjust the critical value according to whether the two means are close together or farther apart in the left-to-right order of magnitude: in the Newman-Keuls test, the critical value of q is less for a pair of means that are adjacent or close together in the ordering than for, say, the greatest and the smallest mean, which are at opposite ends of the ordered array. Tukey's HSD test, therefore, is more conservative than the Newman-Keuls: that is, it gives fewer significant differences.

Procedure

1)   <u>Preparing the DATA LIST command and entering the data</u>

Enter the network and access SPSS/PC+ in the usual way. Restore the command file from Exercise 6 to the scratch pad by pressing [F1] and ⅃, then [F3] and I, and finally typing in the file name. Edit the commands, so that you have, in the scratch pad, the following:

DATA LIST FREE/ group score.
BEGIN DATA.
1 3 1 5 . . . 1 10
2 10 2 8 . . . 2 10
3 20 3 15 . . . 3 19
END DATA.
VARIABLE LABELS group 'TYPE OF TRAINING'.
VALUE LABELS group 1 'NO MNEMONIC' 2 'MNEMONIC 1' 3 'MNEMONIC 2'.
ONEWAY/score BY group(1, 3).

2)   <u>Specifying the Tukey HSD test</u>

Leave the cursor on the period at the end of the ONEWAY command. Return to the Menu system by pressing [Esc], find the ONEWAY menu and note the items /RANGES and /OPTIONS. Highlight /RANGES and press ⅃ to paste it in. Now choose TUKEY. The ONEWAY command is now:

ONEWAY/score BY group(1, 3)/RANGES TUKEY.

Save the commands to a file on your disk, choosing a name such as A:1waytuky.CMD, and then execute them, remembering to do so only after the cursor has been moved to the line of the DATA LIST command.

Examine the screen carefully as the commands are executed. There may be a long pause after the Oneway Table is completed before the word MORE appears in the top right corner of the screen. That is your cue to press a key (any key) to obtain the listing of the Tukey output.

An explanation of the Tukey listing is given on pages 91-92.

The meaning of
The value actually compared with Mean(J) - Mean(I) is
$2.4863 * Range * Sqrt(1/N(I) + 1/N(J))$

is explained in the appendix to this exercise.

- From the listing for the Tukey test, construct your own table of means and differences, making it clear which differences are significant.

3)   <u>Terminating the session</u>

If a printed listing is required, insert a SET/LISTING command at the head of the commands in the scratch pad, and re-execute all the commands. Exit from SPSS/PC+ with FINISH.

Appendix to Exercise 7

One item in the Tukey listing requires further explanation. At one point, there appears the statement:

The value actually compared with Mean(J) - Mean(I) is
$2.4863 * Range * Sqrt(1/N(I) + 1/N(J))$

In this formula, Range is the critical value of the Studentised range statistic ($q_{critical}$) for an array of 3 treatment means and an ANOVA error term with 27 degrees of freedom. This critical value of q is 3.50.

From the definition of the Studentised range statistic and the foregoing discussion, it is clear that the critical difference between means (CD) is given by

$$CD = q_{critical} \times \sqrt{(MS_{WITHIN}/n)},$$

where n is the supposedly fixed number of subjects in each treatment group.

This formula can be generalised to a situation where one sample is of size n_1 and the other n_2. For n in the above formula, substitute the harmonic mean (h), where $h = 2/(1/n_1 + 1/n_2)$. The formula for the critical difference (CD) then becomes

$$CD = q_{critical} \times [\sqrt{(MS_{WITHIN}/2)}] \times [\sqrt{(1/n_1 + 1/n_2)}]$$

Thus $CD = 3.50 \times 2.4863 \times \sqrt{(1/n_1 + 1/n_2)}$ which is the formula given in the output listing.

EXERCISE 8

FACTORIAL ANALYSIS OF VARIANCE
Completely Randomised Factorial Experiment

The last two exercises have concerned the analysis of data from an experiment with just one independent variable (or factor) with three levels. Provided there are no contraindications in the data (heterogeneity of variance, markedly skewed distributions and so on), the null hypothesis that, in the population, all treatment means have the same value can be tested with the one-way analysis of variance, which is performed by the SPSS/PC+ program ONEWAY. In this exercise, we turn to the analysis of data from an experiment with **two** independent variables, or factors. Specifically, we shall be concerned with the ANOVA of data from a two-factor factorial experiment with no repeated measures (see Section 8.1 for an explanation of these terms). This type of experiment is also said to be of completely randomised factorial design. In factorial experiments, the factors are said to cross, each level of either factor being found in combination with every level of the other. The specification of no repeated measures implies that there is a fresh sample of subjects for every treatment combination.

For the analysis of variance of data from completely randomised factorial experiments (no repeated measures), the SPSS/PC+ command is ANOVA. The following discussion assumes that the reader has a firm understanding of the ANOVA of factorial experiments, especially the distinction between main effects and interactions. These terms are all explained in Chapter 8.

The data

'Must have a marvellous memory!'. This is something often said of a good chess player; but do good chess players necessarily have better memories than those who are mediocre? To find out, a psychologist tested chess players at three levels of proficiency on their ability to reconstruct board positions they had just been shown. Some of the positions used were from real games selected from tournaments; but others were merely random placings of the same pieces. The psychologist predicted that whereas the better players would show superior reconstructions of real board positions, this superiority would disappear when they tried to reproduce random placements.

The dependent variable in this experiment is a subject's score on reconstruction. There are two independent variables (factors):

(1) Competence (3 levels: Novice, Average, Good);
(2) Position (2 levels: Real, Random).

What the psychologist is predicting is that, when performance is averaged over Random and Real positions, the better players will achieve higher performance means; but this will turn out to be because of their superior recall of Real board positions only, and the beginners will be just as good at reconstructing Random positions. The two-factor ANOVA, therefore, should show a significant <u>interaction</u> between the factors of Competence and Position, as well as (possibly) a main effect of Competence. The latter might arise because the better players' superior reconstruction of real board positions should pull up the mean value of their performance over both Real and Random positions, even though they may not excel beginners on the Random task.

The design of this two-factor factorial experiment is tabled below. Note carefully that, for the purposes of this exercise, we assume that there is a fresh sample of subjects for every combination of the two treatment factors, so that each subject (whatever his or her level of ability) is tested with either Real or Random positions, not both.

FACTORS

COMPETENCE:	Novice		Average		Good	
POSITION :	Real	Random	Real	Random	Real	Random
Subject Group:	Gp1	Gp2	Gp3	Gp4	Gp5	Gp6

The data are tabulated below:

CHESS COMPETENCE

		Novice	Average	Good
TYPE OF PROBLEM	Real	38 39 42 40 40	65 58 70 61 62	88 97 79 89 89
	Random	50 53 40 41 36	50 40 43 37 38	41 40 50 42 41

Procedure

Before proceeding further, we strongly recommend you to study Section 8.2.1.

1)   Preparing and entering the data

The data will comprise three variables: the first and second are the Competence (*compet*) and Position (*position*) factors (each a grouping variable); the third is the dependent variable (*score*). The first and second variables will contain code numbers identifying the level of each factor at which the score at the end of the row was achieved. The three levels of the Competence factor (Novice, Average, Good) can be given the code numbers 1, 2 & 3, respectively; and the two levels of the Position factor (Real, Random) can be given the code numbers 1 & 2, respectively.

Since the data set is a small one, the values can be typed in the scratch pad after DATA LIST, between the BEGIN DATA and END DATA commands. With typical data sets, however, it is much better practice to store them separately, in a named data file.

2)   Preparing the DATA LIST command and entering the data

Write the DATA LIST command (Sections 3.2 and 8.2.1).   The command is:

DATA LIST FREE/ compet position score.

Type in the data between the BEGIN DATA and END DATA commands (Section 3.5). It is convenient (from the point of view of checking for accuracy) to write each subject's grouping (factor) codes and score on a single line, taking a fresh line for the next subject. The row of values

3 2 41

would signify that a player of good standard, faced with the task of reconstructing random positions, got a score of 41. <u>Note carefully that this order of interpretation has been specified in DATA LIST and the data must conform to it.</u>

3)   Adding VARIABLE LABELS and VALUE LABELS commands

To clarify the listing, you should include both VARIABLE LABELS and VALUE LABELS commands. Do not bother trying to paste these with the menu: just get into the scratch pad with [Alt]/E and type in the commands directly. Use the examples in (Section 3.7) as models. The commands are:

VARIABLE LABELS compet 'Level of Play' position 'Board Position'.
VALUE LABELS compet 1 'Novice' 2 'Average' 3 'Good' /position 1 'Real' 2 'Random'.

Note carefully that in the VALUE LABELS command, the information about one variable must be followed by a slash (/) before proceeding to the next variable. Save and execute all the commands written so far.

4)   Exploring the data

Before proceeding with the ANOVA, it is important to explore the data to check for contraindications, such as heterogeneity of variance. Since the samples are small, stem-and-leaf displays or boxplots of the data in the six cells of the experiment are unlikely to be illuminating. We suggest, therefore, that the MEANS command, which gives cell means and standard deviations, is the most appropriate for present purposes. To obtain a table of means and standard deviations, the syntax *dependent variable* BY *first independent variable* BY *second independent variable* after the subcommand /TABLES must be used. To obtain the overall means for *position*, an extra MEANS command is needed. Save and execute the following MEANS commands:

MEANS/TABLES score BY compet BY position.
MEANS/TABLES score BY position.

- Prepare a table of cell means and marginal means laid out in the same way as the original data table. Are the standard deviations reasonably similar in magnitude? Do there seem to be main effects (inspect the marginal means)? Is there any sign of an interaction (inspect the cell means and draw a graph as described below)?

To see whether there is an interaction, draw a graph profiling the cell means for the three classes of player for the Real and Random positions (use the graph in Section 8.2.2 as a model). You can retrieve these values on the screen after the MEANS command has been executed by pressing [Alt]/S to remove the menu and scrolling up the listing in the upper half of the screen with the ↑ cursor key.

5)   Preparing the ANOVA command

Find the ANOVA command in the Menu and inspect the examples given there. Then prepare a suitable command, remembering that you have two grouping variables. We have already seen that a table of means can be obtained by using the MEANS command; but you can also obtain this table by adding the /STATISTICS subcommand, choosing option 3 by entering that number before the final full stop that indicates the end of the command. Save and execute the complete ANOVA command, which is:

ANOVA/VARIABLES score BY compet(1,3) position(1,2)/STATISTICS 3.

Save and execute this command.

The ANOVA summary table gives F ratios for the main effects of Competence and Position and also for the interaction between the two factors. From inspection of the table of means, you will have discerned any possible main effects or interaction. The formal tests, however, may not confirm these trends; whether they do so or not depends on a number of factors, including the sample sizes, an important factor in determining the power of a statistical test.

- Study the ANOVA table in the listing and construct your own table, giving the values of F (and the associated p-values) for the main effect and interaction terms. Relate these results to the experimental hypothesis about the memory of chess players.

6)   <u>Terminating the session and printing the output</u>

If a printed listing is required, add a SET/LISTING command at the head of all the commands and re-execute all the commands. Terminate the session with FINISH.

Appendix to Exercise 8

Unequal group sizes

It is generally a very good idea to keep the sample sizes in ANOVA experiments as similar as possible. This is partly because the effects of violations of the model's assumptions have much more serious consequences when the sample sizes are unequal (especially when the samples are small).

A further problem is that, with unequal sample sizes, the ANOVA F tests can confound main effects with interactions. Methods (such as <u>unweighted means analysis</u>) have been devised to overcome this problem (see Howell, 1992; Chapter 13); but they are not available on SPSS/PC+. (They are available on some other packages, such as BMDP.)

Unplanned multiple pairwise comparisons

In this section, we offer some outlines for follow-up analysis to elucidate a main effect or an interaction that has been confirmed by an ANOVA F test.

In Exercise 7, Tukey's HSD test was used to make multiple pairwise comparisons among the treatment means, thereby adding considerably to the information given by the omnibus F test. The HSD test was specially designed to control the *per family* type 1 error rate, which could otherwise increase to a dangerously high level, especially when the array of means is large.

Suppose we have a two factor, completely randomised three-by-two factorial experiment, such as the one in the present exercise. A significant main effect of the Position factor implies a significant difference between the two marginal means, so no further testing is necessary. Since there were three types of player, however, a significant main effect of Competence does not show that the difference between any particular pair of means is significant. The Tukey HSD test can be used to make the necessary unplanned pairwise comparisons.

The trick is to pretend that the data are from a one-factor experiment by giving the following ONEWAY command:

ONEWAY/VARIABLES score BY compet(1, 3)/RANGES TUKEY.

Should an interaction prove significant, it will often be illuminating to make pairwise comparisons among the <u>cell means</u>, rather than the marginal means. The Tukey HSD test can be used for inter-cell comparisons also; but this time we must pretend the data are from a one-factor experiment with as many levels of its single factor as there are cell means in the original two-way table of results. This time, we need to construct a new coding variable, which we might call *cellcode*, containing code numbers for each of the six treatment combinations (1,1), (1,2), (2,1), (2,2), (3,1), (3,2), the first and second value of each pair referring to the grouping variables *compet* and *position*, respectively. The new coding variable *cellcode* can be constructed by using the IF command thus:

IF (compet EQ 1 AND position EQ 1) cellcode = 1.
IF (compet EQ 1 AND position EQ 2) cellcode = 2.
. . . .
. . . .
IF (compet EQ 3 AND position EQ 2) cellcode = 6.

The Tukey HSD on the cell means is then accomplished with the command:

ONEWAY/VARIABLES score BY cellcode(1,6)/RANGES TUKEY.

EXERCISE 9

WITHIN-SUBJECTS (REPEATED MEASURES) EXPERIMENTS

An experimental design is said to have repeated measures on a treatment factor when each subject is tested repeatedly, so that they perform (and are measured) at every level of the factor. When a factor has repeated measures, its conditions can be said to vary within subjects, as opposed to between subjects. For fuller details, read Sections 9.1 to 9.3.

SPSS/PC+ works with arrays of data in which each row contains the data on one particular subject. When no subject is tested at more than one level of a treatment factor, only one value in that person's row can be a score: the others could only be that person's identification number, or code numbers in grouping variables representing treatment conditions. When there are no repeated measures, grouping variables are essential; otherwise, it would be quite unclear which scores had been obtained under which conditions.

In a one-factor, repeated measures experiment, where a subject is tested at all levels of the treatment factor, each person's scores at the various levels can be set out in a row. Now each column represents a different level of the treatment factor, and its entries are all the subjects' performance scores at that level. There is therefore no need for a grouping variable to separate the scores obtained under the different conditions: they have already been separated.

The data

Imagine an experiment which measures the time taken for ten subjects to perform an analysis using three statistical computer packages Pack1, Pack2 and Pack3. The experimenter expects that there will be differences among the three packages in performance times. During the course of the experiment, each subject uses every package and the order of use is systematically varied across subjects. The data might be as follows:

	Pack1	Pack2	Pack3		Pack1	Pack2	Pack3
S1	12	15	18	S6	10	12	14
S2	18	21	19	S7	18	17	21
S3	15	16	15	S8	18	17	21
S4	21	26	32	S9	23	27	30
S5	19	23	22	S10	17	25	21

We suggest that the data be entered into SPSS/PC+ in three columns: (1) Pack1, (2) Pack2, (3) Pack3.

Note carefully that what we are after in this exercise is a univariate ANOVA: that is, one where there is only one dependent variable (in this case, time). Unfortunately, where there are repeated measures, we must take a slightly indirect route: our univariate ANOVA is actually carried out by using a command, MANOVA, which is appropriate for multivariate data. (The acronym MANOVA stands for Multivariate Analysis of Variance.)

When a data set comprises several columns of scores, with each column representing performance scores under a different condition, MANOVA regards it as a multivariate data set, that is one where there are two or more dependent variables. We know that in our example, there is really only one dependent variable, time; but as far as MANOVA is concerned, Pack1, Pack2 and so on could contain quite different kinds of measurement: Pack1 could be error scores, Pack2 could be time, and Pack3 income.

Initially, MANOVA assumes that the various levels of a repeated measures factor are separate dependent variables; only by including a special subcommand (/WSFACTORS), can MANOVA be instructed to treat them as different levels of the same factor.

Procedure

1)   Preparing the DATA LIST command and entering the data

Exercises

Prepare a DATA LIST command in the usual way. The command is:

DATA LIST FREE/ pack1 pack2 pack3.

Type in the data between the BEGIN DATA and END DATA commands. Remember that the data must be in the same order as the variables in the DATA LIST command. We suggest that you take a new line for the data from each fresh subject; although, as we have seen, the DATA LIST command has already made it clear that the fourth datum entered will be a *pack1*, the fifth a *pack2* and so on.

Save and execute the data commands. If necessary, correct any errors, resave, and re-execute the commands.

2) Adding a VARIABLE LABELS command

A suitable command is:

VARIABLE LABELS pack1 'Computing Package One' pack2 'Computing Package Two' pack3 'Computing Package Three'.

3) Exploring the data

You might wish to check for the presence of some of the possible contraindications for ANOVA in the data by using the plots in the EXAMINE command, which would be obtained by including the appropriate subcommand:

EXAMINE /VARIABLES pack1 TO pack3/PLOT STEMLEAF BOXPLOT/STATISTICS NONE.

This will show whether there are any outliers. The subcommand /STATISTICS NONE suppresses the copious descriptive statistics which the EXAMINE command would otherwise produce.   A more convenient list of means and standard deviations is obtained by the use of the subcommand /OMEANS in the MANOVA command.

4) Preparing the MANOVA command

Find the **MANOVA** program in the Menu (see Section 9.4.1) and read the overview. Then continue building the command using the menu and table of variable names.

We know that we have a set of data from an experiment with one treatment factor, which has repeated measures and one dependent variable. As explained previously, however, the MANOVA command assumes initially that the levels of a repeated measures factor are separate dependent variables: in fact, a repeated measures factor is not regarded as a factor at all. At this stage, therefore, assume that there are only dependent variables: there are no factors. You will also be asked whether there are any covariates. (A covariate is a measured variable which, although not of central interest, correlates with the principal dependent variables in the analysis. Special methods are available for covariates.) There are no covariates in the present analysis.

It is by inclusion of the subcommand /WSFACTORS that SPSS/PC+ is informed that a univariate analysis is required, and that the dependent variables are to be regarded as different levels of a treatment factor. The name of the factor, of course, cannot be that of any of the existing variables: a factor is a whole set of conditions or categories and, as such, requires its own name. We shall need a new, generic, name for the factor, say *package*. After the factor name, you must move to the !( ) item and insert the number of levels for the factor (3, in the present case).

The output listing for a general MANOVA analysis is truly formidable. For present purposes, we suggest you restrict the output by including the subcommand /PRINT SIGNIF (AVONLY) . This will obtain a listing of the results of the univariate analysis only.

The MANOVA command is:

MANOVA pack1 TO pack3 /WSFACTORS package(3)/PRINT SIGNIF (AVONLY)/OMEANS.

Note carefully that, in the /WSFACTORS subcommand, *package* is not the name of any of the variables given in the DATA LIST command: it is a new, generic, name identifying, for the first time, the repeated measures (within subjects) factor.

The subcommand /OMEANS will tabulate the means and standard deviations of each variable.

5) <u>Interpreting the output</u>

For the moment, the most important item in the output listing is the univariate ANOVA summary table, which appears under the heading: 'AVERAGED Tests of Significance for MEANS1 using UNIQUE sums of squares'.

- What is the value of the F ratio and its associated p-value (tail probability) for *package*? Is F significant? What are the implications for the experimental hypothesis? Construct your own ANOVA summary table, writing down the value of F, the degrees of freedom of the source and error terms, and the p-value.

At this point, however, we must issue a word of warning. In Chapter 9, attention was drawn to the fact that the model for repeated measures ANOVA makes an important assumption, over and above the usual requirements of homogeneity of variance and normality of distribution. This is the assumption of <u>homogeneity of covariance</u>. Often (indeed, usually) the data sets yielded by psychological repeated measures experiments show marked heterogeneity of covariance.

If there is heterogeneity of covariance, the true p-value may be somewhat higher than that given in the ANOVA summary table. If, therefore, the p-value is very small, say, less than 0.01, it is safe enough to say that we have evidence against the null hypothesis. If, however, the p-value is just under 0.05, it may be advisable to consider the use of a <u>conservative F test</u> discussed in Howell (1992, p.446).

6) <u>Printing the listing and terminating the SPSS/PC+ session</u>

If a printed listing is required, add a SET/LISTING command at the head of the commands and re-execute all the commands. Terminate the session with FINISH.

Appendix to Exercise 9

<u>Unplanned multiple comparisons</u>

Unfortunately, SPSS/PC+ does not offer the Tukey HSD test for repeated measures ANOVA. What you must do is to arrange the means in order of magnitude, calculate the differences and find a critical value for the difference (CD) from the formula

$$CD = q\{\sqrt{(MS_{ERROR}/n)}\},$$

where q is the value from the table of critical values for the studentised range statistic (available in Howell, 1992), MS_{ERROR} is the error MS (called 'WITHIN CELLS' in the output listing) and n is the number of subjects in the sample. To obtain q, enter the table with [Number of Steps] = the number of levels comprising the treatment factor, and [Error df] = the degrees of freedom for the ANOVA error MS.

EXERCISE 10

WITHIN SUBJECTS EXPERIMENTS WITH TWO FACTORS

In the previous exercise, the MANOVA command was used to carry out an ANOVA of the results of an experiment with one repeated measures factor. Such an experimental design is also termed <u>within subjects</u>, because the levels of the independent variable vary in the same subjects, rather than between different samples of subjects, as in <u>between subjects</u> experiments. In this exercise, we consider the ANOVA of within subjects factorial experiments, that is, factorial experiments with crossed treatment factors and repeated measures on both factors.

The data

An experiment is carried out to investigate the effects of two factors (independent variables) upon the recognition of Symbols briefly presented on a screen, as measured by the number of correct identifications over a fixed number of trials. The factors are Symbol (Digit, Lower Case, Upper Case) and Font (Gothic, Roman). Both factors are expected to affect the ease with which symbols are recognised. Each of the six subjects in the experiment is tested under all six combinations of the two treatment factors. The data are:

	Digit		Lower case		Upper case	
	Gothic	Roman	Gothic	Roman	Gothic	Roman
S1	2	6	18	3	20	5
S2	4	9	20	6	18	2
S3	3	10	15	2	21	3
S4	1	12	10	9	30	10
S5	5	8	13	8	20	8
S6	6	10	14	10	16	6

Each subject receives six scores, one for each of the six treatment combinations (Digit-Gothic), (Digit-Roman), ..., (Upper-Roman). Abbreviated forms of these labels could be used as labels in the DATA LIST command. There is, however, a shorter way of labelling the columns in the data set, which (especially with more complex designs) is less prone to error. The trick is to assign cryptic variable names that vary only in their final digit: eg *score1*, *score2*, ..., *score6*, by using the keyword TO in an expression such as *score1* TO *score 6*. (As usual, the variable names must not exceed 8 characters.)

Merely labelling the columns, however, does not clarify the treatment combinations under which the scores were obtained. This finer labelling is achieved in the /WSFACTORS subcommand of MANOVA. The order in which the factors are named in the /WSFACTORS subcommand is absolutely crucial.

Look at the table of results once again. Start at the left, with the column of scores that were obtained under the combination (Digit-Gothic). The next combination on the right is (Digit-Roman). The symbol has not varied at this point, but the font has. In this table, therefore, the Symbol factor (*symbol*) can be said to vary 'more slowly' than the Font factor (*font*). The Order Rule for naming factors in the subcommand /WSFACTORS is this: Name the variables in progressive orders of speed, from the slowest (first) to the fastest (last). In the present example, therefore, the order of naming would be: *symbol*, *font*. In correct syntax, the subcommand will be /WSFACTORS symbol(3) font(2).

Within the !/WSFACTORS menu is the prompt **!factor name**. When this is highlighted, the right-hand window shows a statement of the Order Rule and an example. Note, however, that SPSS/PC+ uses the phrase 'across the list of dependent variables'. Recall that, unless the special subcommand /WSFACTORS is included in the MANOVA command, the latter will assume that each column in the data set represents scores on a separate dependent variable. In the present case, MANOVA will initially assume that there are six dependent variables, ie as many as there are columns in the data set (excluding subnum).

Procedure

1)   <u>Preparing the DATA LIST command and entering the data</u>

Having accessed SPSS/PC+ in the usual way, prepare the DATA LIST command, which is:

DATA LIST FREE/ score1 TO score6.

Enter the data in sixcolumns, one column for each of the scores obtained under the six treatment combinations. The data are preceded and followed by the commands BEGIN DATA and END DATA, respectively.

2)   Exploring the data

Check for any distribution problems by using the /PLOT option of the EXAMINE command, as in the previous exercise. Save the EXAMINE command and execute it to check that all is well. The command is:

EXAMINE/VARIABLES score1 TO score6/PLOT STEMLEAF BOXPLOT/STATISTICS NONE.

3)   Preparing the MANOVA command

See Section 9.5.1 for details on how to prepare the MANOVA command with the aid of the menu. It is suggested that the subcommand /OMEANS be included in order to obtain a list of the means and standard deviations for each of the six variables. The MANOVA command is:

MANOVA score1 TO score6/WSFACTORS symbol(3) font(2)/OMEANS/PRINT SIGNIF (AVONLY).

Save and execute the command.

4)   Interpreting the output listing

See Section 9.5.2 for a more detailed explanation of the listing.

The tables of interest are those headed 'AVERAGED Tests of Significance for SCORE using UNIQUE sums of squares'. Note carefully that, while the error terms in the tables are always termed 'WITHIN CELL', the denominator degrees of freedom are 5 for the F test of the Font factor, and 10 for the F test of the Symbol factor and for the test of the Font-by-Symbol interaction. This is because the error mean square is the interaction between the source factor (main effect or interaction) and Subjects, which is treated as if it were a random effects treatment factor (see Howell, 1992, for a lucid discussion of repeated measures ANOVA models, and the correct choice of error terms for ANOVA F tests).

Check the tables to see whether any of the three F tests shows significance (ie the p-value is less than 0.05). If there is an interaction, plot the profiles of the Gothic and Roman Fonts against Symbol. Note that you can retrieve the table of means in the listing by pressing [Alt/S]. The listing will then appear in the upper half of the screen, and you can scroll up to the desired items by using the arrowed cursor keys.

- From the listing, construct your own ANOVA summary table, showing the F ratios, degrees of freedom and p-values for the main effects and the interaction. In your table, make it clear which (if any) factors are significant.

5)   Printing the listing and terminating the SPSS/PC+ session

If a printed listing is required, add a SET/LISTING command above the other commands in the scratch pad. Execute all the commands and terminate the SPSS/PC+ session with FINISH.

Appendix to Exercise 10

Further analyses following ANOVA

The researcher will often want to follow up the ANOVA of a set of data from a within subjects experiment with comparisons among either the marginal or cell means, in order to elucidate a significant main effect or an interaction, respectively. Once again, the Tukey HSD test is not available on SPSS/PC+ for factorial repeated measures analyses. The user must arrange the relevant means in order of magnitude and calculate the appropriate critical difference CD, from the formula:

$$CD = q\{\sqrt{(MS_{ERROR}/n^*)}\},$$

where n^* is the number of scores from which the treatment means to be compared were calculated, MS_{ERROR} is the denominator of the F ratio for the test of the treatment effect concerned, and q is the value obtained from the table of critical values of the Studentised Range Statistic (available in Howell, 1992).

In the present example, for instance, if one wishes to compare the three Symbol means, the number of scores contributing to each mean is <u>twelve</u>: the number of subjects, times the number of fonts. Accordingly $n^* = 12$ in that case.

If, on the other hand, you wish to make comparisons among cell means, $n^* = 6$, because only six scores contributed to the mean obtained under each treatment combination. To obtain the correct value of q, enter the table with two parameters:

      (1)   the number of means in the whole comparisons set;

      (2)   the degrees of freedom of the error term.

Following a significant main effect, the former (1) will be the number of marginal means for the factor concerned; after a significant interaction, it will be the number of cell means. It would be a very useful exercise to follow the ANOVA of the present experimental results with multiple comparisons using the Tukey HSD test as outlined above. Should our instructions prove too sketchy, Howell (1992) provides a detailed account of the procedure.

EXERCISE 11

MIXED (SPLIT-PLOT) ANOVA: TWO-FACTOR EXPERIMENT WITH REPEATED MEASURES ON ONE FACTOR

In many of the factorial designs used in psychological research, only some of the factors have repeated measures: that is, there is a mixture of between subjects and within subjects factors. Such designs are often referred to as mixed designs; but the older term split-plot is also common, an expression arising from the agronomic context in which most of the designs now in use were originally devised.

The data

In an experiment investigating the effect of the colour of the ambient light upon performance of a vigilance task, subjects were asked to press a button when they thought they could discern a signal against a background of random noise. The experimenter expected that the ambient colour would have varying effects upon the detection of different kinds of sound. Three types of signal were used: a horn, a whistle, and a bell. Each sound was presented 30 times in the course of a one-hour monitoring session, during which the subject sat in a cubicle lit by either red or blue light. The dependent variable was the number of correct presses of the button. For theoretical reasons, it was necessary to use different subjects for the different colour conditions; on the other hand, it was considered that there would be advantages in testing each individual with all three kinds of signal. In this experiment, therefore, the factor of Colour was between subjects; whereas the other factor, Signal, was within subjects, ie there were repeated measures on the Signal factor. The results were as follows:

			SOUND		
			Horn	Whistle	Bell
		S1	25	18	22
		S2	22	16	21
	Red	S3	26	19	26
		S4	23	21	20
		S5	19	18	19
		S6	27	23	27
COLOUR					
		S7	19	12	23
		S8	21	15	19
	Blue	S9	23	14	24
		S10	20	16	21
		S11	17	16	20
		S12	21	17	19

Procedure

1)   Preparing the DATA LIST command and entering the data

As usual, the data set will take the form of columns of numbers. This time, because there is a between subjects factor, Colour (levels: Red, Blue), we shall need a grouping variable containing code numbers indicating the ambient colour under which subjects performed their task. The code numbers 1 and 2 could be assigned to the Red and Blue levels, respectively, of the Colour factor. The within subjects factor is Signal (levels: Horn, Whistle, Bell). As before, the scores obtained under each of these conditions will be entered in a separate column. Once again, the MANOVA command will initially treat these as three separate dependent variables; but the subcommand /WSFACTORS obtains the univariate ANOVA.

Prepare the DATA LIST command in the usual way (see Section 10.2.1). The command is:

DATA LIST FREE/ colour horn whistle bell.

The data are best entered in rows (one row for each subject), between the BEGIN DATA and END DATA commands. In the table of experimental results, the top line of entries was:

25 18 22

The line of data for Subject 1 would then be:

1 25 18 22

The line of data for Subject 12 would be:

2 21 17 19

2)   Preparing the VARIABLE LABELS and VALUE LABELS commands.

It is always good practice to include VARIABLE LABELS commands, in order to clarify the meaning of the output listing at a later point.   This is especially so with complex experiments.

VARIABLE LABELS colour 'Ambient Colour During Task'.

For within subjects experiments, the question of a VALUE LABELS command does not arise. In mixed experiments, however, where there are grouping variables, VALUE LABELS commands should be included.

VALUE LABELS colour 1 'Red' 2 'Blue'.

Save and execute the data commands.

3)   Exploring the data

This time, since we have a grouping variable, we can use the MEANS command to obtain means and standard deviations. The command is:

MEANS/TABLES horn whistle bell BY colour.

Save and execute this command.

- Examine the table of means. Plot the profiles of cell means against the different signals for those subjects who performed under red and blue illumination. Are there signs of main effects or an interaction?

4)   Preparing the MANOVA command

In preparing the MANOVA command, bear in mind that, initially, we are classifying the scores on the three 'dependent variables' (Horn, Whistle, Bell) by a grouping factor. Here the keyword BY is used thus:

MANOVA horn whistle bell BY colour(1,2)/WSFACTORS signal(3)/PRINT SIGNIF (AVONLY).

Save and execute this command.

5)   Interpreting the listing

Since there is a between-subjects factor (Colour), the listing starts with a table headed 'Tests of Between-Subjects Effects' (see Section 10.2.2).   Write down the F value for *colour* and its significance.   The second table headed 'AVERAGED Tests of Significance for MEAS.1 using UNIQUE sums of squares' shows the repeated measures factors.   It includes the results of the F tests of the main effect of Signal and of the Colour-by-Signal interaction.

- From the tables in the listing, construct your own ANOVA summary table showing the sources, their degrees of freedom and the values of their F ratios (with tail probabilities). Label any significant results. Relate these findings to the experimental hypothesis.

6)   <u>Printing the listing and terminating the SPSS/PC+ session</u>

If a printed listing is required, add a SET/LISTING command and re-execute all the commands. Terminate the session with FINISH.

EXERCISE 12

MIXED (SPLIT-PLOT) ANOVA: THREE-FACTOR EXPERIMENT WITH REPEATED MEASURES ON TWO FACTORS

From the computational point of view, the analysis of mixed experiments with three factors is a fairly simple extension of the procedure for two-factor mixed experiments. In general, however, the interpretation of data from factorial experiments becomes increasingly problematic as more factors are added. In particular, where there is a complex design with repeated measures on some factors but not on others, the naming of the factors must be carried out with special care.

The data

In an experiment investigating the recognition of shapes under sub-optimal conditions, there were three shapes (Shape1, Shape2, Shape3), each of which could be either Open (outline) or Filled. The experimenter predicted that the ease with which different shapes were recognised would prove to be dependent upon whether the pattern was open or filled. Each subject was tested under all six combinations of these two treatment factors, which can be labelled Shape and Shade. The between subjects factor was the type of observer used: one group consisted of psychology students, the other of engineering students. The dependent variable was the number of correct identifications over a fixed series of trials.

The results are as follows:

FACTORS Shape:		Shape 1		Shape 2		Shape 3	
Shade:		Open	Filled	Open	Filled	Open	Filled
Psychology	S1	2	12	3	1	4	5
Students	S2	13	22	5	9	6	8
	S3	14	20	8	7	5	7
GROUP							
Engineering	S4	12	1	3	9	6	10
Students	S5	11	2	8	10	5	9
	S6	12	7	2	4	4	10

Procedure

1)   <u>Preparing the DATA LIST command and entering the data</u>

The data will comprise seven columns: the grouping variable and a column for each combination of the two treatment factors. The DATA LIST command is:

DATA LIST FREE/ group score1 TO score6.

Note the use of the keyword TO when naming the columns of scores.

Enter the data between the BEGIN DATA and END DATA commands, each row starting with the value of the grouping variable, and concluding with the six values from the results table.

2)   Preparing the VARIABLE LABELS and VALUE LABELS commands

Add the following commands:

VARIABLE LABELS group 'Type of Student' score1 'Shape1 - Open' score2 'Shape1 - Solid' score3 'Shape2 - Open' score4 'Shape2 - Solid' score5 'Shape3 - Open' score6 'Shape3 - Solid'.
VALUE LABELS group 1 'Psychologists' 2 'Engineers'.

Save and execute all the data commands.

3)   Exploring the data

Prepare an appropriate MEANS command and save and execute it. The command is:

MEANS/TABLES score1 TO score6 BY group.

In a three-factor experiment, there is the possibility of a three-way interaction among all three factors. A three-way interaction is said to occur when the interaction between two factors is heterogeneous across the levels of a third factor. This definition might suggest that the presence of a three-way interaction might be rather easy to discern in a three-way table of cell means by simply comparing graphs of two-way interactions at the different levels of a third factor. In fact, the interpretation of graphs drawn from the cell means of three-way tables requires considerable practice. This is because, just as two-way tables of means (and their graphs) reflect the presence of main effects as well as the interaction, three-way tables (and their graphs) reflect the presence of two-way interactions as well as any three-way interaction that might be present. To the untrained eye, two-way graphs may look heterogeneous; but this may arise entirely from the presence of two-way interactions.

- From the listing for the MEANS command, graph the two-way interactions between two of the factors at the different levels of the third factor. {You can retrieve all the values of the means on the screen after the MEANS command has been executed by pressing [Alt]/S to replace the menu with the listing in the upper half of the screen: you can then scroll up and down the listing with the ↑ and ↓ cursor keys. The menu is restored by pressing [Alt]/S again.} Draw two graphs side-by-side: one for Psychologists, the other for Engineers. With the three levels of *shape* on each x-axis and the values of the means on the y-axes, mark in the Open means with dots and the Solid means with crosses. Connect up the dots and connect up the crosses with lines in each graph. Do the patterns of lines seem similar? If not, a three-way interaction may be present.

4)   Preparing the MANOVA command

As in the two-factor within subjects experiment, care is needed when specifying the repeated measures factors in the /WSFACTORS subcommand. As before, the rule is that the 'slowest-moving' factors are named first. The MANOVA command is:

MANOVA score1 TO score6 BY group(1,2)/WSFACTORS shape(3) shade(2)/PRINT SIGNIF (AVONLY).

5)   Interpreting the listing

Look for the tables of 'Between-Subjects effects' for the factor *group* and 'AVERAGED Tests of Significance' for the within-subjects factors.

- Construct your own ANOVA summary table, showing the F ratios (and p-values) for the three factors, their two-way interactions and the three-way interaction, paying particular attention to the degrees of freedom. (Working out the degrees of freedom of the sources before studying the listing is a very good way of keeping track of the sources in complex computer ANOVA output.) Do the values of F confirm the patterns you saw earlier among the treatment means?

6)   <u>Terminating the session</u>

If a printed listing is required, add a SET/LISTING command and re-execute all the commands. Terminate the session with FINISH.

Appendix to Exercise 12

Further analysis: unplanned multiple comparisons

The procedures for making multiple comparisons among the treatment means following the ANOVA of data from an experiment of mixed design are described in Howell (1992; Chapter 14).

EXERCISE 13
THE PEARSON CORRELATION

The Pearson correlation (r) is one of the most widely used of statistics. Despite its apparent simplicity and versatility, however, it is only too easy to misinterpret a correlation. The purpose of the present exercise is not only to show you how to use SPSS/PC+ to obtain correlations but also to illustrate how misleading a given value for r can sometimes be.

The Pearson correlation is a statistic which expresses the strength of a supposed linear (straight line) relationship between two variables, both of which have been measured as they occur in a single sample of individuals: that is, the Pearson r was designed for use with paired data. It follows algebraically from the defining formula for r that this statistic can take values only within the range from -1 to +1, inclusive: if, assuming that there are at least three (X,Y) pairs, r = +1, the two variables have a perfect positive straight line relationship; if r = -1, they have a perfect negative straight line relationship.

If the scatterplot of the two variables is elliptical in shape, we know that the relationship is basically linear, subject to a random error component. If the ellipse is narrow, we can expect a substantial value for r. The converse, however, does not hold: a large correlation does not of itself imply linearity of relationship; indeed, it need not imply any relationship at all! It is essential, therefore, that one always looks at the scatterplot first before calculating the correlation.

This exercise involves the analysis of four sets of paired data, which were contrived by Anscombe (1973). Each set yields exactly the same value for the Pearson correlation. The scatterplots, however, will show that in only one case are the data suitable for a Pearson correlation: in the others, the Pearson correlation gives a highly misleading impression of the relationship between the two variables.

One problem with the Pearson correlation is that it is very vulnerable to the leverage exerted by atypical data points, or <u>outliers</u> as they are termed. Sometimes, it is possible to rectify this by removing the outliers; but that solution is inapplicable when the relationship is basically non-linear.

The data (from Anscombe, 1973)

The four sets of paired data are X1 and Y1, X1 and Y2, X1 and Y3, and X2 and Y4, as presented in the following table:

Subject	X1	X2	Y1	Y2	Y3	Y4
s1	10.0	8.0	8.04	9.14	7.46	6.58
s2	8.0	8.0	6.95	8.14	6.77	5.76
s3	13.0	8.0	7.58	8.74	12.74	7.71
s4	9.0	8.0	8.81	8.77	7.11	8.84
s5	11.0	8.0	8.33	9.26	7.81	8.47
s6	14.0	8.0	9.96	8.10	8.84	7.04
s7	6.0	8.0	7.24	6.13	6.08	5.25
s8	4.0	19.0	4.26	3.10	5.39	12.50
s9	12.0	8.0	10.84	9.13	8.15	5.56
s10	7.0	8.0	4.82	7.26	6.42	7.91
s11	5.0	8.0	5.68	4.74	5.73	6.89

Procedure

1)   Preparing a data file

Since the same data set will be used in a later exercise, it is better to store the data in a separate file, rather than sandwiching them between the BEGIN DATA and END DATA commands below the DATA LIST command. The procedure is simple: just type the data directly into the scratch pad (which must be empty initially), then save using [F9], naming the file in the usual way. Use the extension .DAT to remind you that it is a data file (eg A:anscombe.DAT).

After preparing the data file, erase the data from the scratch pad, using the [F7] and [F8] keys. With the cursor in the bottom row, press [F7] and L for Line, whereupon the row will start flashing yellow. Move the cursor up to the top row and press [F7] again, whereupon the whole block will turn yellow. Then press [F8], followed by D (for Delete) and the block will disappear.

2)   Writing the DATA LIST command

Prepare a DATA LIST command using the FILE option (Section 3.6), inserting in the quotes the name of the data file you have just created. The command is:

DATA LIST FILE 'A:anscombe.DAT' FREE/X1 X2 Y1 TO Y4.

Note that when a file is named in the DATA LIST command, there is no need for the BEGIN DATA and END DATA commands.

Save and execute the DATA LIST command.

3)   Exploring the data

In order to appreciate the distributional peculiarities of some of the data, you should use the **PLOT/PLOT** command to obtain the appropriate scatterplots. Type PLOT/PLOT on the scratch pad and press [Esc] to display the menu for this command. Look at the examples and type in the appropriate variables to get plots of Y1 with X1, Y2 with X1, Y3 with X1, and Y4 with X2. (You can combine the first three in one command; but you will need a second command for Y4 with X2.) The commands are:

PLOT/PLOT Y1 Y2 Y3 WITH X1.
PLOT/PLOT Y4 WITH X2.

Execute these commands and examine the scatterplots on the screen.

The plot of Y1 against X1 shows a substantial linear relationship between the variables. The thinness of the ellipse indicates that the Pearson correlation is likely to be high. These are the kind of data for which the Pearson correlation gives an informative and accurate statement of the strength of linear relationship between two variables.

The other plots, however, are very different: that of Y2 against X1 shows a perfect, but clearly nonlinear, relationship; Y3 against X1 shows a basically linear relationship, which is marred by a glaring outlier; Y4 against X2 shows a column of points with a single outlier up in the top right corner.

4)   Obtaining the Pearson correlations

Now let us obtain the correlations between X and Y for all four sets of paired data. Find CORRELATION in the menu and follow the prompts in order to specify the correlations of X1 with each of Y1, Y2 and Y3, and of X2 with Y4. We suggest you also include the /STATISTICS 1 subcommand to list the means and standard deviations of the variables, and the /OPTIONS 3 subcommand to obtain two-tailed p-values for tests of significance for each correlation. The final command is:

CORRELATION/VARIABLES Y1 TO Y3 WITH X1/STATISTICS 1/OPTIONS 3.
CORRELATION/VARIABLES Y4 WITH X2/STATISTICS 1/OPTIONS 3.

Execute these commands and inspect the listing. The first table displays the descriptive statistics for the variables. Next, there are the correlation coefficients for X1 and so on.

(Incidentally, notice that, in SPSS/PC+'s listing, * denotes 1% significance and ** 0.1% significance. This is not in accord with the usual convention whereby * denotes 5% significance and ** 1% significance.)

- Write down the descriptive statistics for all the columns of data and the values of the correlation coefficients for the four sets of paired data.

The big surprise is that in all cases, the Pearson correlation has the same value (0.817), even in the case where there appears to be no systematic relationship between X and Y at all!

Anscombe's data strikingly illustrate the need to inspect the data carefully to ascertain the suitability of statistics such as the Pearson correlation.

5)   Confirming the effects of removing outliers by using the SELECT IF command

It will be instructive to recalculate the Pearson correlation for the data set (X1, Y3) when the values for Subject 3 have been removed. This is easily achieved by using the SELECT IF command thus:

SELECT IF ($CASENUM NE 3).

This command must be placed before the CORRELATION and PLOT commands. Save the commands and re-execute all those from SELECT IF downwards.

- What is the new value of the Pearson correlation for the data set (X1, Y3) when the data on Subject 3 have been removed? Is this what would could be expected from the appearance of the original scatterplot? Describe the appearance of the new scatterplot.

6)   Printing the output listing and terminating the session

If a printed listing is required, add a SET/LISTING command at the top of the command file and re-execute all the commands. Terminate the session with the FINISH command.

Conclusion

This exercise has demonstrated the value of exploring the data first before calculating statistics such as the Pearson correlation. While it is true that Anscombe's data were contrived to give his message greater force, there have been many misuses of the Pearson correlation with real data sets, where the problems created by the presence of outliers and by basically non-linear relationships are quite common.

EXERCISE 14
OTHER MEASURES OF ASSOCIATION

The Pearson correlation was devised to measure a supposed linear association between quantitative variables, each measured on an independent scale with units, such as a ruler, weighing scales or a psychological test. There are other kinds of data, however, namely those at the ordinal and nominal levels of measurement, to which the Pearson correlation (at least in its usual form) is inapplicable. Moreover, even with scalar data, there may be considerations that debar the use of the Pearson correlation. Fortunately, many other statistical measures of strength of association have been devised, some of which will be considered in this exercise. In this exercise, we shall consider measures of association that are applicable to (1) ordinal data; (2) nominal data.

ORDINAL DATA

The term ordinal data embraces all data on quantitative variables that are not measures on an independent scale with units. For example, if we rank a group of 10 people with respect to height, giving 10 to the tallest and 1 to the smallest, the resulting set of ranks contains ordinal data, because an individual rank does not signify so-many units of the variable of height: it merely states the ordinal position of that person's height in relation to the heights of the other people in the sample.

Often judges are constrained by their instructions to assign a different rank to each object and avoid ties. (This may not always be rigidly enforced and a tie or two may be tolerated.)

In quite another judgemental paradigm, however, ties are built into the judgemental process. Judges may be instructed to assign objects (or people) to one of a set of ordered categories. If there are more objects than there are categories (which is usual), ties are inevitable. The use of rating scales yields ordinal data in the form of assignments to ordered categories.

Measuring strength of association with data in the form of ranks

The Spearman rank correlation: its use as a measure of agreement between two judges who rank a set of objects

Suppose that two judges each rank ten paintings, A, B, ..., J. Their decisions are as follows:

	Best									Worst
First Judge	C	E	F	G	H	J	I	B	D	A
Second Judge	C	E	G	F	J	H	I	B	D	A

It is obvious from this table that the judges generally agree closely in their rankings: at most, the ranks they assign to a painting differ by a single rank. But how can their level of agreement be measured?

The information in this table can be expressed in terms of numerical ranks by assigning the counting numbers from 1 to 10 to the paintings in their order of ranking by the first judge, and pairing each of these ranks with the rank that the same painting received from the other judge thus:

Painting	C	E	F	G	H	J	I	B	D	A
First Judge	1	2	3	4	5	6	7	8	9	10
Second Judge	1	2	4	3	6	5	7	8	9	10

This is not the only way of representing the judgements numerically. It is also possible to list the objects (in any order) and pair the ranks assigned by the two judges to each object, entering two sets of ranks as before. Where the measurement of agreement is concerned, the two methods give exactly the same result.

One way of measuring the level of agreement between the two judges is by calculating the Pearson correlation between the two sets of ranks. This correlation is known as the <u>Spearman rank correlation</u> (or as <u>Spearman's rho</u>), and is usually presented in terms of a formula which, though it looks very different from that of the Pearson correlation, is actually equivalent <u>provided that no ties are allowed</u>.

To obtain Spearman rank correlations on SPSS/PC+, proceed as follows. Write the DATA LIST command thus:

DATA LIST FREE/judge1 judge2.
BEGIN DATA.
1 1 2 2 3 4 . . . 9 9 10 10
END DATA.

Obtain the Pearson correlation by the command:

CORRELATION/VARIABLES judge1 WITH judge2.

Save and execute these commands.

- Write down the value of the Pearson correlation between the two sets of ranks. This is the value of Spearman's rank correlation.

With small samples, it is difficult to obtain an accurate p-value for a Spearman rank correlation, especially when there are tied ranks. When there are no tied ranks (see below), one can obtain critical values for the Spearman rank correlation from tables available in textbooks such as Neave & Worthington (1988).

If the judges are allowed to give equal ranks to objects, for example to say that paintings B, C & F share 2nd place, the rank assigned to each object involved in the tie is the average of the ranks that each would have received had no ties been allowed. For example, if four objects tie for 5th place, the rank assigned to each is $(5 + 6 + 7 + 8)/4 = 6.5$. When ties are present, they must reduce one's confidence in the p-values given by the tables. The user can but hope that when there are only a few ties here and there, the tables will still give serviceable p-values.

<u>The use of the Spearman rank correlation with scalar data showing contraindications for the use of the Pearson correlation</u>

We shall now consider a common problem. We have a set of paired data, consisting of measurements on an independent scale with units. On inspecting the scatterplot, we see that there is a <u>monotonic relationship</u> between the two variables: that is, as X increases, so does Y. On the other hand, the relationship between X and Y is clearly non-linear, and the use of the Pearson correlation is therefore inadvisable. An example of such a data set is the following:

Y	1.00	1.58	2.00	2.32	2.58	2.81	3.00
X	2.0	3.0	4.0	5.0	6.0	7.0	8.0

Enter these values into SPSS/PC+, calculate the Pearson correlation and obtain the scatterplot. The commands are:

DATA LIST FREE/Y X.
BEGIN DATA.
1.00 2 1.58 3 2.00 4 2.32 5 2.58 6 2.81 7 3.00 8
END DATA.
PLOT/PLOT Y WITH X.
CORRELATION/VARIABLES Y WITH X.

- Describe the shape of the scatterplot and write down the value of the Pearson correlation.

Since there is a perfect (but non-linear) relationship between X and Y, ($Y = \log_2(X)$), the degree of association is understated by the Pearson correlation which, though high, is not unity.

Another approach (and arguably a better one) is to convert X and Y to ranks and calculate the Spearman rank correlation. The commands are as follows:

RANK Y X (D)/RANK INTO RY RX.
CORRELATION/VARIABLES RY WITH RX.

The first of these commands converts the values of Y and X into ranks. (The bracketed D obtains ranks descending in value from the highest scalar score to the lowest. This prevents the sign of the correlation changing on conversion of the original data to ranks.)

- Write down the value of the Spearman rank correlation. Compare its value with that of the Pearson correlation. Which, in this case, do you regard as the superior measure of the strength of association between the two variables and why?

Ordinal data consisting of assignments of objects to ordered categories

Kendall's tau

There is available on SPSS/PC+ another measure of agreement between two judges who rank order a set of objects. Since Kendall's tau has a different theoretical rationale from that of Spearman's rank correlation, the two statistics often have appreciably different values for the same set of paired ranks. Kendall's measure has advantages over that of Spearman, the most notable of which is that exact p-values are available even for very small samples and where ties are allowed.

The basic idea is that one set of ranks can be converted into another by a succession of reversals of pairs of ranks in one set: the fewer the reversals needed (in relation to the total number of possible reversals in the data set), the larger the value of tau.

The numerator of Kendall's tau is the difference between the number of pairs of objects whose ranks are concordant (ie they go in the same direction) and the number of discordant pairs. If the former predominate, the sign of tau is positive; if the latter predominate, tau is negative.

There are three different versions of Kendall's tau: tau-a, tau-b and tau-c. (Tau-a, however, cannot be directly requested in SPSS/PC+.) All three measures have the same numerator, the difference between the numbers of concordant and discordant pairs. It is in their denominators that they differ, the difference lying in the way they handle tied observations. The denominator of tau-a is simply the total number of pairs. The problem with tau-a is that when there are ties, its range quickly becomes restricted, to the point where its value becomes difficult to interpret. The correlation tau-b has terms in the denominator that consider, in either variable, pairs that are tied on one variable but not on the other. If no marginal frequency is 0, tau-b can attain a range of -1 to +1; but only with a square table. When there are no ties, the terms involving ties disappear and tau-b and tau-a have identical values.

Tau-c has a denominator which includes the smaller of the numbers of rows and columns. It can come close to attaining a range from -1 to +1 with any two-way table, even if the numbers of rows and columns are different.

Let us return to the problem of measuring the level of agreement between our two assessors' rankings of the ten paintings. This time, we shall simplify matters by supposing that there were just four paintings, and the judgements were as follows:

	Best			Worst
Judge 1	A	B	C	D
Judge 2	B	A	D	C

The command CROSSTABS expects data in the form of rows and columns whose values represent ordered categories. The cell frequencies are represented by a COUNT variable. The information we want to convey to CROSSTABS can be presented in the following matrix, whose entries are the numbers of objects given specified combinations of ranks by Judge 1 and Judge 2:

		Ranks by Judge 2			
		1	2	3	4
Ranks by Judge 1	1		1		
	2	1			
	3				1
	4			1	

Since we are going to weight the category combinations by cell counts, we shall only need to give information about the cells that contain non-zero tallies.

The following command sequence will obtain Kendall's tau-b which, since there are no ties, is in this case equal in value to tau-a.

```
DATA LIST FREE/rjudge1 rjudge2 count.
BEGIN DATA.
1 2 1 2 1 1 3 4 1 4 3 1
END DATA.
WEIGHT BY count.
CROSSTABS/TABLES rjudge1 BY rjudge2/STATISTICS BTAU.
```

• Write down the value of tau for this set of data.

NOMINAL DATA

Measures of association

In an earlier exercise, we considered the use of the chi-square statistic to test for the presence of an association between two qualitative variables. Recall that, provided that the data are suitable, the Pearson correlation measures the strength of a linear association between two scalar variables. In that case, therefore, the same statistic serves both as a test for the presence of an association and as a measure of associative strength. It might be thought that, with nominal data, the chi-square statistic would serve the same dual function. The chi-square statistic, however, cannot serve as a satisfactory measure of associative strength, because its value depends upon the total frequency.

There are several different ways of conceiving 'agreement' and 'association' in two-way tables and as a consequence, many measures have been devised, none of which is suitable in all situations. There are two kinds of measures: one kind is based upon the chi-square statistic; the other measures the proportional reduction in error when predicting category membership on one qualitative variable from knowledge of category membership on another.

Of the chi-square based measures, the phi coefficient is suitable for two-by-two contingency tables only, where it can achieve its full range from 0 to 1. (Note that with qualitative variables, it makes no sense to speak of a 'positive' or 'negative' association, because the categories of the variables are not ordered.)

For two-way tables with three or more degrees of freedom, Cramer's V is regarded as superior to the phi coefficient, because it continues to have a range from 0 to 1.

To illustrate the calculation of measures of association for two-way contingency tables, we can recall the example in Exercise 5, concerning the possibility of a gender difference in the choice of objects by children. Restore the command file to the scratch pad by using [F1], [F3] and Insert. It is shown below:

```
DATA LIST FREE/gender object count.
BEGIN DATA.
1 1 20 1 2 6 2 1 5 2 2 19
END DATA.
WEIGHT BY count.
VALUE LABELS gender 1 'Boys' 2 'Girls'/object 1 'A' 2 'B'.
CROSSTABS/TABLES gender BY object/STATISTICS CHISQ/CELLS COUNT.
```

The keyword PHI, when added to the /STATISTICS subcommand, will obtain phi (for a two-by-two table) and also Cramer's V for tables with two or more degrees of freedom. (Note that in a two-way contingency table with r rows and c columns, the degrees of freedom is (r-1)(c-1). So a 2 × 3 table has 2 degrees of freedom.). Thus edit the /STATISTICS subcommnd of CROSSTABS to:

/STATISTICS CHISQ PHI

Save and execute these commands.

- Write down the values of the chosen measures of association in the present example.

EXERCISE 15

SIMPLE, TWO-VARIABLE REGRESSION

[Before proceeding with this exercise, we strongly recommend you to read Chapter 12.]

The strength of a linear association between two variables can be measured by the Pearson correlation. If the association is both linear and strong, the scatterplot of the variables appears as a thinnish ellipse, with the major axis markedly longer than the minor axis.

But the existence of a substantial association between two variables can also be exploited to predict the scores of individuals on one variable from a knowledge of their scores on the other. This is achieved by drawing the best-fitting straight line (according to the least squares criterion) through the points in the cloud. This straight line, which is known as the regression line, passes through the point whose co-ordinates are the mean scores on the two variables and runs along the length of the ellipse close to (but not coincident with) the latter's major axis. Because the y-co-ordinates of points on the line are often rather close to the true values of the variable represented on the vertical axis, they can give serviceable predictions of individual subjects' scores on one variable from their scores on the other.

Regression is the obverse of correlation and *vice versa*: the former measures the strength of a linear association; the latter exploits it for predictive purposes. In Chapter 12, an example is discussed in which the existence of a substantial linear association between students' marks on their university entrance examinations and their performance later in their university careers (r = 0.671) was used to try to predict university success from the entrance marks. The regression equation is the straight line:

[predicted mark] = 3.23435 × [entrance mark]   -   47.53140

It was seen that many points on the regression line had y-co-ordinates very similar to the true university exam marks. As an exercise, we strongly advise you to work through the example in Chapter 12. In the present exercise, however, the emphasis is upon some of the pitfalls that await the unwary user of regression techniques; in fact, all the cautions and caveats that were made in the last exercise about the Pearson correlation apply with equal force to regression.

In the previous exercise, Anscombe's specially contrived data set (whose columns were named X1, X2, Y1, Y2, Y3, Y4) was saved in a file called A:anscombe.DAT. Scatterplots and correlation coefficients were obtained for the pairings (X1, Y1), (X1, Y2), (X1, Y3) and (X2, Y4). All sets yielded exactly the same value for the Pearson correlation. When the scatterplots were inspected, however, it was seen that the Pearson correlation was appropriate for only one data set: in the other sets, it would give the unwary user a highly misleading impression. One problem with the Pearson correlation is that it is very vulnerable to the leverage exerted by atypical data points, or outliers as they are termed. It can also show large values with monotonic but non-linear relationships.

All this is equally true of the parameters of the regression equation which, it should be noted, are algebraically related to the Pearson correlation: for example, the regression coefficient is actually r times the ratio of the standard deviation of the target (dependent) variable to that of the independent variable (or regressor). In this exercise, we return to Anscombe's data to investigate the statistics of the regression lines for the four sets of paired data.

Procedure

1)   Preparing the DATA LIST command

We shall assume that you have saved Anscombe's data to a separate data file named 'A:anscombe.DAT'. If so, its contents can be accessed by naming it in the DATA LIST command thus:

DATA LIST FILE 'A:anscombe.DAT' FREE/ X1 X2 Y1 TO Y4.

Save and execute this command.

2)   Preparing the REGRESSION command

As when obtaining Pearson correlations, it is essential to explore the data thoroughly, to ascertain the suitability of the statistics. In the previous exercise, for example, it was seen that in all but one case, the scatterplots indicated that the Pearson correlation was an unsuitable statistic for the data. In some of the data sets, it was quite clear that, since the relationship was far from linear, there would be little point either in calculating a Pearson correlation or in carrying out a regression analysis. Sometimes, however, if the purpose of the regression is to acquire a predictive tool, non-linearity of the relationship need not be a major problem, because the regression line can still yield predictions that are a great improvement upon chance. On the other hand, should the user wish to claim, perhaps on the basis of a model, that the relationship is specifically linear, the question of the true nature of the relationship is absolutely crucial.

In regression analysis, there is much emphasis upon a set of methods known as regression diagnostics, which are designed to assess how well a linear model fits the data set concerned. This is ascertained by to the study of residuals which, although there are many different types, are basically the differences, measured along the y-axis, between the points on the regression line and the true values of the dependent variable. In Chapter 12, there is some discussion of the commands that generate specified types of residuals.

It is not merely the size of the residuals that is important; though, of course, the more the points in the scatterplot tend to form a narrowly elliptical cloud, the smaller the residuals will tend to be, in relation to the mean value of the dependent variable. The underlined pattern of the residuals can make it abundantly clear that the relationship between the dependent and independent variables is non-linear.

For present purposes, the subcommand /SCATTERPLOT (*PRED *RESID) should provide illuminating tests of the credibility of the assumption that the data are linear.

The REGRESSION command can be pasted into the scratch pad by (1) typing REGRESSION into the scratch pad and [Esc] to obtain the menu, and (2) following the prompts. The advantage of working with the menu is that at various points the panels opposite keywords and commands offer useful explanations of the various terms. For the moment, however, we suggest you simply type the command shown below directly into the scratch pad.

For the regression of Y1 upon X1, the REGRESSION command is:

REGRESSION/VARIABLES X1 Y1/DESCRIPTIVES/DEPENDENT Y1/METHOD ENTER X1
    /SCATTERPLOT (*PRED *RESID).

Since we want to carry out regression upon all four (X,Y) data sets, it is convenient to request all four analyses with a single command. This can be done by extending the /DEPENDENT and /METHOD subcommands thus:

REGRESSION/VARIABLES X1 X2 Y1 TO Y4/DESCRIPTIVES /DEPENDENT Y1
    /METHOD ENTER X1/SCATTERPLOT (*PRED *RESID)
/DEPENDENT Y2 /METHOD ENTER X1/SCATTERPLOT (*PRED *RESID)
/DEPENDENT Y3 /METHOD ENTER X1/SCATTERPLOT (*PRED *RESID)
/DEPENDENT Y4 /METHOD ENTER X2/SCATTERPLOT (*PRED *RESID).

Save and execute this command.

4)   Interpreting the listing

The listing starts with two tables, one tabulating the descriptive statistics (mean and standard deviation) for each variable, the other tabulating all the correlations. Then there follows a series of tables and plots for each regression.

The main features are as follows:

i) The first regression table gives the multiple correlation coefficient R. This is the Pearson correlation between the true values of the dependent variable and the corresponding points on the regression line and is thus a measure of the association between the predicted and true values. The statistic R arises naturally in the context of multiple regression, in which the dependent variable is predicted from several independent variables. The value of R can never be negative, irrespective of the sign of the correlations between the dependent and independent variables. In the special case of simple regression, where there is only one independent variable, the multiple correlation is the absolute value of the Pearson correlation between the dependent and independent variables. The multiple R is followed by an analysis of variance of the components of regression.

- Write down the value of R.

ii) The next table contains the regression constants.

- Write down the regression equation. In the table, the regression coefficient (ie the slope of the regression line) is given in the column labelled 'B', in the row labelled with the name of the independent variable. Below the coefficient is the intercept (SPSS/PC+ terms this the 'constant') of the regression equation. Construct the regression equation by reading down the values in the B column thus:

  predicted value Y' = [upper value in B] × *independent variable* + [lower value in B]

iii)   The next table can be ignored for the time being. It lists statistics for various residual variables, the meaning of which is explained in good textbooks on regression such as Cook & Weisberg (1982). Howell (1992; Ch. 15) provides a helpful introduction to this difficult and technical topic.

iv)   Finally the scatterplot of Predicted value *PRED (Y') against Residual *RESID is shown. If all is well, the points on the graph should show no particular pattern (ie they should be randomly distributed).

- Describe the form of the scatterplot. Is it a circular cloud?

Note that the foregoing tables will appear for each of the regression analyses requested. From each set of tables, record the regression constants and statistics.

- Within rounding errors for numbers, what do you notice about the four regression equations and the four values of R, despite the differences among the scatterplots?

5) **Printing and terminating the SPSS/PC+ session**

If a printed listing is required, add a SET/LISTING command and re-execute all the commands. Terminate the session with FINISH.

EXERCISE 16
MULTIPLE REGRESSION

[We strongly recommend that the reader study Section 12.3 before proceeding with this exercise.]

Multiple regression is the construction of a linear equation by which the values of a dependent (target) variable can be estimated from two or more independent variables (regressors).

The data

Reading is a complex skill, so much so that many would argue that reading actually comprises many different component skills, all converging on the extraction of meaning from print.

A reading researcher hypothesises that certain specific kinds of pre-reading abilities and behaviour can predict later progress in reading, as measured by performance on reading tests taken some years after the child's first formal lessons. Let us, therefore, label the dependent variable in this study 'Progress'. While they are still very young indeed, many children evince a considerable grasp of English syntax in their speech. Our researcher devises a measure of their syntactic knowledge, 'Syntax', based upon the average length of their uttered sentences. Some researchers, however, argue that an infant's prelinguistic babbling (which we shall label 'Vocal') also plays a key role in their later reading performance. This variable, therefore, is also included in the study.

At the pre-reading stage, some very young children can acquire a sight vocabulary of several hundreds of words. The ability to pronounce these words on seeing them written down is known as Logographic reading; but many authorities do not regard logographic reading as 'reading' in the true sense, since the child evinces sight vocabulary long before acquiring any awareness of the alphabetic principle. Our researcher, who views the logographic strategy as important, includes a measure of this skill, *Logo*, in the study. Fifty children are studied over a period beginning in infancy and extending through their school years. Their subject numbers (Su) and scores on the four measures, *Progress* (P), *Logo* (L), *Vocal* (V) and *Syntax* (S), are listed in the appendix to this exercise.

Since it would be very laborious for you to type in all the data during the exercise, we must hope that your instructor has already stored them in a file which you can access. Let us suppose that the data are available in a file under the name reading.DAT.

Procedure

1) **Preparing the data commands**

The data can be accessed by writing the following DATA LIST command:

DATA LIST FILE 'A:reading.DAT' FREE/ progress logo vocal syntax.

Add a VARIABLE LABELS command:
VARIABLE LABELS progress 'Later Reading Performance' logo 'Early Sight Vocabulary' vocal 'Babbling' syntax 'Early Spoken Syntax'.

Save and execute these data commands.

2) Exploring the data

First use the methods of Exercise 2 to obtain descriptive statistics of the four variables in the study and to ascertain the distributions of the scores. The commands are:

DESCRIPTIVES/VARIABLES progress logo vocal syntax.
EXAMINE/VARIABLES progress logo vocal syntax/PLOT BOXPLOT/STATISTICS NONE.

Save and execute these commands. You will find that the four variables have distributions with rather similar values for their means and standard deviations. The boxplots confirm that their distributions are fairly symmetical.

3) Obtaining the correlations among the four variables

The intercorrelations among the four variables can be obtained with the CORRELATION command, which is:

CORRELATION/VARIABLES progress logo vocal syntax.

Save and execute this command. This will obtain a correlation matrix, ie a square array showing the correlation of each of the four variables in the study with each of the other variables, each row or column containing all the correlations involving one particular variable.

Notice that the dependent variable (*progress*) shows substantial correlations with both *logo* and *syntax*. On the other hand, there is no appreciable correlation between *logo* and *syntax*. The remaining variable (*vocal*) shows little association with any of the other variables; although there is a hint of a negative correlation with *logo*.

4) Carrying out the multiple regression analysis

Note that the following command can be pasted into the scratch pad by (1) typing REGRESSION and [Esc] to obtain the menu, and (2) following the prompts. The advantage of working with the menu is that at various points, the panels opposite keywords and commands offer useful explanations of the various terms. For the moment, however, we suggest you simply type the command directly into the scratch pad:

REGRESSION/VARIABLES progress logo syntax vocal/DEPENDENT progress/METHOD STEPWISE.

5) Inspecting the regression output

i)   The first table has the heading: 'Variable(s) Entered on Step Number'. This table shows which variable was entered at Step 1. It is followed by the multiple correlation coefficient R, R Squared, Adjusted R Squared, and the Standard Error. R Squared is an important statistic, because it provides a measure of the proportion of variation in the dependent variable that is predictable from the best linear combination of the independent variables - the higher the value, the better the prediction.

Note that in the present example, the value of R squared is considerably larger when a second regressor (independent variable) is entered into the equation.

There is also an ANOVA of the regression, showing that the slope is significant with a very small tail probability.

ii)   The next tables have the captions, 'Variables in the Equation' and 'Variables not in the Equation'. These show which variables have been included and which excluded at this Step. There follows a similar table for

Exercises

Step 2.

- From the table at Step 2, write out the multiple regression equation. Note that the values of the regression parameters are given in column B. You will need the values in this column to write the equation.

iii) The table with the caption 'Variables not in the Equation' shows any variables that have been excluded from the equation because they fail certain criteria for inclusion.

- Which variable has been excluded at Step 2? Does this surprise you? Write down your explanation.

6) <u>Using the multiple regression equation to estimate a person's later reading score from variables measured in infancy</u>

The multiple regression equation will be of the general form:

$$progress = \text{constant} + \text{coefficient} \times logo + \text{coefficient} \times syntax$$

By substituting a particular person's scores on *logo* and *syntax* into the equation, that person's *progress* score can be estimated.

Suppose we want to use the multiple regression equation to estimate the *progress* score of person number 22. This can be done by using the PROCESS IF, COMPUTE and LIST commands (see Section 4.5.2 for PROCESS IF). The COMPUTE command calculates the value of the estimate (represented by the new variable name *est*) from the values of *logo* and *syntax* multiplied by their respective coefficients from the regression equation. In writing the COMPUTE command, you must substitute the values of the coefficients for each *coefficient*, and the value of the constant for *constant*, in the command below. (The symbol * represents multiplication in computer usage and must be used in place of the arithmetical sign ×.) The LIST command will tabulate the resulting estimate, along with the values of the other variables.

The commands are as follows:

```
PROCESS IF ($SUBNUM EQ 22).
COMPUTE est = coefficient*logo + coefficient*syntax + constant.
LIST est progress.
```

Save and execute these commands.

- Compare the estimate with the subject's true Progress score. Write down the value of the residual. Was the estimate accurate?

7) <u>Terminating the session and printing the output listing</u>

If a printed listing is required, add a SET/LISTING command and re-execute all the commands. Terminate with FINISH.

Appendix to Exercise 16

The data are as follows:

Su	P	L	V	S
1	65	75	34	48
2	46	55	75	32
3	65	50	75	68
4	34	32	42	27
5	58	29	18	67
6	51	31	50	66
7	71	65	23	64
8	54	64	55	32
9	42	40	43	38
10	61	69	59	46
11	60	56	52	44
12	81	82	60	69
13	55	55	9	48
14	45	19	71	59
15	17	10	64	20
16	77	66	50	79
17	68	81	41	54
18	53	48	44	45
19	55	41	41	55
20	57	30	20	54
21	59	28	72	68
22	46	45	29	45
23	69	51	14	62
24	80	82	65	58
25	50	39	31	42

Su	P	L	V	S
26	25	28	58	28
27	47	49	46	59
28	89	51	52	48
29	50	26	78	56
30	71	70	51	54
31	53	14	53	77
32	50	34	45	60
33	71	84	46	50
34	30	55	42	25
35	50	40	51	31
36	69	49	72	72
37	65	71	30	52
38	62	53	52	57
39	80	45	59	90
40	71	69	57	60
41	34	30	30	20
42	47	20	78	69
43	51	18	22	61
44	39	25	81	49
45	44	71	79	22
46	60	46	80	67
47	79	58	13	82
48	47	62	26	30
49	70	66	40	61
50	51	43	31	50

EXERCISE 17

FACTOR ANALYSIS

Suppose that a battery of tests is given to a group of 200 subjects, with a view to exploring the relationships between anxiety and a number of clinical and personality measures. When the data have been gathered, the correlation between each test and every other test in the battery can be arrayed in a correlation matrix (R). Correlation matrices can be very large, depending, of course, on the size of the test battery.

In factor analysis, it is assumed that performance on a variety of tests may tap relatively few psychological dimensions. The purpose of a factor analysis is to use the information in the correlation matrix to classify the tests with respect to a relatively small number of axes, or factors as they are termed. It is assumed that if this is possible, these mathematical factors can be taken to represent the latent dimensions.

The first product of a factor analysis is an unrotated factor matrix. In the cells of this matrix are the weightings, or loadings, of the tests on the factors specified by the column headings. A loading, like the Pearson correlation, can vary within the range from -1 to +1 (though these end values are never obtained in practice). Each test can be thought of as a point in a space whose dimensions are the factors: the loadings of a test are its coordinates with respect to the factor axes. The loading of a test on a factor is a measure of the importance of that factor in accounting for the variance that that particular test shares with others in the battery.

The factors (or axes) in a factor analysis are constructed, or extracted, one at a time, this process being repeated until it is possible, from the loadings of the tests on all the factors so far extracted, to generate good approximations to the correlations in the original R matrix. Factor analysis tells us how many axes (or factors) are necessary to achieve a reconstruction that is sufficiently good to account satisfactorily for R.

If we think of the tests in the battery and the origin of the axes as stationary points and rotate the axes around the origin, the values of all the loadings will change. Nevertheless, the new set of loadings on the axes in any position can still be used to produce as good an approximation of R as when the axes were in their original position. In this sense, the position of the axes is arbitrary. At the first stage, factor analysis only tells us <u>how many</u> axes are necessary to classify the data adequately: it does not thereby establish that the initial position of the axes is the most appropriate one.

In <u>rotation</u>, the factor axes are rotated around the fixed origin until the loadings meet a certain criterion. The set of loadings that satisfies the criterion is known as the <u>rotated factor matrix</u>. The purpose of any rotation is to achieve a configuration of loadings having the qualities collectively known as <u>simple structure</u> which, loosely conceived, is the set of loadings that shows the maximum number of tests loading on the minimum number of factors. The rationale of simple structure is that the fewer the factors that are involved in accounting for the correlations among a group of tests, the easier it is to invest those factors with psychological meaning. In fact, simple structure is an ideal never achieved in practice, partly because the concept as originally formulated is actually rather vague and embodies contradictory qualities. Computing packages such as SPSS/PC+ offer a selection of rotation methods, each based upon a different (but reasonable) interpretation of simple structure. The most common rotation method is known as <u>varimax</u>.

The Data

Suppose that a group of 200 subjects is given a battery of personality tests, comprising the following items:

Anxiety; Agoraphobia; Arachnophobia; Extraversion; Adventurousness; Sociability.

The first step is to generate a correlation matrix from the data on all these tests using the CORRELATIONS command, as described in Section 15.2.1. There is obviously not enough time for you to do this now, so we shall input a correlation matrix (R) directly, as described in Section 15.2.5. Suppose the matrix is as shown below:

	Anxiety	Agora	Arachno	Advent	Extrav	Sociab
Anxiety	1.0000	0.8560	0.7845	0.0820	0.0560	0.0995
Agora	0.8560	1.0000	0.8271	0.0564	0.0283	0.0752
Arachno	0.7845	0.8271	1.0000	0.0624	0.0369	0.0795
Advent	0.0820	0.0564	0.0624	1.0000	0.8652	0.8396
Extrav	0.0560	0.0283	0.0369	0.8652	1.0000	0.8560
Sociab	0.0995	0.0752	0.0795	0.8396	0.8560	1.0000

Procedure

1) Preparing the DATA LIST command

Since the data will comprise the correlation coefficients in R (the correlation matrix), the DATA LIST command must contain reference to as many variables as there are columns (or rows) in R. Notice the keyword MATRIX: this tells SPSS/PC+ that the data will be in the form of a matrix for reading by a later command. The correct command (assuming that the data will be entered after DATA LIST) is:

DATA LIST MATRIX FREE/anxiety agora arachno advent extrav sociab.

2) Entering the size of n

Specify the number of subjects in the study by typing the following into the scratch pad:

n 200.

3)   Typing in the correlation matrix

A correlation matrix is <u>square</u>, that is, there are as many rows as there are columns. The diagonal of cells running from top left to bottom right is known as the <u>principal diagonal</u> of the matrix. Since the variables are labelled in the same order in the rows and columns of R, each of the cells along the principal diagonal contains the corrrelation of one of the variables with itself (ie 1). The correlations in the off-diagonal cells are the same above and below the principal diagonal (the correlation of agora with sociab is identical with the correlation of sociab with agora). A <u>triangular matrix</u> is that part of a square matrix comprising the entries along the principal diagonal and the off-diagonal entries either above or below: the <u>upper triangular matrix</u> comprises the entries in the principal diagonal plus the off-diagonal entries above it; the <u>lower triangular matrix</u> comprises the entries in the principal diagonal and the off-diagonal entries below it. Either of the triangular versions of R contains all the information in R. We shall enter the correlations in the form of a lower triangular matrix. Type in the correlation matrix between the BEGIN DATA and END DATA commands, just as in Section 15.2.5, taking a new line for each new variable and concluding each line with the value 1.0 as follows:

```
BEGIN DATA.
1.00
0.8560 1.00
0.7845 0.8271 1.00
. . . . . . . . . . . . . . . . .
. . . . . . . . . . . . . . . . . . . . . .
0.0995 0.0752 0.0795 0.8396 0.8560 1.00
END DATA.
```

Having checked the contents of the scratch pad to make sure there have been no transcription errors, save and execute the data commands to ensure that the DATA LIST command has been correctly prepared.

4)   Preparing the FACTOR command

Note that the FACTOR command can be pasted into the scratch pad by (1) moving into the <u>extended menus</u> with [Alt]/X, (2) typing FACTOR into the scratch pad and [Esc] to obtain the menu, and (3) following the prompts. The advantage of working with the menu is that at various points, the panels opposite keywords and commands offer useful explanations of the various terms. For the moment, however, we suggest you simply type the command directly into the scratch pad.

First, type in the basic FACTOR command, which is as follows:

FACTOR /VARIABLES ALL/READ CORRELATION TRIANGLE.

Associated with each factor is a quantity called the <u>eigenvalue</u>, which, in the present context, is a number expressing the amount of variance in the scores that is accounted for by that particular factor. As factors continue to be extracted, their eigenvalues diminish. The plot of eigenvalue against ordinal position of factor falls sharply at first, but then straightens out into a straight, gradual decline which has been fancifully likened to the scree on a mountainside. At this stage, further factors account for very little variance, and factor extraction ceases when it is reached. The keyword EIGEN draws the 'scree' graph of the factors in the listing.

The subcommand /FORMAT allows the user to instruct SPSS/PC+ to suppress loadings of less than a specified value. This can make a factor matrix much easier to interpret.

Finally the /ROTATION subcommand allows the user to specify the rotation method (we shall choose the varimax method).

Now complete the FACTOR command as follows:

FACTOR/VARIABLES ALL/READ CORRELATION TRIANGLE/FORMAT SORT BLANK(.5)
/PLOT EIGEN/ROTATION VARIMAX.

Save and execute this command.

5)   Interpreting the listing

The listing for FACTOR is very extensive; although our omission of the subcommand /PRINT ALL has shortened it somewhat. You should find it helpful to read Section 15.2.4 for explanations of some features of the output.

The most important table is the penultimate one, with the title: 'Rotated Factor Matrix'.

- Construct your own table from the rotated factor matrix in the listing, showing the loadings of each of the variables on the two factors that have emerged from the analysis. State clearly whether there is a tendency for different groups of variables to load upon different factors.

6)   Terminating the session

If a printed listing is required, add a SET/LISTING command, and execute the entire set of commands. Terminate with FINISH.

EXERCISE 18
LOGLINEAR ANALYSIS

The psychologist is often faced with the problem of analysing nominal data in the form of multi-way contingency tables, the cells of which contain counts for combinations of three of more qualitative or categorial variables. The common (but very bad) practice of 'collapsing' across some of the variables to produce two-way tables that can be subjected to the traditional Pearsonian chi-square test (see Exercise 5) is fraught with danger. Fortunately, recent years have seen great developments in this area, including the advent of loglinear models. These methods allow the researcher to study the often intricate interplay among the factors at work in complex contingency tables.

A statistical model is an interpretation of a data set, usually in the form of an equation, stating how the data have been generated and accordingly predicting certain aspects of the data. The closeness with which the predictions approximate the true data is a measure of the adequacy of the model in accounting for the data.

Superficially, a loglinear model looks rather like a model for factorial ANOVA: there are main effect terms, each relating to just one of the qualitative variables in the classification; and there are interaction terms, involving two or more variables. Also, as in the ANOVA, the estimate is obtained by summing the main effect and interaction terms. Yet there are also important differences between the two kinds of model.

In ANOVA, the model interprets an individual score *partly* as a linear combination of main effects and interaction terms. Since there is always a random error component, however, the exact prediction of an individual score is impossible, and so a random error term appears in the model's equation.

In a loglinear model, the target for estimation is the cell count, not an individual's category membership. You may recall, however, that estimates of cell frequencies (the expected frequencies) under the null hypothesis that the variables are independent are obtained by multiplicative probability rules. By making the subject (ie the left hand side) of the equation the logarithm of the cell frequency, rather than the cell frequency itself, these multiplicative expressions are transformed to summations. (Recall that the logarithm of a product of terms is the sum of the logarithms of those terms.) So it is that a loglinear model expresses the log of a cell count as the sum of main effect and interaction terms (which are themselves based upon the logs of the original frequencies).

Another important difference between loglinear and ANOVA models is that a loglinear model containing all the possible main effect and interaction terms can predict the cell counts exactly. Such a model is known as a saturated model. The purpose of the exercise, however, is to ascertain which effect terms (if any) can be dropped from the full model to produce an adequate interpretation of the data. The process of constructing a loglinear model is described more fully in Section 13.1.3.

Exercises

There are different kinds of loglinear models. In <u>hierarchical</u> models, the presence of an interaction effect term implies that all lower-order effects involving terms (exclusively) from the interaction must also be present in the model. In specifying such a model, therefore, it is only necessary to present the highest-order interaction term, which is known as the <u>generating class</u> of the model.

Recall that in a factorial ANOVA (with a fixed number of observations per cell), the total sum of squares can be <u>partitioned</u> into (ie expressed as the sum of) a set of components associated with the various main effects and interactions. In a similar way, in loglinear analysis, the total value of a statistic known as the <u>likelihood-ratio chi-square statistic</u> can similarly be partitioned into components representing the various effect terms. The difference, however, is that, since the saturated model predicts the (logs of the) cell frequencies perfectly, the value of the likelihood-ratio chi-square statistic must be zero for the saturated model. As effects are progressively, removed, however, the value of chi-square increases, and the summative property is used to appraise the contributions of the different orders of effect components, with a view to possibly discarding them from the final model. This is the basis of the strategy known as <u>backward elimination</u>.

In this exercise, a hierarchical loglinear analysis will be applied to a multi-way contingency table, with a view to teasing out the relationships among the variables involved. In SPSS/PC+, hierarchical loglinear analyses are carried out by a program called HILOGLINEAR, and the backward elimination procedure is specified by the subcommand /METHOD BACKWARD.

The Data

In the literature on helping behaviour by (and towards) men and women, there is much interest in three questions:

(1) Are women more likely to receive help?

(2) Are women more likely to give help?

(3) Are people more likely to help members of their own sex?

A male or female confederate of the experimenter approached male and female students who were entering a university library and asked them to participate in a survey. The following table shows the incidence of helping in relation to the sex of the confederate and that of the subject.

CONFEDERATE (sex of)	SUBJECT (sex of)	HELP Yes	No
Male	Male	52	35
	Female	21	43
Female	Male	39	40
	Female	23	75

In order to answer the three research questions, these results will be subjected to a hierarchical loglinear analysis, following the backward elimination strategy with a view to fitting the most parsimonious unsaturated model.

Before carrying out any formal analysis, however, a brief inspection of the contingency table may prove informative. First of all, we notice that, on the whole, help was more likely to be refused than given; moreover, the females helped less than did the males. In view of the generally lower rate of helping in the female subjects, therefore, there seems to be little support for the hypothesis that females help more. Finally, turning to the third question, although the male subjects did help the male confederate more often, the female subjects tended to be more helpful towards the male confederate. From a superficial inspection, therefore, the present data do not seem to affirm any of the three research questions.

Procedure

1)   Entering the data and preparing the DATA LIST command

There are three variables in the contingency table: (1) Confederate's Sex (*confsx*); (2) Subject's Sex (*subjsx*); (3) Subject's Response (*help*). Since there must be a coding variable for each of these, plus another variable of cell counts, the data set will comprise four variables in all. Write the DATA LIST command as follows:

DATA LIST FREE/confsx subjsx help count.

Let us assign the code numbers 1 and 2 to the categories of the three variables *confsx*, *subjsx* and *help* where, in the case of the first two variables, 1 = 'Male' and 2 = 'Female', and in the third, 1 = 'Yes' and 2 = 'No'. The data can be entered between the BEGIN DATA and END DATA commands as follows:

```
BEGIN DATA.
1 1 1 52
1 1 2 35
1 2 1 21
1 2 2 43
2 1 1 39
2 1 2 40
2 2 1 23
2 2 2 75
END DATA.
```

(2)   Adding the VARIABLE LABELS and VALUE LABELS commands

As always, it is essential to clarify the output by using the labelling commands to supply keys to the code numbers that were assigned to the categories. For present purposes, suitable commands are as follows:

VARIABLE LABELS confsx 'Sex of Confederate' subjsx 'Sex of Subject' help 'Whether Help was Given'.
VALUE LABELS confsx 1 'Male' 2 'Female' /subjsx 1 'Male' 2 'Female'/help 1 'Yes' 2 'No'.

3)   Adding the WEIGHT BY command

In an actual research situation, the data on each subject would be entered individually into the data set, and the CROSSTABS command would be used to construct the contingency table. In this case, however, we begin at the point where the contingency table has already been constructed. Accordingly, we must weight the combinations of coding variables by the cell frequencies by adding a WEIGHT BY command thus:

WEIGHT BY count.

Save and execute all these data commands.

(4)   Preparing the HILOGLINEAR command

The following command obtains a hierarchical loglinear analysis, following the backward-elimination procedure:

HILOGLINEAR confsx subjsx help(1,2) /METHOD BACKWARD.

Save and execute this command.

(5)   Interpreting the listing

Fuller details are given in Section 13.2.2. The first item is of little interest, since it shows the observed and expected frequencies generated by the fully saturated model which, as we have seen, must be a perfect fit. Notice that the likelihood ratio chi-square is zero, and the p-value is 1.

The next table, with the caption 'Tests that K-way and higher order effects are zero' is much more interesting. Since the highest-order term is the three-way interaction, the first row of the table (K = 3) tests the null hypothesis that there is no three-way interaction. The very low value of the L-R chi-square (0.009) and its very high p-value (0.9261) show that there is no evidence against the null hypothesis: we can conclude that there is no three-way interaction.

The next row (K = 2) shows that if the two-way interaction terms are removed, the model is a very poor fit (p-value < 0.00005). The L-R chi-square is also very substantial (35.336). Clearly, there is at least one two-way interaction in the table. But which are the real contributors?

Tables of 'Estimates of Parameters' appear now. Of interest is whether any of the interactions or main effects have an absolute Z-Value (the fourth column in the table) greater than 1.96 (the 5% significance level).

- Which interactions or main effects have a Z-Value greater than 1.96 (ignore any negative signs)?

The listing now proceeds to report tests of models in which one of the two-way interaction terms has been left out. It can be seen that only the interaction between *confsx* and *subjsx* can be removed so that the increment in the L-R chi-square has a p-value not less than 0.05. That term, therefore, is dropped from the model.

The final model has two interaction terms: *confsx*help* and *subjsx* help*.

- Note down the value of the L-R chi-square associated with the best-fitting model. This is a measure of the failure of the model to predict the cell frequencies.

Finally the listing shows a table of 'Observed, Expected Frequencies and Residuals'. Notice how small the residuals are.

Now that we know there are two interactions present in the data, these can be explored by constructing two-way tables.

- Construct tables showing the total counts for confsx*help and subjsx*help. Relate the patterns in the tables to the original experimental hypotheses. What are your answers to the three research questions?

(6)   Testing the hypothesis of total independence

It is interesting to compare the value of the L-R chi-square for the final loglinear model with the value of chi-square that would have been obtained from a test of the model of total independence of all three variables. Despite the fact that it contains the word 'HILOGLINEAR', the following command does not obtain a loglinear analysis: it will result in the traditional chi-square test of independence of all three variables in the three-way classification:

HILOGLINEAR confsx subsx help (1,2)/DESIGN confsx subsx help.

Save and execute this new command.

- Compare the value of chi-square with that for the final loglinear model.

Conclusion

It should be quite clear from the foregoing comparisons that the final loglinear model is a very considerable improvement upon the model of total independence. Log-linear models provide a powerful tool for teasing out the relationships among the variables in multi-way contingency tables.

EXERCISE 19

PREDICTING CATEGORY MEMBERSHIP: DISCRIMINANT ANALYSIS

We have seen that in multiple regression, the aim is to predict the values of a target or <u>dependent variable</u> from the values of two or more <u>independent variables</u>, or <u>regressors</u>. This is achieved by constructing a linear function of the independent variables whose value varies as closely as possible with the values of the dependent variable. The situation often arises, however, where what is of interest is the prediction of <u>category membership</u>, rather than values of a quantitative variable. Of the youngest children at a school, for example, which will subsequently go on to higher education? Of premature babies, which will survive and which will perish? Which road users will have fatal accidents?

The problem has been likened to one of trying to see the future in a crystal ball. We can suppose, however, that, unlike the fortune-teller, the forecaster has available data on a number of relevant variables, and the question is whether this information can be used to predict category membership. We can also suppose that our data base, like those used by insurance companies, includes a sufficiency of past cases where the eventual category membership is known, so that we can attempt to formulate precise rules to aid us in our predictions of future category membership. In <u>discriminant analysis</u>, the aim is construct, from the independent variables, linear functions which, because they differentiate as much as possible between the cases in the different groups, are known as <u>discriminant functions</u>. Provided they are sufficiently effective in doing this, such functions can be used to predict category membership.

More precisely, the purpose of discriminant analysis is this: Given the independent variables IV1, IV2, . . ., IVp, the object is to find a linear function (D) of the IVs such that when a one-way ANOVA is carried out to compare the categories of the qualitative dependent variable with respect to D, the ratio $SS_{between}/SS_{total}$ is as large as possible. D will be of the general form:

$$D = b_0 + b_1(IV1) + b_2(IV2) + . . . + b_p(IVp)$$

As in multiple regression, it is possible to identify those variables that make significant contributions to the predictive process and drop the others from the final function. There are many other parallels between the two statistical techniques.

Recall that in one-way ANOVA, the total sum of squares (SS_{total}), which is a measure of the total dispersion of the scores around the grand mean, can be partitioned into two components: (1) $SS_{between}$; (2) SS_{within}. The first of these components is the dispersion of the group means around the grand mean; the second is the dispersion of the scores around their group means. The three sums of squares are related according to the identity:

$SS_{total} = SS_{between} + SS_{within}$

Other things being equal, the ANOVA is more likely to show significance if the ratio ($SS_{between}/SS_{total}$) is close to unity: that is, the group means show large dispersion, whereas the individual scores lie close to their group means.

The quantity ($SS_{between}/SS_{total}$) is known as the <u>correlation ratio</u> (eta squared). The correlation ratio is the oldest of various ANOVA measures of the strength of the effect that a treatment factor exerts upon the dependent variable.

The idea of strength of effect can be expressed in another way. In the univariate case (i.e. where there is just one dependent variable), the ratio SS_{within}/SS_{total} gives the value of a statistic known as <u>Wilks' lambda</u>. Wilks' lambda is the complement of the ratio $SS_{between}/SS_{total}$, that is

Wilks' lambda + correlation ratio (eta squared) = 1

The <u>smaller</u> the value of Wilks' lambda, the more chance there is of a significant ANOVA result, because the relatively small dispersion of the individual scores around their group means implies a relatively large dispersion among the group means.

In discriminant analysis, the question of whether a function can be found which reliably discriminates among the categories of the dependent variable is answered by a chi-square test of the value of Wilks' lambda, rather than an ANOVA. The two tests, however, will give exactly the same result.

For each of the categories of the dependent variable, there will be a (supposedly normal) distribution of D for the members of that category. The distributions will usually overlap, of course; but the goal of discriminant analysis is to find values for the constants $(b_0, b_1, \ldots, b_p)$ in the discriminant function such that the overlap among the distributions of D is minimised. In other words, the idea is to spread out the distributions of D to the greatest possible extent.

If there are only two categories in the dependent variable, only one discriminant function can be constructed. If the qualitative dependent variable comprises three or more categories, a discriminant analysis can yield several D functions: in general, if there are k categories in the qualitative variable, it is possible to construct (k - 1) independent D functions, each accounting for less association than its predecessor. It has been found, however, that usually only the first one or two of these discriminate significantly among the categories of the dependent variable.

The data

Just before they leave school, students in the most senior class of a school are regularly tested on their comprehension of a difficult reading passage. Typically, only 50% of students can perform the task. We shall also suppose that, for a substantial number of past pupils, we have available data not only on their performance on the comprehension passage but also on the very same variables that were investigated in the exercise on multiple regression, namely, the reading-related measures that we have referred to as *logo*, *syntax* and *vocal*, all of which were taken in the very earliest stages of the children's education.

The full data set is given in the appendix of this exercise. As with the multiple regression example, we can only hope that the data have already been stored in a file with a name such as **discrim.DAT**, the contents of which you can access by using the DATA LIST command. The first and last few lines of the data set are as follows:

Logo	Syntax	Vocal	Comprehension
10	20	64	1
28	28	58	1

. . . .

BODY OF DATA SET   (The whole set has fifty rows)

. . . .

82	69	60	2
51	48	52	2

The rightmost variable, Comprehension, is a coding variable whose values, 1 and 2, denote, respectively, failure and success on the comprehension task.

Procedure

(1)   <u>Entering the data</u>

The data set can be accessed by writing the following DATA LIST command:

DATA LIST FILE 'A:discrim.DAT' FREE/ logo syntax vocal comp.

(2)   <u>Writing the VARIABLE LABELS and VALUE LABELS commands</u>

The following commands will clarify the output:

VARIABLE LABELS logo 'Logographic' comp 'Comprehension'.
VALUE LABELS comp 1 'Failure' 2 'Success'.

Save and execute these data commands.

(3)   Exploring the data

Before moving on to the main analysis, a preliminary exploration of the data will bring out at least some of the important features. For example, if a particular variable is going to be useful in assigning individuals to categories, one might expect that, if its scores are subdivided according to category membership, there should be a substantial difference between the group means; if, on the other hand, there is no such difference, that would suggest that the variable will play a minimal role in the final discriminant function. To investigate these differences, one-way ANOVAs can be used to compare the group means on the various independent variables. These tests are requested by options within the subcommand /STATISTICS of the command for discriminant analysis. We shall therefore return to the descriptive statistics when we come to write the main discriminant command.

Since discriminant analysis assumes that the distribution of the independent variables is multivariate normal, we shall also need to look at their empirical distributions to ascertain the credibility of that assumption.

(4)   Obtaining displays of the distributions of the dependent variables

The following commands will obtain displays of the empirical distributions of the predictor variables.

EXAMINE/VARIABLES logo syntax vocal BY comp/PLOT BOXPLOT/STATISTICS NONE.

The listing from EXAMINE will describe each IV in turn, first ignoring the dependent variable *comp*, and then showing side-by-side displays for each category. Save and execute this command.

- Study the output and note whether the boxplots reveal any outliers. Do the side-by-side boxplots show anything of interest?

(5)   Obtaining point-biserial correlations

At this point, it should be noted that, if there are only two groups, there is a close link between the comparison of the two group means on one of the independent variables and the correlation of that independent variable with the (qualitative) target variable. This correlation is found by taking the absolute value of the Pearson correlation between the scores on the independent variable and the code numbers representing group membership. (The values of the code numbers are quite arbitrary: they need only be different.) This correlation is known as the point-biserial correlation.

It can be shown that, in this special two-group case, the square of the point-biserial correlation is equal to the ANOVA statistic eta squared (i.e. $SS_{between}/SS_{within}$), so that the point-biserial correlation itself is equal to eta.

The following command will obtain the point-biserial correlations between each of the three IVs in the study and the qualitative, two-group dependent variable.

CORRELATION/VARIABLES log syntax vocal WITH comp.

Save and execute this command.

- Write down the values of the point-biserial correlations between each of the three independent variables and the dichotomous target variable *comp*.

(6)   Writing the command for discriminant analysis

Type DSCRIMINANT (or DSCR as a short-cut) in the scratch pad (note the spelling - there is no I after the D) and press [Esc] to get the menu. To obtain some of the options in the subcommand /STATISTICS, it is necessary to type [Alt]/X to access the extended menu. Read through the relevant items in order to understand the construction of the command given below, which you can subsequently type directly in the scratch pad:

DSCRIMINANT/GROUPS comp(1,2) /VARIABLES logo syntax vocal/STATISTICS 1 2 6 11 13 15.

The /STATISTICS options are as follows:

1	means of variables
2	standard deviations of variables
6	univariate F ratios (ie oneway ANOVAs comparing the two groups on each of the three IVs)
11	unstandardised discriminant function coefficients
13	classification results table (or confusion matrix)
15	histogram of discriminant scores (D).

SPSS/PC+ uses the discriminant function D and a rule in probability known as Bayes' theorem to allocate cases to the categories of the dependent variable. Since the correct category membership is known, the accuracy of this allocation can be also be determined. The confusion matrix is a table showing the numbers of cases in each group that have been accurately categorised.

The all-groups histogram is a display showing the degree of overlap between the distributions of D in the two groups.

The discriminant function itself is requested by option 11. In the output, it will appear under the heading: 'Unstandardised Canonical Discriminant Function Coefficients'.

Notice that, in contrast with the command described in Chapter 14, no /METHOD subcommand has been included here. In Chapter 14, we recommended the stepwise method of minimisation of Wilks' lambda (/METHOD WILKS). In the present example, because of its simplicity, it is better to use the default method known as DIRECT or (forced entry), in which all the variables are entered simultaneously (provided they meet certain tolerance criteria). Since forced entry is the default method, there is no need to specify it in a subcommand.

Now save and execute the DSCRIMINANT command.

(7)   Interpreting the listing

The first table shows the number of cases in each of the categories of the variable *group*.

The next tables give the means and standard deviations requested by options 1 and 2.

- Note the variables with substantial differences between the groups. Compare the differences between group means with the values of the point-biserial correlations that you recorded earlier.

The next table, headed 'Wilks' lambda (U-statistic) and univariate F-ratio', shows the F-ratios (and their associated p-values) for the comparisons between the groups on each of the three independent variables.

The value of Wilks' lambda given in each of the ANOVAs is equal to one minus the square of the point-biserial correlation of each variable with the dependent variable: lambda is the complement of the correlation ratio.

- Which variables have significant F ratios and which do not?

There now follows the first of the tables showing the output of the discriminant analysis proper. Its title is 'Canonical Discriminant Functions'. Because there are only two groups, there is only one function.

The most important entries in the table are the statistic lambda, its chi-square value and the associated p-value. You will notice immediately that the value of lambda is smaller than the value for any of the three IVs considered separately. That is well and good: the discriminant function D, which uses the information in all the IVs should do a better job than any one IV alone. Here there is an obvious parallel with multiple regression, in which the predictive ability of the multiple regression equation cannot be less than the simple regressions of the target variable on any one regressor alone. Just as, in multiple regression, predictions can only improve when more regressors are added, the addition of another variable to the discriminant function can only improve its efficacy (although, in the case of the variable *vocal*, the improvement is negligible).

Since, however, two of the IVs can each discriminate reliably between the groups, the result of the chi-square test of lambda in the discriminant analysis table is a foregone conclusion. As expected, the p-value is very small. The discriminant function D can indeed discriminate reliably between the two groups on the basis of performance on the independent variables.

Ignore the table of standardized Canonical Discriminant Function Coefficients.

A more useful table is the next one, labelled 'Structure Matrix: Pooled-within-groups correlations between discriminating variables and canonical discriminant functions'.

- Which variables have the larger correlations and which has the smallest? Does this correspond with previous observations?

The next table, entitled 'Unstandardized Canonical Discriminant Function Coefficients', gives the values of the parameters of the discriminant function D.

The entries in the first three rows are presented in what is known as <u>scientific notation</u>, in which the term 'E-01' means 'multiplied by ten to the power of -1', which is the same as 'divided by ten to the power of +1'. So divide the numbers in the first row by ten, and the third row by 1000 (i.e. 10^{+3}).

- Write out the discriminant function D.

Examine the 'All-groups stacked histogram' to ascertain the success of the discriminant function in minimising the overlap between the distributions of D in the two groups. Notice that, although the groups are generally well separated, some 2s intrude into the area dominated by the 1s and *vice versa*. This means that, if category membership is unknown, SPSS/PC+ will misassign some of the cases to the wrong group.

We have shown that the discriminant function D discriminates effectively between the two groups; but <u>how effectively</u> does it do this? This is shown by the confusion matrix, which appears under the heading: 'Classification Results'.

- Note down the percentage of grouped cases correctly classified, the percentage of correct group 1 predictions and the percentage of correct group 2 predictions.

Conclusion

This exercise is intended to be merely an introduction to the use of a complex and sophisticated statistical technique. Accordingly, we chose an example of the simplest possible application, in which the dependent variable comprises only two categories. The simplicity of our interpretation of a number of statistics such as Wilks' lambda breaks down when there are more than two categories in the dependent variable. For a treatment of such cases, see Tabachnick & Fidell (1989).

Appendix to Exercise 19

A) Some further explorations

From the foregoing discussion, we know that the value of the point-biserial correlation between the discriminant function D and the dependent variable should be the square root of the complement of Wilks' lambda.

Exercises

Use the discriminant function D to calculate a D score for each person. Ignore the IV 'vocal', whose coefficient is miniscule compared with the those of the other IVs. The command is:

COMPUTE dscore = b_0 + b_1*logo + b_2*syntax.

where b_0, b_1 and b_2 are the parameters whose values were noted earlier from the table showing the unstandardized canonical discriminant function coefficients.

Save and execute this COMPUTE command.

Next, calculate the point-biserial correlation between dscore and comp, using the command:

CORRELATIONS/VARIABLES dscore WITH comp.

- Write down the value of the correlation so obtained. Compare this value with the point-biserial correlations for the individual independent variables. Confirm that $(1 - r^2)$ is the value of lambda given in the discriminant table.

As a final exercise, carry out a one-way ANOVA comparing the means of the two groups with respect to D. The command is:

ONEWAY/VARIABLES dscore BY comp(1,2).

- Obtain the values of $SS_{between}$ and SS_{total} from the Sum of Squares column of the ANOVA table. Confirm that the ratio $(SS_{between}/SS_{total})$ is the square of the point-biserial correlation between D and the dependent variable. Check also that the complement of this is the value of lambda given in the output.

B) The data

10 20 64 1	45 45 29 1	43 50 31 1	56 44 52 2	84 50 72 2
28 28 58 1	62 30 26 1	48 45 44 1	69 46 59 2	70 54 51 2
55 25 42 1	20 69 78 1	14 77 53 1	53 57 52 2	65 64 23 2
30 20 30 1	49 59 46 1	64 32 55 1	75 48 34 2	69 60 57 2
32 27 42 1	39 42 31 1	55 48 9 1	71 52 30 2	66 79 50 2
25 49 81 1	26 56 78 1	41 55 41 1	50 68 75 2	58 82 13 2
40 38 43 1	40 31 51 1	30 54 20 2	81 54 41 2	45 90 59 2
71 22 79 1	34 60 45 1	29 67 18 2	51 62 14 2	82 58 65 2
19 59 71 1	31 66 50 1	28 68 72 2	49 72 72 2	82 69 60 2
55 32 75 1	18 61 22 1	46 67 80 2	66 61 40 2	51 48 52 2

REFERENCES

Anderson, A. J. B. (1989). **Interpreting Data: A First Course in Statistics.** London: Chapman and Hall.

Anscombe, F. J. (1973). Graphs in statistical analysis. **American Statistician**, 27, 17 - 21.

Cohen, J., & Cohen, P. (1983). **Applied Multiple Regression/Correlation Analysis for the Behavioral Sciences. 2nd Edition.** Hillsdale, N. J.: Lawrence Erlbaum.

Cook, R.D. & Weisberg, S. (1982). **Residuals and Influence in Regression.** London: Chapman and Hall.

Darlington, R. B. (1968). Multiple regression in psychological research and practice. **Psychological Bulletin, 69**, 161 - 182.

Delucchi, K. L. (1983). The use and misuse of chi-square: Lewis and Burke revisited. **Psychological Bulletin, 94,** 166 - 176.

Everitt, B. S. (1977). **The Analysis of Contingency Tables.** London: Chapman and Hall.

Gravetter, F. J., & Wallnau, L. B. (1992). **Statistics for the Behavioral Sciences: A First Course for Students of Psychology and Education. 3rd Edition.** St. Paul: West.

Hartwig, F., & Dearing, B. E. (1979). **Exporatory Data Analysis.** Sage University Paper Series on Quantitative Applications in the Social Sciences, 07-016. Newbury Park, CA: Sage.

Howell, D. C. (1992). **Statistical Methods for Psychology. 3rd Edition.** Belmont, CA: Duxbury.

Kim, J., & Mueller, C. W. (1978a). **Introduction to Factor Analysis: What It Is and How To Do It.** Sage University Paper Series on Quantitative Applications in the Social Sciences, 07-013. Newbury Park, CA: Sage.

Kim, J., & Mueller, C. W. (1978b). **Factor Analysis: Statistical Methods and Practical Issues.** Sage University Paper Series on Quantitative Applications in the Social Sciences, 07-014. Newbury Park, CA: Sage.

Kirk, R. E. (1982). **Experimental Design: Procedures for the Behavioral Sciences. 2nd Edition.** Belmont: Brooks/Cole.

Lewis, D., & Burke, C. J. (1949). The use and misuse of the chi-square test. **Psychological Bulletin, 46,** 433 - 489.

Lovie, P. (1991). Regression diagnostics: a rough guide to safer regression. In P. Lovie & A. D. Lovie, **New Developments in Statistics for Psychology and the Social Sciences.** London and New York: The British Psychological Society and Routledge.

Meddis. R. (1984). **Statistics Using Ranks: A Unified Approach.** Oxford: Basil Blackwell.

Myers, J. L. (1979). **Fundamentals of Experimental Design. 3rd Edition.** Boston: Allyn and Bacon.

References

Neave, H.R. & Worthington, P.L. (1988). **Distribution-Free Tests.** London: Unwin Hyman.

Reynolds, H. T. (1984). **The Analysis of Nominal Data. 2nd Edition.** Sage University Paper Series on Quantitative Applications in the Social Sciences, 07-007. Newbury Park, CA: Sage.

Tabachnick, B. G., & Fidell, L. S. (1989). **Using Multivariate Statistics. 2nd Edition.** New York: Harper and Row.

Tukey, J.W. (1977). **Exploratory Data Analysis.** Reading, MA: Addison-Wesley.

Upton, G. J. G. (1978). **The Analysis of Cross-tabulated Data.** Chichester: John Wiley.

Upton, G. J. G. (1986). Cross-classified data. In A. D. Lovie (ed.) **New Developments in Statistics for Psychology and the Social Sciences.** London and New York: The British Psychological Society and Methuen.

Winer, B. J. (1971). **Statistical Principles in Experimental Design. 2nd Edition.** Tokyo: McGraw-Hill Kogakusha.

INDEX

Index

SPSS FOR WINDOWS MADE SIMPLE

PAUL R. KINNEAR & COLIN D. GRAY
(University of Aberdeen)

Like its predecessor SPSS/PC+ Made Simple, SPSS for Windows Made Simple is the product of many years of teaching experience. There is an abundance of worked examples, which include annotated SPSS output listings and actual screen images of windows, icons and dialog boxes. These are accompanied by comments clarifying the points that have arisen most frequently from students' queries during practical classes.
At the end of the book, is a complete course of practical exercises in statistical computing with SPSS for Windows, covering all the topics considered in the text; indeed, the opportunity is frequently taken to expand upon some points merely touched upon in the chapters themselves.
As the title suggests, a premium has been placed upon simplicity rather than comprehensiveness. Nevertheless, the range of problems and techniques covered is much wider than in comparable introductory texts.
The first five chapters introduce the reader to some basic terms from computing, research methodology and Windows, and describe the use of SPSS to explore a data set thoroughly. There is also some advice on the selection of statistical tests. The remaining chapters are relatively self-contained, each dealing with a particular test or procedure, with preliminary comments about its use and the conditions that must be satisfied for its correct application.

In summary, SPSS for Windows Made Simple:
- Introduces the reader, with a minimum of fuss and detail, to Windows and the basics of SPSS operation in a graphics environment
- Shows how to get the most out of a set of data
- Offers cautions and caveats about the misuse of computing packages and statistics
- Advises on the choice of a statistical test
- Covers a much wider range of topics than other introductory texts
- Illustrates techniques with fully annotated SPSS output
- Makes extensive use of screen images
- Contains an abundance of worked examples
- Includes a course of practical exercises
- Has a useful and comprehensive index

Contents: The Personal Computer. Some Basic Windows Operations for SPSS. Inputting and Editing Data. Listing and Exploring Data. Choosing a Statistical test. Comparing the Averages of Two Samples. Factorial Experiments with No Repeated Measures. Experiments with Repeated Measures on All Factors. Experiments of Mixed Design. Measuring Statistical Association. Regression. Loglinear Analysis. Prediction of Group Membership. Discriminant Analysis. The Search for Latent Variables: Factor Analysis.

ISBN 0-86377-350-8 1994 288pp. $19.95 £11.50 pbk

Published by Lawrence Erlbaum Associates Ltd.